INSTRUCTOR'S MANUAL

WITH TESTS

Catherine A. Teare-Ketter
University of Georgia

ESSENTIALS OF OCEANOGRAPHY

EIGHTH EDITION

Alan P. Trujillo • Harold V. Thurman

PEARSON
Prentice
Hall

Upper Saddle River, NJ 07458

Assistant Editor: Melanie Cutler
Executive Editor: Patrick Lynch
Editor-in-Chief, Science: John Challice
Vice President of Production & Manufacturing: David W. Riccardi
Executive Managing Editor: Kathleen Schiaparelli
Assistant Managing Editor: Becca Richter
Production Editor: Dana Dunn
Supplement Cover Manager: Paul Gourhan
Supplement Cover Designer: Joanne Alexandris
Manufacturing Buyer: Ilene Kahn

© 2005 Pearson Education, Inc.
Pearson Prentice Hall
Pearson Education, Inc.
Upper Saddle River, NJ 07458

Printed in the United States of America

10   9   8   7   6   5   4   3   2   1

ISBN 0-13-144785-8

Pearson Education Ltd., *London*
Pearson Education Australia Pty. Ltd., *Sydney*
Pearson Education Singapore, Pte. Ltd.
Pearson Education North Asia Ltd., *Hong Kong*
Pearson Education Canada, Inc., *Toronto*
Pearson Educación de Mexico, S.A. de C.V.
Pearson Education—Japan, *Tokyo*
Pearson Education Malaysia, Pte. Ltd.

Table of Contents

Test Bank Contents

Instructor's Manual

CHAPTER

1

Introduction to Planet "Earth"

Learning Objectives

The instructional objectives are performance-based and detail specific learning outcomes for Chapter 1. The test items contained in the Test Bank are keyed to the learning objectives and the Key Questions at the beginning of the chapter. The order of the objectives mirrors the content presentation in Chapter 1.

Upon completion of this chapter, the student should be able to:

1.   Describe the principal oceans of the Earth including the following:
A. location
B. relative size
C. land forms that border the ocean

2.   Name the deepest ocean trench and describe its exploration by humans.

3.   Discuss early ocean exploration, including the contributions of:
A. early Pacific islanders (4000 B.C.-900A.D.)
B. significance of the *Kon Tiki* voyage
C. Phoenicians
D. Greeks
E. Romans

4.   Describe the contributions to oceanic exploration during the Middle Ages and the Ming Dynasty including the:
A. Arabs
B. Vikings
C. Chinese during the Ming Dynasty (1405-1433)

5.   Elaborate on the contributions to oceanic exploration made by European explorers during the Renaissance (Age of Discovery) including:
A. Prince Henry the Navigator
B. Vasco da Gama
C. Christopher Columbus
D. John Cabot
E. Vasco Nùñez de Balboa
F. Ferdinand Magellan
G. Juan Sebastian del Caño

Introduction to Planet "Earth"

6.   Discuss the contributions of James Cook to early ocean science.

7.   List and describe the systematic steps of the **scientific method**.

8.   Distinguish between a **hypothesis** and a **theory**.

9.   Describe the formation of the **solar system** as outlined by the **nebular hypothesis**.

10.   Compare and contrast **Protoearth** and modern Earth.

11.   Describe **density stratification** in the Earth and the resultant chemical structure including:
    A. **crust**
    B. **mantle**
    C. **core**

12.   Describe the physical structure of the Earth including:
    A. **inner core**
    B. **outer core**
    C. **mesosphere**
    D. **asthenosphere**
    E. **lithosphere**

13.   Distinguish between **continental crust** and **oceanic crust** including location, chemical, and physical properties of the crust.

14.   Differentiate between **isostatic adjustment** and **isostatic rebound**.

15.   Describe the formation of the Earth's initial atmosphere.

16.   Describe the formation of the Earth's oceans and discuss the origin of the salts in ocean water.

17.   Discuss the implications of **Stanley Miller's** experiment involving the simulation of the primitive Earth's atmosphere on the origin of life on Earth.

18.   Discriminate between **evolution** and **natural selection.**

19.   Define the following terms:
    A. **autotroph**
    B. **heterotroph**
    C. **anaerobic**
    D. **chemosynthesis**
    E. **photosynthesis**
    F. **respiration**
    G. **endothermic (endergonic)**
    H. **exothermic (exergonic)**

20.   Outline the effects of photosynthesis on the primitive Earth's atmosphere.

21.   Describe the process of **radiometric dating** and its implications in estimating the Earth's age.

Overview

Chapter 1 is an introduction to the Earth and its oceans, including a discussion of the history of ocean exploration. The scientific method is presented in this chapter so that students will have a framework for understanding the nature of scientific inquiry. Theories that describe the origin of the solar system, the Earth, the atmosphere, and the oceans are presented in addition to a discussion of the origin of life on Earth. The chapter is completed with a presentation of the geologic timescale and radiometric age dating.

Chapter Outline

Headings covered in this chapter include:
    Geography of the Oceans
        The Four Principal Oceans, Plus One
        The Seven Seas?
        Comparing the Oceans to the Continents
    Explorations of the Oceans: Some Historical Notes About Oceanography
        The Middle Ages
        The Age of Discovery in Europe
        The Beginning of Voyaging for Science
        History of Oceanography…To Be Continued
    The Nature of Scientific Inquiry
        Observations
        Hypothesis
        Hypothesis Testing
        Scientific Theories and Truth
    Origins
        Origin of the Solar System and the Earth
        Origin of the Atmosphere and the Oceans
    Life Begins in the Oceans
        The Importance of Oxygen to Life
        Plants and Animals Evolve
        Radiometric Dating and the Geologic TimeScale
    Special Features:
        Box 1-1: Voyages to Inner Space: Visiting the Deep Ocean Floor in Submersibles
        Box 1-2: How Do Sailors Know Where They are at Sea? From Sticks and Charts to Satellites
        Box 1-3: The Bermuda Triangle: Fact or Fiction?
        Box 1-4: Charles Darwin and the Voyage of HMS Beagle
        Box 1-5: Deep Time

Teacher's Resources

Films/Videotapes
Films and videotapes that present an overview of topics covered during the semester appropriate to show during the first week of class include:
- Challenge of the Oceans (McGraw-Hill), 29 min
- Scripps Institute of Oceanography Today (Regents of the University of California), 30 min
- The Boundless Sea (Bell System), 54 min (two 27-min filmstrip reels)
- Plant Earth: The Blue Planet (Program #2) (WQED, Pittsburgh, PBS), 58 min
- The World's Deepest Dive (The History Channel), 60 min (about the record-setting deep dive of the *Trieste*)

Other films/videotapes that cover topics within this chapter are:
- Darwin and the Theory of Natural Selection (Coronet), 14 min
- Evolution and the Origin of Life (CRM), 33 min
- Sea Power: A Depth of Knowledge (Program #6) (Ambrose Video), 55 min (topic: history of oceanography)

CD-ROMs
- Explorers of the New World (Softkey Multimedia, Inc.) (topic: ocean exploration during the Age of Discovery)
- Exploring the Ocean (Tasa Graphic Arts, Inc.)
- The Water Planet (Videodiscovery, Inc.)
- The Universe (Videodiscovery, Inc.)

Answers to End-of-Chapter Questions and Exercises

1.   How did the view of the ocean by early Mediterranean cultures influence the naming of the planet "Earth"?

Early Mediterranean cultures envisioned that marginal bodies of water similar to the Mediterranean Sea surrounded most of the continents. The name "Earth" describes the portion of the planet that is inhabited by man in spite of the fact that the majority of the planet's surface is covered by water. Our planet was named before ocean exploration began.

2.   What is the difference between an ocean and a sea? Which [AQ1]ones are the seven seas?

In common use the terms "sea" and "ocean" are synonymous. Technically, seas are distinct from oceans in that:
- Seas are smaller in size and are relatively shallow. (The Arctic Ocean would be a "sea" using these criteria.)
- Seas are salty, although the Caspian Sea in Asia is basically a very large freshwater lake.
- Seas are usually enclosed by land, although strong ocean currents can define an area (example: Sargasso Sea in the Atlantic Ocean).

The seven seas are the North Pacific, the South Pacific, the North Atlantic, the South Atlantic, the Indian, the Arctic, and the Antarctic (or Southern).

3.   Describe the development of navigation techniques that have enabled sailors to navigate in the open ocean far from land.

The Polynesians were probably some of the first sailors to navigate far from land. The tools they used to assist them in navigating between islands included the Sun, the Moon, nighttime stars, marine organism behavior, ocean characteristics, and the stick chart that mapped the pattern of ocean waves.

Later, latitude (location north and south) and longitude (location east and west) were used to determine ship location. Latitude was estimated using celestial navigation, while longitude was calculated using time. As a result, to navigate accurately, a reliable timepiece had to be onboard the ship. The first chronometer was invented by John Harrison and was invaluable to eighteenth- and nineteenth-century navigators.

Currently, ocean navigation uses Global Positioning System (GPS) technology. A series of geostationary orbiting satellites is used to determine the exact latitude and longitude of a ship. GPS navigation is accurate to a few meters at sea.

Using a diagram, illustrate the method used by Pytheas to determine the latitude in the Northern Hemisphere.

Pytheas determined the angle between the horizon and the Northern Hemisphere and the North Star to determine latitude.

1.   While the Arabs dominated the Mediterranean region during the Middle Ages, what were the most significant ocean-related events taking place in northern Europe?

The Vikings roamed the North Atlantic from the eighth to the thirteenth centuries. Erik, the Red, sailed to establish colonies in Baffin Island in 891, and his son, Leif Eriksson, visited Vineland (now Newfoundland, Canada) in 995.

2.   Describe the important events in oceanography that occurred during the Age of Discovery in Europe.

During the 30-year period from 1492 to 1522 (the Age of Discovery), the western world came to realize the vastness of the Earth's oceans. Europeans explored the continents of North and South America. The circumnavigation of the Earth was completed for the first time. Europeans discovered populations of indigenous peoples on other continents and islands. Bartholomew Diaz, Vasco da Gama, Christopher Columbus, Vasco Núñez de Balboa, and Ferdinand Magellan made important contributions to ocean exploration during the Age of Discovery.

3.   List some of the major accomplishments of Captain James Cook.

During his three ocean voyages, Captain James Cook (1728–1779)
*   explored the southern oceans and charted the coasts of New Zealand and Australia;
*   was the first person to cross the Antarctic Circle in his search for a southern continent, Terra Australis;
*   discovered the Sandwich Islands and South George Island after failing to find the southern continent;

- found a means of preventing scurvy, a disease resulting form Vitamin C deficiency;
- proved the value of John Harrison's chronometer for determination of longitude;
- determined the outline of the Pacific Ocean;
- led the way in sampling subsurface water temperatures, measuring winds and ocean currents;
- sounding to estimate depth, and data collection on coral reefs;
- discovered the Hawaiian Islands and looked for the Northwest Passage around North America.

8. What is the difference between a fact and a theory? Can either (or both) be revised?

A scientific fact is an observation that has been repeatedly confirmed by independent testing (so many times that it is assumed to be valid). A theory is a well-substantiated explanation that incorporates facts, descriptive generalizations about the behavior of an aspect of the natural world (laws), logical inferences, and tested hypotheses. A theory is not an educated guess or a scientific hunch. A theory is an understanding that develops from extensive, independent observation, experimentation, and data interpretation/reflection.

Facts and theories can be modified and/or revised as new data are collected and interpreted. Scientific facts are more likely to change with time and new technology than scientific theories.

9. Briefly comment on the phrase "scientific certainty." Is it an oxymoron (a combination of contradictory words) or are scientific theories considered to be absolute truth?

Knowledge about the natural world is constantly changing because we are always adding new observations and data to our knowledge base. As new data become available (frequently due to new technologies giving more detailed and accurate data), hypotheses, theories, and scientific facts are reexamined for consistency with the new information. As long as new data is being added, the nature of scientific truth will be subject to change. Thus, the phrase "scientific truth" is an oxymoron. Over time, scientific statements generally form a sequence of increasingly accurate statements, eventually coming to a point where they are no longer questioned. It is accurate to say that science arrives at that which is probably certain, based on available data.

10. Discuss the origin of the solar system using the nebular hypothesis.

The nebular hypothesis (refer to Figure 1-11) suggests that bodies of the solar system formed from an enormous nebular cloud composed predominantly of hydrogen and helium with a small fraction of heavier elements. As the large dust cloud revolved around its rotational center, the Sun began to form because of the concentration of particles under gravitational forces. In the earliest stages, the volume of the Sun may have been equal to the diameter of our solar system today.

As the nebular matter that formed the Sun contracted, a small percentage of it was left behind in small eddies (similar to whirlpools in a stream). This material flattened itself into an increasingly compact disc. The disc became so compact that it became gravitationally unstable and broke apart into separate smaller clouds. These smaller clouds were the protoplanets and their orbiting satellites. These bodies became the modern day planets and their moons.

11. How was Protoearth different from today's Earth?

Protoearth was a large mass with perhaps a 1000 times greater diameter than the present Earth, and Protoearth was 500 times more massive than the Earth today. Protoearth was devoid of life or oceans. It is believed that Protoearth was a homogenous planet with uniform composition throughout the planet. Protoearth had an atmosphere that was largely hydrogen and helium.

12.   What is density stratification, and how did it change Protoearth?

Density stratification is a result of gravitational forces and results in the layering of materials as a function of density. The denser (heavier) material is found beneath the lower density (lighter) material. This caused Protoearth (and other protoplanets) to undergo internal rearrangement as the heavier materials migrated to the center to form a heavy core. The result is a layered Earth with the lowest density material on the surface and the greatest density material in the core.

13.   Discuss how the chemical composition of the Earth's interior differs from its physical properties. Include specific examples.

Figure 1-12 illustrates the distinction between the Earth's interior as a function of chemical and physical composition. If you consider the chemical composition of the Earth, the interior can be divided into three layers: the crust, the mantle, and the core. The crust is the lowest density layer composted mostly of silicate minerals. The mantle below the crust is the largest layer and is composed of denser iron and magnesium silicate rock. The high-density core is predominately metal (mostly iron and nickel). In contrast, considering the physical characteristics of the Earth and how the layers respond to temperature and pressure, the Earth is composed of five layers: the lithosphere, the asthenosphere, the mesosphere, the outer core, and the inner core. The lithosphere is the outermost layer or brittle rock that fractures when pressure is applied. The asthenosphere is a plastic layer; it flows when a gradual force is applied. The mesosphere is below the asthenosphere (corresponds to the middle and lower mantle) and is rigid because of the increased pressure at depth. The outer core below the mesosphere is liquid (capable of flow), and the inner core is rigid. Like the mesosphere, the pressure on the inner core produces a rigid layer incapable of flow when pressure is applied.

14.   What are the differences between the lithosphere and the asthenosphere?

The lithosphere is a thin, relatively cool, rigid layer that includes all of the crust and the topmost portion of the mantle that acts as a single unit floating on the asthenosphere. It is about 100 km, or about 62 mi thick. In contrast, the asthenosphere is a relatively thick, hot, highly viscous, plastic region of the Earth. The asthenosphere corresponds to the upper mantle, and it is about 700 km, or about 430 mi, thick. When force is applied to the lithosphere, it will fracture. When a gradual force is applied to the asthenosphere, it will deform without fracturing.

15.   What is the origin of the Earth's oceans, and how is it related to the origin of the Earth's atmosphere?

Evidence suggests that the oceans came from inside Earth by the process of outgassing. About four billion years ago, the surface of the Earth cooled sufficiently to allow the water vapor being pumped into the atmosphere by volcanoes to condense and settle on Earth's surface. Earth's initial atmosphere was also outgassed from the Earth's interior along with the Earth's oceans, but its composition has changed through time.

16.   Have the oceans always been salty? Why or why not?

Evidence suggests that the oceans have always been salty, because many of the compounds eroded from surface rocks (that is where the ocean's salinity originated) contain elements that comprise salt: chlorine, sodium, magnesium, and potassium.

17.   How does the presence of oxygen in our atmosphere help to reduce the amount of ultraviolet radiation that reaches the Earth's surface?

Ultraviolet radiation absorbed by oxygen (O_2) molecules breaks the bonds between the atoms:
$$O_2 + \text{Ultraviolet light} \rightarrow O + O$$

18.   What was Stanley Miller's experiment, and what did it demonstrate?

Laboratory experiments by Stanley Miller in 1952 showed that exposing a mixture of compounds that were thought to exist in the early atmosphere (hydrogen, carbon dioxide, methane, ammonia, and water) to ultraviolet light and an electrical spark (simulating the effect of lightning) will produce a large assortment of organic molecules that are the basis for life.

19.   Earth has had three atmospheres (initial, early, and present). Describe the composition and origin of each.
Earth's initial atmosphere was composed of hydrogen and a small amount of helium. The atmosphere was outgassed from the Earth's interior, and it was replaced by the release of gases from the mantle by outgassing through volcanic activity to form an early atmosphere. These gases included water vapor, carbon dioxide, and smaller concentrations of other gases. The present atmosphere is composed mostly of nitrogen and oxygen gas. Atmospheric oxygen resulted from photosynthetic activity (or possibly outgassing from the mantle about 2.5 billion years ago). Oxygen began to be a significant constituent of the Earth's atmosphere about two billion years ago.

20.   Construct a representation of the geologic timescale using an appropriate quantity of any other substance (other than dollar bills or toilet paper). Be sure to indicate some of the major changes that have occurred on Earth since its origin.

Just about any substance or length can be used to represent a geologic timescale. In past years, some students have used dump trucks full of jellybeans, stacks of playing cards, crates of toothpicks, the distance (or flight time) between Los Angeles and New York, or laps around the athletic track to illustrate the immensity of geologic time. Whatever scale is used, it should be appropriately labeled with significant events that are shown on the geologic timescale (refer to Figure 1-20).

2

Plate Tectonics
and the Ocean Floor

Learning Objectives

The instructional objectives are performance-based and detail specific learning outcomes for Chapter 2. The test items contained in the Test Bank are keyed to the learning objectives and the Key Questions at the beginning of the chapter. The order of the objectives mirrors the content presentation in Chapter 2.

Upon completion of this chapter, the student should be able to:

1. Restate the theory of **plate tectonics**.

2. List the evidence used by Alfred Wegener to formulate his **continental drift** theory including:
    A. continental fit, especially South America and Africa
    B. similarities in the rock sequences (age and structure) on opposite sides of ocean basins.
    C. occurrence of past glacial activity in tropical areas
    D. similar fossil distributions in continents that were once connected

3. Distinguish between Alfred Wegener's continental drift theory and the modern theory of plate tectonics. Be certain that you outline the early ideas about continental drift that are extant in the modern theory.

4. Describe the evidence that supports the current version of the theory of plate tectonics including:
    A. orientation of magnetic particles in the Earth's crust
    B. magnetic dip (function of the latitude at which the rock cooled)
    C. apparent polar wandering
    D. magnetic polarity reversals
    E. ocean floor magnetic anomalies
    F. sea floor spreading
    G. uneven heat flow in the Earth's crust
    H. worldwide earthquake distribution

5. List the features found in the following types of plate boundaries:
    A. divergent plate boundary
    B. convergent plate boundary
    C. transform plate boundary

6. Distinguish between **mantle plumes** and **hotspots**.

Plate Tectonics and the Ocean Floor

7.   Describe how the occurrence and distribution of mantle plumes and hot spots supports the current theory of plate tectonics.

8.   Illustrate the arrangement of the continents when the supercontinent Pangea existed.

9.   Make predictions about continental position in the geologic future.

Overview

Chapter 2 is a discussion of the nature of Earth's crustal movements in the context of plate tectonic theory. This chapter presents a discussion of the historical development of our understanding of continental drift and how new discoveries shaped the development of current plate tectonic theory. The current knowledge of the Earth's internal structure is covered, and the implications of near surface structure for plate movement are presented. Different types of plate boundaries and the types of crustal movements associated with each type of boundary are discussed. An emphasis on sea floor plate boundaries and plate movement is included in this chapter. The chapter concludes with some discussion of plate tectonic applications that include paleoceanography and predictions for future continental locations.

Headings covered in this chapter include:
Evidence for Continental Drift
       Fit of the Continents
       Matching Sequences of Rocks and Mountain Chains
       Glacial Ages and Other Climate Evidence
       Distribution of Organisms
       Objections to the Continental Drift Model
Evidence for Plate Tectonics
       Earth's Magnetic Field and Paleomagnetism
       Sea Floor Spreading and Features of the Ocean Basins
       Other Evidence from the Ocean Basins
       The Acceptance of a Theory
Earth Structure
       Chemical Composition Versus Physical Properties
       Near the Surface
       Isostatic Adjustment
Plate Boundaries
       Divergent Boundaries
       Convergent Boundaries
       Transform Boundaries
Testing the Model: Some Applications
       Mantle Plumes and Hotspots
       Seamounts and Tablemounts
       Coral Reef Development
       Detecting Plate Movement with Satellites
       The Past: Paleoceanography
       The Future: Some Bold Predictions

Special Features:
> Box 2-1: *Research Methods in Oceanography: Do Sea Turtles (and Other Animals) Use Earth's Magnetic Field for Navigation?*

Teacher's Resources

There is a wide assortment of good films/videos on plate tectonics, including:

- Boundary Creation (NOAA), 26 min.

- Continental Drift and Plate Tectonics (Tanya Atwater/University of California Santa Barbara), 19 min.
- Continents Adrift (American Educational), 15 min.
- Earth Revealed: The Restless Planet (Program #2) (The Annenberg/CPB Collection), 30 min.
- Earth Revealed: Plate Dynamics (Program #6) (The Annenberg/CPB Collection), 30 min.
- Not So Solid Earth (Time-Life Film and Video), 30 min.
- Restless Earth, Plate Tectonics (Indiana University), 100 min (two 50-min filmstrip reels).
- This Land (Shell Oil), 41 min.
- Volcano Surtsey (North Shore News), 26 min.

CD-ROMs
- The Theory of Plate Tectonics (Tasa Graphic Arts, Inc.) (introductory college level).
- Plate Tectonics and How the Earth Works (Tasa Graphic Arts, Inc.) (advanced college level).
- Understanding Earth (Videodiscovery, Inc.).

Answers to End-of-Chapter Questions and Exercises

1.   When did the supercontinent of Pangea exist? What was the ocean that surrounded the supercontinent called?

   Pangea existed about 200 million years ago. The single largest ocean surrounding Pangea was Panthalassa (refer to Figure 2-5, Ice age on Pangea).

2.   Cite the lines of evidence Alfred Wegener used to support his idea of continental drift. Why did scientists doubt that continents drifted?

   Alfred Wegner used the following evidence to support continental drift:
   ✓ The fit of the continental margins across ocean basins.
   ✓ Matching rock sequences and mountain ranges on different continents.
   ✓ Climatic evidence such as glacial deposits in areas that are now close to the Equator.
   ✓ The distribution of organisms across continents that are separated by oceans that these organisms could not have crossed.
   > Although the evidence in support of continental drift seems compelling, scientists in Wegener's time rejected the idea of continental drift because the mechanisms Wegener proposed as driving continental movement seemed too far-fetched to be plausible. Some scientists felt that Wegener's proposal ran contrary to the understanding of the laws of physics in the early twentieth century. When sea floor spreading data became available in the 1950s and 1960s,

Plate Tectonics and the Ocean Floor

Wegener's ideas about continental movement were combined with these data to provide a more current model that explained crustal movement.

3.   If you could travel back in time with three figures (illustrations) from this chapter to help Alfred Wegener convince scientists of his day that continental drift does exist, what would they be and why?

Wegener was unable to describe the process that caused continental movement because there was an incomplete understanding of the structure of the Earth in 1912. Figure 2-10, Process of plate tectonics, would provide Wegener with a modern understanding of the Earth's structure and the processes that drive plate movement. Two additional figures that provide supporting evidence for Wegener's theory are Figures 2-13 (a) and (b), Earthquakes and Lithospheric Plates. Please note that student answers may vary.

4.   Describe Earth's magnetic field, including how it has changed through time.

The Earth's magnetic filed resembles the magnetic field produced by a large bar magnet. Bar magnets have ends that are oppositely charged. The magnet ends are usually designated by "+" and "-" or "N" (for north) and "S" (for south). This opposite polarity causes magnetic objects to align parallel to the magnetic field produced by the bar magnet. Although the Earth does not actually have a bar magnet inside, it behaves as if it does. Invisible lines of magnetic force originating from within the Earth travel through Earth and out into space (see Figure 2-7, Nature of Earth's magnetic field).

The strength of the Earth's magnetic field has changed through time (on the geologic time-scale). Additionally, the Earth has experienced many dozens of magnetic field polarity reversal during the last 100 million years.

5.   Describe how sea turtles use Earth's magnetic field for navigation.

Research in the field of magnetoreception, the study of an animal's ability to sense magnetic fields, suggests that sea turtles and some marine mammals may use the Earth's magnetic field for navigation. It has been demonstrated that hatchling sea turtles can distinguish between different magnetic inclination angles; this in effect, allows sea turtles to sense latitude. Recent research indicates that sea turtles can also sense magnetic field intensity, a rough indication of latitude. Using the ability to sense magnetic field intensity and magnetic inclination, the sea turtles can construct a magnetic map with grid coordinates that can be used for navigation. A sea turtle can use the magnetic map to determine its location and navigate to a tiny island that is hundreds or thousands of miles away for breeding.

6.   Why is the pattern of alternating reversals of the Earth's magnetic field as recorded in the sea floor rocks such an important piece of evidence for advancing plate tectonics?

The alternating (or striped pattern) reversals of the Earth's magnetic field recorded in sea floor rocks could be created when newly formed rocks at the mid-ocean ridges are magnetized and align with the direction of the Earth's magnetic field at the time of their formation. As these rocks move slowly away from the crest of the mid-ocean ridge, periodic magnetic pole reversals produce rocks with different magnetic orientation, recording polarity changes in sea floor rocks.

This produces a pattern of magnetic polarity stripes in the sea floor that are symmetrical on either side of the mid-ocean ridge (refer to Figure 2-12). This pattern strongly supports the existence of sea floor spreading at mid-ocean ridges.

7. Describe sea floor spreading and explain why it is an important piece of evidence for advancing plate tectonics.

The age relationships and pattern of symmetric stripes on the sea floor with respect to the axis of the mid-ocean ridge indicate that sea floor spreading occurs along the mid-ocean ridge. With sea floor spreading as a mechanism, many of the arguments against continental drift could no longer be supported, so it helped to advance the development of continental drift and the formation of plate tectonic theory.

8. Describe the general relationships that exist among the following: distance from spreading centers, heat flow, age of ocean crustal rock, and ocean depth.

With increasing distance in either direction from the spreading center, the amount of heat flowing through the Earth's surface decreases and the age of the ocean floor increases along with ocean depth.

9. Why does a map of worldwide earthquakes closely match the locations of worldwide plate boundaries?

Plate boundaries are locations where plates interact. Earthquakes frequently occur in areas with convergent or transform plate movements. There is a high correlation between worldwide earthquake location and plate boundaries.

10. List and describe the three types of plate boundaries. Include in your discussion any sea floor features that are related to these plate boundaries, and include a real-world example of each. Construct a map and cross-section showing each of the three boundary types and the corresponding direction of plate movement.

Figure 2-14 (Three types of plate boundaries) illustrates the three types of plate boundaries (convergent, divergent, and transform) and shows the corresponding direction of plate movement. Convergent plate boundaries move away from the plate boundary; the direction of movement is perpendicular to the plate boundary (example: mid-ocean ridge). Plate movement in which the two plates move toward one another characterizes divergent plate boundaries. In the case of an oceanic plate (basalt) and a continental plate (granite), the denser oceanic plate is thrust below the continental plate. The area of plate overlap is called a subduction zone. Transform faults occur in areas where the movement of the two plates is in opposite directions and parallels the plate boundary.

11. Most lithospheric plates contain both oceanic- and continental-type crust. Use plate boundaries to explain why this is true.

Plate boundaries rarely follow continental margins, so most large plates contain a continent (continental crust) as well as a large area of ocean floor (oceanic crust).

Plate Tectonics and the Ocean Floor

12.   Describe the differences between oceanic ridges and oceanic rises. Include in your answer why these differences exist.

Spreading rates (the total widening rate of an ocean basin resulting from the motion of *both* plates away form the spreading center) vary along the mid-ocean ridge and profoundly affect the slope of the mountain range. The faster the spreading rate, the broader the mountain range associated with the spreading center. The rapidly spreading and gently sloping portion of the mid-ocean ridge are called oceanic rises. The slower and steeper-sloped areas of the mid-ocean ridge are called oceanic ridges. Oceanic ridges and oceanic rises are both part of the global mid-ocean ridge system.

13.   Convergent plate boundaries can be divided into three types on the basis of the type of crust contained in the two colliding plates. Compare and contrast the different types of convergent boundaries that result from these collisions.

Oceanic–Continental Plate Convergence: When an oceanic and a continental plate converge, the denser oceanic plate will be subducted, forced below the continental plate. As the plate descends, some of the material is melted and mixes with other melted rock to produce an andesitic continental arc.
    Oceanic–Oceanic Plate Convergence: When two oceanic plates converge, the denser oceanic plate will be subducted. As the plate descends, some of the material is melted and mixes with other melted rock to form a basaltic island arc.
    Continental–Continental Plate Convergence: When two continental plates converge, neither plate will be subducted. No volcanic arc is created. In contrast to collisions with oceanic plates, a tall, uplifted mountain range forms that is composed of folded and deformed sedimentary rock.

14.   Describe the difference in earthquake magnitudes that occur between the three types of plate boundaries, and include why these differences occur.

Divergent plate boundary: The magnitude of energy release along divergent plate boundaries is closely related to the spreading rate. Earthquakes in the rift valley of the slow-spreading Mid-Atlantic Ridge reach a maximum magnitude of about M_W=6.0, whereas those occurring along the axis of the fast-spreading East Pacific Rise seldom exceed M_W=4.5. These earthquakes are shallow, usually less than 10.0 km (6 mi) in depth. Compared to the other types of plate boundaries, earthquakes along divergent plate boundaries are numerous, but relatively small because the sea floor is continually pulling apart, or rifting, here.
    Convergent plate boundary: The forces involved in convergent plate boundary collisions are enormous and create infrequent but powerful earthquakes. Convergent plate boundaries are associated with some of the most powerful earthquakes in the world. Currently, the largest earthquake ever recorded was the Chilean earthquake of 1960 that occurred near the Peru–Chile Trench and had a magnitude of M_W=9.5. Earthquakes associated with convergent boundaries vary from shallow depths near the surface down to 6709 km (415 mi deep); these are the deepest earthquakes in the world. These earthquakes are clustered in a band about 20 km (12.5 mi) thick that closely corresponds to the location of the subduction zone.
    Transform plate boundary: As one plate slowly moves past another, shallow but frequently strong earthquakes are produced. Magnitude M_W=7.0 have been recorded along some

oceanic transform faults, and the San Andreas Fault (a continental transform fault) has experienced earthquakes up to $M_w=8.5$. These earthquakes are not as strong as those associated with convergent boundaries because the direction and type of plate movement is different.

15. How can plate tectonics be used to help explain the difference between a seamount and a tablemount?

Most oceanic islands form because of the volcanic activity at oceanic spreading centers. As the lithospheric plates move away from the oceanic ridge, ocean depth increases because of thermal contraction in the lithosphere. The islands will become inactive volcanoes within 30 million years because by that time they would have moved too far away from the volcanically active spreading center. Being inactive, they will be carried beneath the ocean's surface. Those that have their surfaces flattened by wave erosion will become tablemounts.

16. How is the age distribution pattern of the Emperor Seamount and Hawaiian Island chains explained by the position of the Hawaiian hotspot? What could have caused the curious bend in between the two chains of seamounts/tablemounts?

From the island of Hawaii, the only active volcano in the chain, there extends a northwest trending line of islands and seamounts to about 188° west longitude. At this point, it makes a bend and turns sharply north as the Emperor Seamount Chain. These volcanoes increase in age from Hawaii to about 40 million years at the bend between two chains and about 81 million years at the north end of the Emperor Seamount Chain. This evidence indicates that all of the volcanoes that make up the chains formed when a portion of the ocean floor from which they extend passed over a stationary volcanic hotspot that now underlies the island of Hawaii and Loihi.
      The bend probably indicates a change in the direction of the movement of the Pacific Plate. During eruptions of the Emperor Seamounts, the plate was moving past the hotspot in a northerly direction. About 40 million years ago, Pacific Plate movement changed to a northwesterly direction, thus creating the bend in between the two island chains.

17. Describe the differences in origin between the Aleutian Islands and the Hawaiian Islands. Provide evidence to support your explanation.

The Aleutian Islands are created by the subduction of the Pacific Plate into the Aleutian Trench. As the subducted plate melts, the material mixes with other molten rocks and creates an andesitic volcanic island arc. Any of the volcanoes in the island arc could be active at anytime because of continuing subduction.
      The Hawaiian Islands are created by the Pacific Plate passing over the Hawaiian hotspot. The eruptions associated with the Hawaiian hotspot produce mostly basaltic lava. Only the volcanoes on the island (or two) directly over the hotspot are active, and each island further from the hotspot is progressively older.

18. What are the differences between a mid-ocean ridge and a hotspot?

A mid-ocean ridge is a divergent boundary where two plates are splitting apart. As the plates pull away from one another, there is an abundance of volcanic activity. Hotspots are areas of intense volcanic activity as well, but they are not necessarily associated with any particular type of plate

Plate Tectonics and the Ocean Floor

boundary. The vast majority of hotspots do not coincide with plate boundaries; those that do not are concentrated along divergent boundaries where lithospheric plates are relatively thin.

19.   Using the paleogeographic reconstructions shown in Figure 2-31, determine when the following events first appear in the geologic record:
    A. North America lies on the Equator—480 million years ago
    B. The continents come together as Pangaea—240 million years ago
    C. The North Atlantic Ocean opens—120 million years ago
    D. India separates from Antarctica—60 million years ago

20.   Assuming that a continent moves at a rate of 10 cm per year, how long would it take to travel from your present location to a nearby large city?

The answer to this question will vary as a function of location. As an example, if the nearest large city is 100 km (60 mi away), then

100 km X (1000 m/km) X (100 cm/m) X (1 year/10 cm) = 1,000,000 or 10^6 years. One million years is a surprisingly short length of geologic time for moving such a large distance.

CHAPTER

3

Marine Provinces

Learning Objectives

The instructional objectives are performance-based and detail specific learning outcomes for Chapter 3. The test items contained in the Test Bank are keyed to the learning objectives and the Key Questions at the beginning of the chapter. The order of the objectives mirrors the content presentation in Chapter 3.

Upon completion of this chapter, the student should be able to:

1. Define **bathymetry**.

2. Describe the techniques used by early oceanic navigators to estimate the ocean depth.

3. Relate the **fathom** to vertical distance measured in meters and feet.

4. Distinguish among the following terms, and describe how each technology is used to make estimates of the ocean depth including:
    A. **echo sounding**
    B. **precision depth recording (PDR)**
    C. **SONAR (sound navigation and ranging)**
    D. **Sea MARC (Sea mapping and remote characterization**
    E. **GLORIA (geological long-range inclined acoustical instrument)**
    F. **seismic reflection profiles**

5. Describe a **hypsographic curve** and discuss the information that this graph illustrates.

6. List the three major marine provinces and give the distinguishing features of each marine province.

7. Distinguish between **passive continental margins** and **active continental margins,** and describe the tectonic processes occurring at each continental margin.

8. Differentiate between **convergent active continental margins** and **transform active continental margins.** Provide a specific example of a location of each type of oceanic active margin.

9. Discriminate between the **continental shelf** and **continental slope**.

10. Give an example of a **submarine canyon**.

Marine Provinces

11. Discuss the relationship between **turbidity currents** and the formation of **submarine canyons**.

12. Describe the topographic features of the **continental rise** including:
    A. **graded bedding**
    B. **turbidite deposits**
    C. **deep-sea fans (submarine fans)**

13. Describe the characteristic features of the **abyssal plain** including:
    A. **seamounts**
    B. **abyssal hills (seaknolls)**
    C. **abyssal hill provinces**

14. Discuss the relationship between the formation of an **ocean trench** and a **volcanic island arc**. Describe the tectonic processes that create these features.

15. Distinguish between a **guyot** and a **tablemount**.

16. Explain the relationship between the **Pacific Ring of Fire** and the location of plate margins in the Pacific Ocean. Include a discussion of the type of continental margins in these locations.

17. List the features that characterize the **mid-ocean ridge**.

18. Differentiate between a **rift valley**, an **oceanic ridge**, and an **oceanic rise**.

19. Distinguish among the following types of **hydrothermal vents**: **warm-water vents**, **white smokers**, and **black smokers**.

20. Compare and contrast **transform faults** and **fracture zones** found on the sea floor.

Overview

Chapter 3 presents a brief discussion of the major geomorphic oceanic provinces and ocean floor features, especially as they relate to plate tectonics. The theory of plate tectonics is covered in Chapter 2. Bathymetry and bathymetric techniques are included in this chapter to help students understand how ocean scientists collect information about areas of the sea floor that have not been explored by man. On surveying ocean floor features from nearshore environments to the mid-ocean ridge, the major marine provinces are presented. This material may be presented as a "virtual field trip" or "tour of the ocean floor".

Headings in this chapter include:
Bathymetry
        Bathymetric Techniques
Provinces of the Ocean Floor
        Features of the Continental Margins
        Features of the Deep-Ocean Basin

Features of the Mid-Ocean Ridge

Special Features:
> *Box 3-1: Research Methods in Oceanography: Sea Floor Mapping from Space*
> *Box 3-2: Historical Feature: Experiments in Underwater Living*
> *Box 3-3: Research Methods in Oceanography: A Grand "Break": Evidence for Turbidity Currents*

Teacher's Resources

Films/Videotapes
- Earth Revealed: The Sea Floor (Program #4) (The Annenberg/CPB Collection), 30 min.
- The Earth Beneath the Sea (McGraw-Hill), 29 min.

Answers to End-of-Chapter Questions and Exercises

1. What is bathymetry?
Bathymetry is the measurement of ocean depths and the charting of ocean floor topography (shape and relief). Determining bathymetry involves measuring the vertical distance form the ocean surface down to the mountains, valleys, and plains on the sea floor.

2. Discuss the development of bathymetric techniques, including significant advances in technology.

Since early history, humans have determined water depth using depth soundings made by attaching a heavy weight to a long line and lowering it over the side of a vessel. The first systematic bathymetry of the oceans was made in 1872, when the HMS *Challenger* began its historic three-and-a-half-year voyage. Throughout the voyage, the *Challenger*'s crew stopped to make depth soundings every few thousand kilometers. They also recorded various seawater properties at these locations.

In the1920s, the invention of the echo sounder advanced ocean floor mapping. An echo sounder sends a sound signal (a ping) into the ocean. The sound signal bounces off any object that has a density different than seawater (such as live organisms or the ocean floor). Analogous to the use of radar on land, the echosounder records echoes that have bounced off objects. The time that it takes for the echoes to return is used to determine ocean depth and the shape of the ocean floor. In 1924, the German vessel *Meteor* was the first vessel to use an echosounder to map the sea floor. One problem with this technique is that it lacked the resolution to show detailed sea floor features.

The precision depth recorder (PDR) was developed in the 1950s. With a more focused high-frequency sound beam (in comparison to the echosounder), it could provide depths to a resolution of about 1 m (3.3 ft). Throughout the 1960s, PDRs were used extensively to provide a reasonable good representation of the ocean floor. Data collected by thousands of research vessel tracks produced the first reliable global sea floor bathymetric maps. These maps provided important evidence that supported plate tectonic theory and the idea of sea floor spreading.

Today, multibeam echosounders and side-scan sonar give oceanographers a far more precise picture of the ocean floor. The first multibeam echosounder, Seabeam, made it possible for a survey ship to map the features of the ocean floor along a strip up to 60 km (37 mi) wide. The system uses sound emitters directed away from both sides of the ship, with receivers permanently mounted on the ship's hull.

Marine Provinces

With these data, a map of the sea floor can be computer-generated. Sea MARC and GLORIA are types of side-scan sonar devices that are towed behind a survey ship.

To obtain a more detailed picture of the ocean floor, a side-scan sonar instrument must be towed behind a ship on a cable so that it "flies" just above the ocean floor. The most recent technology in these deep-sea tow systems combines a side-scan sonar instrument with a sub-bottom imaging package. This allows a simultaneous view of the ocean floor surface and a cross section of the sediment below water depths of 6500 m (21,325 ft).

The sea floor can also be mapped by using satellites that can detect slight irregularities in the height of the ocean surface caused by gravitational attraction of different sea floor features. Various satellite missions and their objectives are listed in Table 3-1.

3. Describe what is shown by a hypsographic curve, and explain why its shape reflects the presence of active tectonic processes on Earth.

A hypsographic curve is used by oceanographers to graphically represent the relationship between land elevation and water depth (refer to Figure 3-4). The curve is constructed as a plot of the percentage of the Earth's surface (area of the Earth's surface) on the horizontal axis and elevation/ocean depth on the vertical axis. The two flat areas and the three sloped areas on the Earth's hypsographic curve illustrate that there is a very uneven distribution of area at different land elevations and ocean depths. The flat portions of the curve represent features within a plate. The sloped portions of the curve represent the continental slopes, the deep-ocean trenches, mid-ocean ridges, and mountains. The existence of these features suggests that some physical mechanism produces the uneven folding of the Earth's surface such as plate tectonics. If there were no tectonic activity, the area of the Earth's surface would be constant at every elevation/depth, producing a straight line instead of a curve.

4. Describe the differences between active and passive continental margins. Be sure to describe how these features relate to plate tectonics, and include an example of each type of margin.

Active margins are continental margins that are associated with lithospheric plate boundaries, and they are marked by a high degree of tectonic activity (refer to Figure 3-7, right). Active margins are further divided into two types: transform active margins and convergent active margins. Transform active margins are associated with transform plate boundaries where transform or strike-slip faulting occurs. An example of a transform active margin is in the western United States along the San Andreas Fault. Convergent active margins are associated with oceanic–continental convergent plate boundaries. An island arc and an offshore trench delineate the plate boundary. An example of a convergent active plate margin is along the coast of western South American where the Nazca Plate is being subducted beneath the South American Plate. There is an abundance of active margins in the Pacific Ocean.

Passive margins are continental margins that are embedded within the interior of lithospheric plates and are not in close proximity to any plate boundary. Rifting of continental landmasses produces passive margins. An example of a passive margin exists along the east coast of the United States where there is no plate boundary. Passive margins lack tectonic activity (earthquakes, volcanoes, and mountain building). A passive continental margin includes the continental shelf and shelf break, the continental slop and the continental rise that extends toward the deep-ocean basins (refer to Figure 3-7, left). In contrast with the Pacific Ocean, the Atlantic Ocean has an abundance of passive plate margins.

5. Describe the major features of a passive continental margin: continental shelf, continental slope, continental rise, submarine canyon, and deep-sea fans.

The *continental shelf* extends seaward from the shoreline as a gently sloping surface with an average

slope of about one-tenth of a degree. Its topography is usually similar to that of the coastal region of the continent. It is very narrow in some areas, such as off California, and reaches widths as great as 1300 km off the Siberian coast; its average width is about 70 km. The average depth at which the shelf break that marks its seaward limit occurs is about 135 m, but the break is as deep as 350 m off Antarctica.

The *continental slope*, which extends from the continental shelf to the deep-ocean basins, has an average slope of 4°. In the Pacific Oceans where mountainous coasts are common, the continental slope averages 5° in contrast to the Atlantic and Indian Oceans where it averages 3°. Submarine canyons resulting from turbidity currents cut the slopes and may even extend across the continental shelf in some cases.

The *continental rise* is a gently sloping surface that has about the same slope as the continental shelf. It extends from the base of the continental slope into the deep-ocean basins as a thinning wedge of sediment, most of which is probably deposited by turbidity currents when they reach the base of the continental slope and loose their energy. This sediment is greatly modified by deep boundary currents that erode it from some locations and deposit it as drifts as the currents slow while turning at bends in the continental slope.

Submarine canyons are similar in size and design to river-cut canyons on land. They are found mostly on the continental slope, but some canyons extend landward across the continental shelf (such as the Hudson Canyon that extends toward the mouth of the Hudson River in New York).

Deep-sea fans are formed when the turbidity currents reach the base of the continental slope and lose speed moving across the flatter deep-ocean floor. The sediment settles out of the slow moving water to create deep-sea fans at the base of the slope. As the fans grow from deposits of distributary channels flowing across their surface, they merge to produce the gently sloping continental rise at the base of the continental slope.

6. Explain how submarine canyons are created.

The most widely accepted phenomenon that has been used to explain the existence of submarine canyons is turbidity currents. Although no one has directly witnessed turbidity currents in action, there is good evidence to support their existence and erosive power. It is believed that the sediment on the continental slope may be dislodged by an event such as oversteepening of sediment, an earthquake, a hurricane, or some other disturbance. The dislodged sediment mixes with water as it moves down the slope under the influence of gravity to produce a turbidity current. This flow of dense fluid is erosive and cuts a gully in the slope. Subsequent turbidity currents deepen it to canyon proportions.

7. What are the differences between a submarine canyon and an ocean trench?

A *submarine canyon* is a deep gouge that exists on continental slopes/continental shelves, and it is thought to have been created by turbidity currents. An *ocean trench* is a much deeper and a larger feature that is the physiographic representation of a subduction zone where one tectonic plate plunges beneath another.

Marine Provinces

8. Explain what graded bedding is and how it forms.

Graded bedding is a type of sediment layering that becomes progressively finer within a sequence, and it is the result of deposition by turbidity currents. Material that was suspended in a turbidity current settles out in a distinct pattern: the larger pieces settle first, then progressively smaller pieces settle, and eventually even very fine pieces settle out. The settling process may take weeks or months. This creates a

graded bedding sequence of coarser material at the bottom, becoming progressively finer toward the top.

9. Describe the process by which the abyssal plain was created.

Abyssal plains are formed by fine particles of sediment slowly drifting down onto the crust of the deep-ocean floor and, over millions of years, producing thick sedimentary deposits analogous to marine dust. This process is called suspension settling because fine sediment is constantly settling out of suspension in the water column. With enough time, most irregularities of the deep ocean are covered by these deposits.

10. Discuss the origin of the various volcanic peaks of the abyssal plains: seamounts, tablemounts, and abyssal hills.

Seamounts are cone-shaped volcanic peaks that stand more than 1 km above the sea floor. *Tablemounts* are seamounts that have had their tops flattened by wave energy. Most are now submerged beneath 1800 to 3000 meters (5900 to 9800 ft) of ocean water. *Abyssal hills* (seaknolls) are small gently rounded volcanic hills that stand less than 1 km above the ocean floor.

11. In which ocean basin are most ocean trenches found? Use plate tectonic processes to help explain why.

Most ocean trenches are located in the Pacific Ocean because of the prevalence of convergent plate boundaries (with subduction zones) that ring the Pacific Ocean basin.

12. Describe the characteristics and features of mid-ocean ridge, including the difference between oceanic ridges and oceanic rises.

The global mid-ocean ridge is a continuous, fractured-looking submarine mountain range that extends through the middle of all the ocean basins and extends for some 65,000 km (40,400 mi). The width of the mid-ocean ridge varies along its length, but averages about 1000 km (620 mi). The mid-ocean ridge is a topographically high feature, extending an average of 2.5 km (1.5 mi) above the surrounding sea floor. The mid-ocean ridge
- is entirely volcanic in origin;
- is composed of lavas with a basaltic composition;
- has along its crest a central down dropped rift valley created by sea floor spreading processes where two plates are diverging;
- has an abundance of earthquake activity in the form of small, shallow quakes;
- has a variety of volcanic features, including seamounts, and recent underwater lava flows (pillow lava);

- is associated with hydrothermal vents where hot water seeps out of the sea floor and unusual life exists;
- has deposits of metal sulfides that contain economic mineral deposits.

Segments of the mid-ocean ridge are called *oceanic ridges* where they are mountainous with steep irregular slopes and *oceanic rises* where the slopes are gentler. As explained in Chapter 2, the differences in overall shape between ridges and rises are due spreading rate differences: oceanic ridges have slower spreading rates than oceanic rises.

13. List and describe the different types of hydrothermal vents.

Hydrothermal vents are hot springs associated with mid-ocean ridge rift valleys that are caused by seawater seeping along fractures in the ocean crust. The water is heated when it comes in contact with underlying magma and then rises upward and spews out of the sea floor. There are three types of hydrothermal vents:
- *Warm-water vents* have water temperatures below 30 °C (86 °F).
- *White smokers* have water that is white in color as a result of dissolved barium sulfate particles and a water temperature between 30 and 350 °C (662 °F).
- *Black smokers* have water that is black in color as a result of dissolved dark-colored metal sulfides and a water temperature above 350 °C (662 °F). Many of these black smokers spew water out of chimney-like structures composed of metal sulfide deposits up to 20 m (66 ft) high.

14. What kinds of unusual life can be found associated with hydrothermal vents? How do these organisms survive?

Hydrothermal vent communities include large clams, mussels, vestimeniferan tubeworms, and other animals. The vents discharge hydrogen sulfide gas, which is oxidized by bacteria and archaeons to provide the starting products to fix organic carbon in the absence of sunlight.

15. Use pictures and words to describe the differences between a fracture zone and a transform fault.

Refer to Table 3-3 (Comparison between transform faults and fracture zones) and Figure 3-15.

CHAPTER

4
Marine Sediments

Learning Objectives

The instructional objectives are performance-based and detail specific learning outcomes for Chapter 4. The test items contained in the Test Bank are keyed to the learning objectives and key questions. The order of the objectives mirrors the content presentation in Chapter 4.

Upon completion of this chapter, the student should be able to:

1. Define **lithogenous sediment** and discuss the origin of this type of sediment.

2. Discuss the chemical (mineral) composition of lithogenous sediments.

3. Describe the **Wentworth scale of grain size** for sediments including the sizes of:
    A. boulders.
    B. cobbles.
    C. pebbles.
    D. granules.
    E. sand.
    F. silt.
    G. clay.

4. Explain the impact of sediment **sorting** and **maturity** on sediment texture.

5. Differentiate between **neritic** and **pelagic sediment deposits**.

6. Distinguish between the various types of neritic sediment deposits including:
    A. beach deposits.
    B. continental shelf deposits.
    C. turbidite deposits.
    D. glacial deposits.

7. Describe the mineral composition and texture of pelagic lithogenous sediments.

8. Define **biogenous sediment** and discuss the origin of this type of sediment.

9. Explain the difference between **macroscopic** and **microscopic biogenous sediment** and give an example of each.

10. Discuss the chemical (mineral) composition of biogenous sediments and list the organisms from which these sediments are derived.

11. Define **ooze**. Distinguish between calcareous and siliceous oozes and list the organisms responsible for the formation of the different oozes.

12. Discuss the distribution of biogenous sediments in neritic and pelagic environments including:
    A. carbonate deposits including **limestone** and **stromatolites**.
    B. siliceous ooze.
    C. calcareous ooze.

13. Outline the relationship between the **calcite compensation depth (CCD)** and the formation of calcareous oozes.

14. Define **hydrogenous sediment,** and discuss the origin of this type of sediment.

15. Discuss the chemical (mineral) composition and the distribution of hydrogenous sediments including:
    A. manganese nodules.
    B. phosphates.
    C. carbonates.
    D. metal sulfides.
    E. evaporites.

16. Define **cosmogenous sediment,** and discuss the origin of this type of sediment.

17. Describe the chemical (mineral) composition and distribution of cosmogenous sediments.

18. Explain how sea floor sediments mirror surface ocean conditions.

19. Summarize the relationship between sea floor sediments and the Earth's history.

20. List the commercially important resources provided by ocean sediments.

Overview

This chapter focuses on how deep-sea sediments are collected, the types of marine sediment, and what the analysis of deep-sea sediments reveals about the Earth's history. A classification scheme for marine sediments is presented. There are four main types of marine sediments: lithogenous, biogenous, hydrogenous, and cosmogenous. The origin, composition, and distribution of each of the four types of sediments are discussed, including a section on mixtures. A summary of neritic (continental margin) and pelagic (deep-ocean) sediment is presented, followed by information about ocean sediments as a resource.

Headings covered in this chapter include:
Lithogenous Sediment
        Origin
        Composition
        Sediment Texture

Marine Sediments

       Distribution
Biogenous Sediment
       Origin
       Composition
       Sediment Texture
       Distribution
Hydrogenous Sediment
       Origin
       Composition and Distribution
Cosmogenous Sediment
       Origin, Composition, and Distribution
Mixtures
Distribution of Neritic and Pelagic Deposits: A Summary
Events Revealed by Sea Floor Sediments
Ocean Sediments as a Resource
       Petroleum
       Gas Hydrates
       Sand and Gravel
       Evaporative Salts
       Phosphorite (Phosphate Minerals)
       Manganese Nodules and Crusts
Special Features:
       Box 4-1: Diatoms: The Most Important Things You Have (Probably) Never Heard Of.
       Box 4-2: Research Methods in Oceanography: When a Sea was Dry: Clues from the Mediterranean.
       Box 4-3: Research Methods in Oceanography: When the Dinosaurs Died: The Cretaceous-Tertiary (K-T) Event.
       Box 4-4: Historical Feature: Collecting the Historical Record of the Deep-Ocean Floor.

Teacher's Resources

There is a wide assortment of good films/videos on marine sediments including:

Films/Videotapes
- A Planet in Motion (Ocean Drilling Program), 22 min.
- Deep Sea Drilling Project (Association Sterling Films), 28 min.
- History, Layer by Layer (McGraw-Hill), 23 min.
- The Bahamas: Where Limestones Grow Today (Modern Talking Picture Service), 40 min.
- The Ring of Truth: Clues (Phillip Morrison/PBS), 60 min (examines evidence for the drying of the Mediterranean Sea).
- Windows to the Past: Discovering the Earth's Future (Ocean Drilling program), 13 min.

CD-ROMs
- ODP: From Mountains to Monsoons (Joint Oceanographic Institutions)
- ODP: From Gateways to Glaciations (Joint Oceanographic Institutions)

Answers to End-of-Chapter Questions and Exercises

1. List and describe the characteristics of the four basic types of marine sediment.

Lithogenous: composed of fragments of preexisting rock material.
Biogenous: composed of the hard remains of dead marine organisms.
Hydrogenous: composed of material that is dissolved in water and precipitates to form deposits.
Cosmogenous: composed of material of extra-terrestrial origin.

2. How does lithogenous sediment originate?

Lithogenous sediment begins as rock material on continents or islands. Agents of weathering break the rock material into smaller pieces. Once the rock is in smaller pieces, it can be more easily eroded (picked up and transported) because smaller pieces require less energy to move. This eroded material is the basic component from which all lithogenous sediment is composed.

Eroded material form the continents is carried into the oceans by a variety of transporting media including streams, wind, glaciers, and gravity. The sediment can be deposited in bays or lagoons near the ocean, it can be transported further by waves along the beach to produce beach deposits along the shoreline, or it may be spread along the continental margin by currents. It can also be carried beyond the continental margin to the deep-ocean basin.

3. Why is lithogenous sediment composed of quartz grains? What is the chemical composition of quartz?

Most lithogenous sediments are composed of quartz grains because quartz is one of the most abundant and chemically stable minerals in the Earth's crust. Quartz is resistant to abrasion, and as a result, quartz can be transported large distances and deposited far from the source area. It should be no surprise that the majority of lithogenous sediment deposits are composed of quartz. Quartz is composed of silicon and oxygen (SiO_2).

4. If a deposit has a coarse grain size, what does that indicate about the energy of the transporting medium? Give several examples of various transporting media that would produce such a deposit.

Since sediment size is related to the energy condition under which the deposit was laid down, a coarse grain size indicates that the deposit was produced under high-energy conditions. Examples of high-energy transport media include streams with high velocity (such as flood conditions), strong wave energy, gravity, or glaciers.

5. What characteristics of marine sediment indicate increasing maturity? Give an example of a mature and immature sediment.

Sediment maturity increases with
*   decreasing clay content.
*   increased degree of sorting.
*   decrease of non-quartz minerals.
*   increasing rounding of particles

Marine Sediments

Well-sorted beach sand is an example of a mature sediment. A poorly sorted glacial deposit composed of angular fragments of different sizes is an example of an immature sediment.

6. List the two major chemical compounds of which most biogenous sediments are composed and the organisms that produce them. Sketch these organisms.

- Calcium carbonate ($CaCO_3$): Foraminiferans and coccolithophorids; also pteropods and ostracods. Sketches of foraminiferans and coccolithophorids should resemble Figure 4-10.
- Silica (SiO_2): Diatoms and radiolarians; also silicoflagellates. Sketches of diatoms and radiolarians should be similar to Figure 4-9.

7. What are the several reasons that diatoms are so remarkable? List the products that contain or are produced using diatomaceous earth.

Diatoms are microscopic, photosynthetic organisms with ornate cell walls. They reproduce both sexually and asexually, they exist as individual cells or colonial organisms, they are found in a diversity of habitats, and they are among the most abundant organisms on Earth. As primary producers in aquatic ecosystems, diatoms are at the base of the food chain in marine and freshwater environments.

The main commercial uses for diatomaceous earth include filters (sugar refinement, brewing, and swimming pool filters), mild abrasives (in products such as toothpaste, facial scrubs, and household cleaning and polishing compounds), and absorbents (chemical spills and as pest control), and as a chemical carrier (in paint and dynamite). Other products from diatomaceous earth include optical quality glass (because of the pure silica in diatom cell walls), space shuttle tiles (because they are lightweight and provide good insulation), and additive in concrete, a filler and anti-caking agent, and in building stone for housing construction.

8. If siliceous ooze is slowly but constantly dissolving in seawater, how can deposits of siliceous ooze accumulate on the sea floor?

One way that siliceous oozes accumulate on the ocean floor is for the rate of deposition of siliceous tests to exceed the rate of dissolution for the tests. In this case, siliceous tests will accumulate faster than they can be dissolved.

9. How do oozes differ from abyssal clay? Discuss how productivity, destruction, and dilution combine to determine whether an ooze or abyssal clay will form on the deep-ocean floor.

Oozes contain at least 30% biogenous particles (by weight), in contrast to abyssal clay that contains less than 30% biogenous material. The bulk of the remaining percentage (up to 70%) of abyssal clay deposits is comprised of lithogenous clays.

Whether an ooze forms is dependant on the relative rates of biogenous and lithogenous particle deposition. The deposition rate of biogenous particles is a function of the rate at which they are produced (productivity) versus the dissolution rate (destruction) in ocean water. The seawater dissolution rate for silica is slow and steady at all ocean depths, but increases significantly with increasing water depth for calcium carbonate. Finally, if the deposition rate for lithogenous particles is greater than the deposition rate for biogenous particles, the lithogenous particles will dilute the concentration of biogenous particles and biogenous ooze will never form as a result of this dilution.

10. Describe the environmental conditions (e.g. surface water temperature, productivity, dissolution, etc.) that influence the distribution of siliceous and calcareous ooze.

Deposits of siliceous and calcareous ooze are only found beneath areas where silica- or calcite-secreting organisms live in the surface waters above. Both are affected by dilution or other sediment types or dissolution at depth, which also limits their distribution (refer to Table 4-3).

    Deposits of siliceous ooze are generally found on the sea floor beneath cool surface water in high latitudes or on the sea floor beneath upwelling areas (such as near the Equator), where cool water is found at the ocean surface. Conversely, deposits of calcareous ooze are generally found on the sea floor beneath warm surface water in low latitudes and [AQ1]at not too great a depth (dissolved below the CCD).

11. Explain the stages of progression that results in calcareous ooze existing below the CCD.

Initially, calcareous ooze is deposited above the CCD (and there it will not dissolve) on a topographically high feature such as the mid-ocean ridge. Then, the calcareous ooze is covered by a deposit that is unaffected by the CCD such as an abyssal clay or siliceous ooze so that it is isolated from the environment. Finally, over millions of years, the ocean floor that was once at shallower depths is moved away from the mid-ocean ridge by the process of sea floor spreading, carrying with it the calcareous ooze covered by another sediment.

12. Describe manganese nodules, including what is known about how they form.

Manganese nodules are rounded, hard lumps of manganese, iron, and other metals up to 30 cm (12 in) long. When cut in half, the nodules often reveal that they have been formed by precipitating layers around a central nucleation object.

    The origin of manganese nodules continues to elude scientists. It is widely believed that the concentric layers of a manganese nodule form as a hydrogenous deposit around a central nucleation object. Scientists are still working on answering questions such as why manganese nodules have such high concentrations of manganese and why they are not buried by ocean floor sediment. Recent research suggests that the formation of manganese nodules may be aided by as not-yet-identified marine organisms.

13. Describe the most common types of cosmogenous sediment and give the probable source of these particles.

Cosmogenous sediment consists of the following main types:
- Microscopic spherules that are microscopic globular masses composed of silicate rock material (called tektites) or composed mostly of iron and nickel. Although they were once thought to be the product of meteors, it is now believed they are produced by collisions between asteroids, which produce microscopic space dust particles that drift harmlessly through the Earth's atmosphere.
- Macroscopic meteor debris that forms near an impact site when meteors collide with Earth at great speeds.

14. Describe the K-T event, including evidence for it and its effect on the environment.

The K-T event is a major extinction on Earth that occurred about 65 million years ago between the Cretaceous and Tertiary Periods of geologic time. Evidence indicates that a 16-km (10-mi) wide meteor

Marine Sediments

collided with the Earth off the Yucatan coast in the Gulf of Mexico during this time, leading to the extinction of dinosaurs and two-thirds of all plant and animal species on Earth (including marine species). The meteorite caused a gigantic splash wave and left a 190-km (120-mi) wide 30-km (20-mi) deep impact crater. It also ripped up large fragments from the sea floor and deposited iridium and shocked quartz around the globe, which have been recovered in core samples from the deep ocean. The impact could have kicked up so much dust that it blocked sunlight, chilled the Earth's surface, and brought about the extinction of dinosaurs and other species. Acid rains and global fires may have added to the environmental disaster. Additionally, such a large impact on Earth could easily have caused major volcanic activity to occur.

15. Why is lithogenous sediment the most common neritic deposit? Why are biogenous oozes the most common pelagic deposits?

Why is lithogenous sediment by far the most common type of neritic deposit? Why are biogenous oozes the most common pelagic deposits?

Lithogenous sediment is by far the most common type of neritic deposit because lithogenous material is derived in great quantity from the rocks on the nearby landmasses. The material is deposited rapidly near continental margins. It is such deposits that constitute the wedge of sediment underlying the continental shelf, slope, and rise.

One of the main reasons that biogenous oozes are the most common pelagic (deep-ocean) deposits is because there is so little lithogenous sediment deposited at great distance from the continents. Even though pelagic environments contain identifiable and even significant percentages of lithogenous and hydrogenous material, the deposition rates for sediments are low in the ocean basins that biogenous material dominates.

16. How do fecal pellets help explain why the particles found in the ocean surface waters are closely reflected in the particle composition of the sediment directly beneath? Why would one not expect this?

The small particle common to pelagic sediment would require form 10 to 50 years to sink to the ocean floor, so the sediment on the ocean floor would not be expected to be similar to makeup to the particle concentrations in the surface water immediately above. The slightest current would be expected to carry them from 3000 to 15,000 km (1860 to 9320 mi) laterally before they could reach the bottom. The fecal pellets incorporate small particles into larger packages that can sink to the ocean floor in 10 to 15 days, allowing the composition of bottom sediment to resemble closely the composition of the particle content of the surface water immediately above.

17. What kind of information can be obtained by examining and analyzing core samples?

By examining sediment cores retrieved form ocean drilling and interpreting them, oceanographers can ascertain events such as
- the timing of major extinctions
- global climate change
- plate movements
- historical information about the Earth's geology and biology.

18. Describe the process of how a drilling ship like the *JOIDES Resolution* obtains core samples from the

deep-ocean floor.

The drill ship *JOIDES Resolution* uses the rotary drilling method while holding its position at the surface constant with a dynamic positioning system to obtain deep-sea cores. The *Resolution* contains a tall metal drilling rig that is used to lower sections of drill pipe through an opening in the middle of the ship. The pipe is in individual sections of 9.5 m (31 ft), but can be screwed together to make a single string of pipe up to 9150 m (30,000 ft). The pipe string has on its end a rotating drill bit as it is pressed against the bottom rock, allowing the ship to drill deeper and deeper into the ocean floor. Like a twirling soda straw drilling into a layer cake, the drilling operation crushes rock around the outside and retains a cylinder of rock (core sample) on the inside of the pipe. The drill crew lowers the core-recovering equipment through the string of drill pipe. Once cores are retrieved form inside the pipe, they are collected and processed by scientists.

19. Discuss the present importance and the future prospects for the production of petroleum; sand and gravel; phosphorite; and manganese nodules and crusts.

Petroleum production from marine deposits represents more than 95% of the value of nonliving resources exploited from oceans. Offshore petroleum will provide an increasing percentage of the oil and gas that provides most of our energy requirements in future years. Beyond the year 2020, the availability of conventionally produced petroleum will probably not be sufficient to meet the demand, and more exotic forms of petroleum recovery will be exploited.

    Sand and gravel recovered from offshore is the next most valuable marine mineral resource after petroleum. It is used for beach fill, landfill, and concrete aggregate. Also, diamonds, tin, platinum, and gold have been recovered by offshore dredging. Nearshore mining operations may damage present beaches. If they are conducted too close to the beaches, they may cause beach sediment to move offshore.

    Phosphorite is used as fertilizer but has not been mined commercially from the marine environment and probably will not be until well in the future.

    Polymetallic crusts and nodules have created a lot of interest in the past three decades because of the abundance of manganese and other metals contained within them, but they will not be likely mined until later in the twenty-first century.

20. What are gas hydrates, where are they found, and why are they important?

Gas hydrates (also known as clathrates) are a combination of two substances: water and natural gas, usually methane. They are found in deep-ocean sediments where pressures are high and temperatures are low. Generally, they are found at depths below 525 m (1720 ft) and are concentrated along continental margins, where high productivity waters enrich ocean floor sediments below with organic matter. Here, natural gas is trapped inside a lattice-like cage of water molecules.

    Gas hydrates have generated much scientific interest because their methane content may be potentially the world's largest useable energy source today. Also, there is interest in knowing what role they play in sea floor instability and as contributors to global warming. Additionally, methane seeps support a rich community of organisms, many of which are species new to science.

5
Water and Seawater

Learning Objectives

The instructional objectives are performance-based and detail specific learning outcomes for Chapter 5. The test items contained in the Test Bank are keyed to the learning objectives and key questions. The order of the objectives mirrors the content presentation in Chapter 5.

Upon completion of this chapter, the student should be able to:

1. Differentiate between an **atom** and a **molecule**.

2. Describe the structure of an atom including the arrangement, relative size, and charge of the subatomic particles, **proton**, **neutron**, and **electron**.

3. Define **ion** and give an example.

4. Discuss the formation of **covalent bonds** between atoms.

5. Explain how the geometry of the water molecule contributes to its **polarity**.

6. Describe the formation of **hydrogen bonds** and discuss how hydrogen bonding between water molecules affects the physical and chemical properties of water.

7. List the reasons why water is considered a universal solvent.

8. Outline how hydrogen bonding affects the thermal properties of water.

9. Distinguish between **heat** and **temperature** and give the units of measurement for each.

10. Define:
    A. **melting point**.
    B. **freezing point**.
    C. **boiling point**.
    D. **condensation point**.

11. Compare and contrast **heat capacity** and **latent heat**.

12. Discuss how the physical properties of water affect global climate including marine and continental effects.

13. Explain how the geometry of the water molecule affects the density of water as it changes states of matter.

14. Define **salinity** and discuss its origin and concentration in seawater.

15. Restate the **principle of constant proportions**.

16. Name the instrument used to accurately measure dissolved salts in seawater.

17. Discuss the factors that affect the salinity of coastal and surface ocean waters.

18. List the processes that decrease seawater salinity.

19. List the processes that increase seawater salinity.

20. Draw and explain the hydrologic cycle.

21. Define **residence time** and discuss the implications of residence time for substances dissolved in seawater.

22. Distinguish between an **acid** and an **alkaline** (**base**) and describe how the relative concentrations of ions are measured.

23. Discuss the forms of dissolved carbon dioxide that exist in the ocean and the relationship between water pH and the form of dissolved carbon dioxide that is present.

24. Outline how salinity varies with depth in the ocean.

25. Outline how density varies with ocean depth.

26. Differentiate between a **halocline**, a **pycnocline**, and a **thermocline** and discuss the location of each in the ocean.

27. Discuss the two box ocean (mixed surface layer and deep water) and describe the separation of these water masses.

28. Outline common methods for desalination and discuss their commercial viability.

Overview

This chapter presents an overview of one of the most remarkable substances on Earth, water. Important aspects of the chemical and physical properties are discussed. Many students will find that the background information on atomic structures is a review. Reviewing atomic structure is essential to understanding the basis for water's unusual geometry, the polarity resulting from geometric spacing of oxygen and hydrogen atoms, and the ability of water to serve as a universal solvent. Additional information about chemistry is included at the end of the book in Appendix IV, *A Chemical Background:*

Water and Seawater

Why Water Has 2H's and 1O. A discussion of water's thermal properties follows, in addition to

information about the factors affecting the density of water. The focus of the chapter is the properties of seawater. Topics include various aspects of seawater salinity such as salinity variations, how dissolved components are added and/or removed form seawater, acidity and alkalinity of seawater, processes affecting salinity variation and how salinity affects seawater density. In summary, the properties of pure water are contrasted with seawater. The chapter concludes with a discussion of desalination techniques.

Teacher's Resources

There is a wide assortment of good films/videos on introductory chemistry, including:

Films/Videotapes
- Chemical Bond and Atomic Structure (University of Illinois),16 min.
- Chemical Changes All About Us (Coronet), 14 min.
- Physics and Chemistry of Water (BFA Educational Media), 21 min.
- The World of Chemistry: Water (Program #12) (The Annenberg/CPB Collection), 28 min.

Answers to End-of-Chapter Questions and Exercises

1. Sketch a model of an atom, showing the positions of the subatomic particles protons, neutrons, and electrons.

The sketch should look like Figure 5-1.

2. Describe what conditions exist in water molecules to make them dipolar.

The unusual geometry of the water molecule is what causes water molecules to be dipolar. Both hydrogen atoms are on the same side of the oxygen atom, separated by 105°. This makes the side of the oxygen atom where they attach possess an excess of positive charge as the hydrogen nuclei are somewhat exposed. The electrons from the hydrogen atoms are spending most of their time on the side near the oxygen atom, which gives that side of the water molecules a net negative charge. As a result, water molecules are dipolar (having separate charges).

3. Sketch several water molecules, showing all covalent and hydrogen bonds. Be sure to indicate the polarity of each water molecule.

The sketch should resemble Figure 5-3, with covalent bonds within the water molecule and hydrogen bonds between adjacent water molecules. The side of the water molecule that has two hydrogen atoms has a net positive charge.

4. How does hydrogen bonding produce the surface tension phenomenon of water?

Within a mass of water, hydrogen bonds can be oriented in all directions, but they must be oriented sideways or down in the surface molecules. There is a greater amount of energy put into the lateral bonds at the water surface. This results in a strong skin-like surface layer of water molecules that creates the phenomenon known as surface tension.

5. Discuss how the dipolar nature of the water molecule makes it such an effective solvent of ionic compounds.

Because of their dipolar nature, water molecules can weaken an electrical field to 1/80th of its normal intensity by aligning themselves in it. This reduces the strength of the electrical bond between ions in an

Water and Seawater

ionic compound, and as the positive ends of the water molecule are attracted to the negative ends and vice versa, this further reduces the energy available for ion-to-ion bonds. Eventually, each ion is hydrated, or surrounded, by water molecules and pulled out of the crystalline network.

6. Describe the differences between the three states of matter, using the arrangement of molecules in your explanation.

The three states of matter are solid, liquid, and gas.
- In the *solid* state (ice), water has a rigid form and structure and does not flow. Bonds are constantly being broken and reformed. Nonetheless, the prevailing bond between molecules is one of rather stable attachment produced by the nearness of the molecules; this causes the van der Waals force to be greater. In the solid state, the molecules vibrate with energy but remain in relatively fixed positions.
- In the *liquid* state (water), water molecules are unstructured and can flow and take the shape of the container. The molecules have gained enough energy to overcome many of the van der Waals forces that bound them together in the solid state. The molecules are free to move relative to one another, but they are still attracted to one another. Bonds are being formed and broken at a much greater rate than in the solid state.
- In the *gaseous* state (water vapor), molecules are unstructured and flow very freely, filling the volume of whatever container they are placed in. Molecules now are moving at random, and there exists no significant attraction among individual molecules (the molecules are independent of one another). The only effect that one molecule may have on another results form the collision during random movement.

7. Why are the freezing and boiling points of water higher than would be expected for a compound of its molecular makeup?

This is because not only van der Waals bonds (these must be overcome in changing the state of matter in all substances) but also hydrogen bonds (that are stronger than intermolecular bonds) must be overcome in the change of state for water. It takes more energy to overcome these bonds, resulting in a much higher freezing and boiling point for water when compared to other similar chemical compounds.

8. How does the heat capacity of water compare with that of other substances? Describe the effect that this has on climate.

The heat capacity of water is higher than that of most commonly occurring substances. As a result, coastal climates are milder with a much narrower temperature range than inland regions. This is because coastal water can gain or loose the same amount of heat as inland rocks and soil while undergoing only about half of the temperature change.

9. The heat energy added as latent heat of melting and latent heat of vaporization does not increase water temperature. Explain why this occurs, and where the energy is used.

The heat energy added as latent heat of melting and latent heat of vaporization is used to break hydrogen bonds, so the water temperature does not increase.

10. Why is the latent heat of vaporization so much greater than the latent heat of melting?

The latent heat of vaporization is much greater because to change water from a solid to a liquid, only a small percentage of the hydrogen bonds need to be broken. To convert liquid water to water vapor, every hydrogen bond must be broken.

11. Describe how excess heat absorbed by Earth's low-latitude regions is transferred to heat-deficient higher latitude through a process that uses water's latent heat of vaporization.

To evaporate one gram of water from the ocean in the subtropics where the temperature of water is 20°C requires 585 cal of heat energy. This energy is contained in the evaporated water molecules as they are transported to higher latitudes by the westerly wind belts. At about 60° latitude, the air that is carrying the water rises, cools, and the water condenses as precipitation. For every gram of water that condenses, 585 cal of heat is released into the atmosphere at this latitude.

12. As water cools, two distinct changes take place in the behavior of the molecules: their slower movement tends to increase density, whereas the formation of bulky ice crystals decreases density. Describe how the relative rates of their occurrence cause pure water to have a temperature of maximum density at 4°C (32.9°F) and make ice much less dense than liquid water.

In liquid water at all temperatures, there are molecules in two stages:
1. bound to one another by hydrogen bonds, and
2. free unbound molecules.
As the molecules loose energy and the water cools, the unbound molecules occupy less space making the water denser. At the same time, more and more of the low energy molecules will form hydrogen bonds with their neighbors. As water cools above 4°C, density increases because the dominant process is the clumping together of unbound molecules. However, below a temperature of 4°C, the dominant process is the formation of clusters of molecules held together by hydrogen bonds. This process produces an increase in the volume of water with decreasing temperature, because the crystalline lattice is an open structure that increases the distance between water molecules. Eventually, almost all of the water molecules will be part of this crystalline structure held together by hydrogen bonds, and the liquid water will become ice.

13. What is your state sales tax, in parts per thousand?

This answer will vary depending upon the state and location. Here in Athens, Georgia (where the University of Georgia is located), sales tax in 2004 is 8%, or 80 ‰.

14. What are goiters? How can they be avoided?

Goiters are an enlargement of the human thyroid gland caused by iodine deficiency. Goiters can be avoided by including trace amounts of iodine in the diet. Products of marine origin contain trace amounts of iodine.

15. What condition of salinity makes it possible to determine the total salinity of ocean water by measuring the concentration of only one constituent, the chloride ion?

The *Principle of Constant Proportions* states that the major dissolved constituents that comprise the salinity of seawater occur nearly everywhere in the ocean in the exact same proportions, independent of

Water and Seawater

salinity. Since the relative abundance of the major constituents of salinity is essentially constant, one can calculate the total salinity after determining the concentration of a single major constituent. The most abundant major constituent in seawater is the chloride ion (Cl^-), which is most commonly used to determine salinity. Its concentration (called *chlorinity*) is also expressed in parts per thousand. The conversion formula is:

$$\text{Salinity (\%o)} = \text{Chlorinity (\%o)} \times 1.80655$$

16. List some major achievements of the voyage of the HMS *Challenger*.

In its nearly three-and-a-half year voyage, the crew of the HMS *Challenger* made 492 deep-sea soundings, 133 bottom dredges, 151 open water trawls, and 263 serial water temperature observations. The crew also accomplished netting and classifying 4717 new species of marine life, measuring a record depth of 8158 m in the Mariana Trench, and collecting 77 ocean water samples that were later analyzed by chemist William Dittmar.

17. What physical conditions create brackish water in the Baltic Sea and hypersaline water in the Red Sea?

The Baltic Sea is an enclosed sea that receives much freshwater input from streams that drain much of Europe, producing brackish water there. Conversely, the Red Sea is an enclosed sea that receives little freshwater input owing to the dry climate. It is characterized by a high evaporation rate that removes mostly freshwater and causes the Red Sea to have hypersaline conditions.

18. Describe the ways that dissolved components are added and removed from seawater.

Dissolved components of seawater are primarily added by streams that dissolve the ions from continental rocks and carry them to the sea and by volcanic eruptions, both on land and on the sea floor. Other sources of dissolved components include the atmosphere (which contributes gases that are dissolved in seawater) and biological interactions.

Dissolved components of seawater are removed in many ways. Along mid-ocean ridges, the infiltration of seawater near hydrothermal vents causes magnesium and sulfate ions to become incorporated into sea floor mineral deposits. These hydrothermal vents directly and actively influence the chemical composition of seawater. It has been estimated that the *entire volume of ocean water* is recycled through this hydrothermal circulation at the mid-ocean ridge every three million years. Therefore, the chemical exchange between ocean water and basaltic crust has a major influence on the nature of ocean water. Other methods of removal include the formation of salt spray by waves; deposition in ocean sediments within the shells of dead microscopic organisms and animal feces; the drying of inland arms of the sea; and by adsorption (physical attachment) to the surfaces of sinking clay and biological particles.

19. List the components (reservoirs) of the hydrologic cycle that hold water on earth and the percentage of Earth's water in each one. Describe the processes by which water moves among these reservoirs.

Earth's water reservoirs:
- Oceans=97%
- Glaciers=2%
- Groundwater=0.6%

- Rivers and lakes=0.02%
- Atmosphere=0.001%

Water is evaporated from the surface of the oceans, rivers, and lakes, is transported while stored as water vapor in the atmosphere, and eventually returned to the Earth's surface as precipitation. The precipitation that falls on the continents is transported back into the oceans by flowing through lakes and rivers and as groundwater.

20. Explain the difference between an acid and an alkali (base) substance. How does the ocean's buffering system work?

An acid is a compound containing hydrogen that when dissolved in water, releases hydrogen ions (H^+), increasing the number of these ions per unit of water mass. A strong acid is one whose molecules readily release hydrogen ions when present in a dilute solution. The term alkali or base refers to compounds that when dissolved in water, dissociate and increase the presence of hydroxyl ions (OH^-). A strong base is a compound whose molecules readily release hydroxyl ions in dilute solutions.

The carbonate buffering system serves to moderate changes in the pH of the ocean and has kept the ocean at a stable pH for long periods of time. If for any reason the pH of the ocean rises, chemical reactions proceed to release H^+ and lower the ocean's pH. If the pH of the ocean decreases, chemical reactions raise the pH by removing H^+. Buffering has been responsible for maintaining the ocean's pH at an average of 8.1 with little variation through time.

21. Explain why there is such a wide variation of surface salinity, but such a narrow range of salinity at depth.

The wide range of salinity at the surface results from the processes that affect seawater salinity: precipitation, runoff, iceberg melting, sea ice melting or forming, and evaporation. All of these are surface processes and do not occur at depth.

22. Why is there such a close association between (a) the curve showing seawater density variation with ocean depth and (b) the curve showing seawater temperature variation with ocean depth?

The similarity between the two curves is not surprising because the main factor affecting seawater density is temperature.

23. Compare and contrast the following seawater desalination methods: distillation, solar humidification, and reverse osmosis.

- *Distillation*: water is boiled and the vapors are collected as freshwater in a condenser. This method requires a large energy input.
- *Solar humidification*: Solar heat evaporates water from a seawater reservoir that is covered. The vapor condenses on the cover and runs into trays around the edge of the cover to be collected in a freshwater reservoir. It has been used in large-scale projects and requires no additional energy input.
- *Reverse osmosis*: Seawater is separated from a freshwater reservoir by a water-permeable membrane. Normally, freshwater would flow through the membrane into the seawater, but in reverse osmosis, pressure is applied to the seawater reservoir forcing seawater molecules through the membrane into the freshwater reservoir—the reverse of osmosis.

Water and Seawater

24. Explain how an ocean thermal energy conversion (OTEC) unit generates electricity (a labeled diagram might help).

Responses to this question will vary. The drawing should resemble Figure 5C; alternately, a flow diagram should include these steps:
1. Vaporized ammonia passes through turbines to generate electricity.
2. Cold water pumped up from beneath the thermocline cools the vaporized ammonia, converting it to a liquid.
3. Warm surface water is used to vaporize the ammonia again so that it can pass through the turbine again to generate more electricity.

CHAPTER
6
Air-Sea Interaction

Learning Objectives

The instructional objectives are performance-based and detail specific learning outcomes for Chapter 6. The test items contained in the Test Bank are keyed to the learning objectives and key questions. The order of the objectives mirrors the content presentation in Chapter 6.

Upon completion of this chapter, the student should be able to:

1. Define the Earth's **ecliptic** and describe its effect on the Earth's climate.

2. Describe the Earth's season including the:
    a. **vernal equinox.**
    b. **summer solstice.**
    c. **autumnal equinox.**
    d. **winter solstice.**

3. Define **declination** as it relates to the Sun, the Earth, and global climate variation.

4. Describe the location of the following:
    a. **Tropic of Cancer.**
    b. **Tropic of Capricorn.**
    c. **Arctic Circle.**
    d. **Antarctic Circle.**

5. Define **albedo** and the effect of differential albedo (ice/snow, land, and water) on climate.

6. Detail the following atmospheric properties:
    a. chemical composition.
    b. temperature.
    c. density.
    d. water vapor content.
    e. pressure.
    f. movement.

7. Explain the relationship between the solar heating of the Earth and convection cells on a non-spinning Earth.

8. Discuss the effect of a rotating Earth on the direction of wind and water movement.

Air-Sea Interaction

9. Draw and label the major global circulation patterns and the corresponding wind belts (remember that winds are named for the direction from which they blow) including: **Hadley cells, Ferrel cells,** and **polar cells, trade winds (northeast trades & southeast trades), westerlies,** and **polar easterlies.**

10. Describe the location, direction of air movement, and corresponding air pressure for: **subtropical highs, polar highs, equatorial lows,** and **subpolar lows.**

11. Distinguish between the **doldrums,** the **horse latitudes,** and the **polar front** and give the location of each.

12. Define the **Intertropical Convergence Zone (ITCZ)** .

13. Differentiate between **weather** and **climate.**

14. Describe the relationship between air pressure and wind direction in **cyclonic flow** and **anticyclonic flow.**

15. List the factors in the development of **land breezes** and **sea breezes.**

16. Explain how **storms** form, the relationship between **jet stream** position and storm movement, and make the distinction between **warm fronts** and **cold fronts.**

17. Give the distinction between a **hurricane,** and **typhoon,** and a **cyclone** and the location where these weather phenomena occur.

18. Provide a brief explanation of the **Safir-Simpson Scale.**

19. List the severe hurricanes, typhoons, and cyclones (and the location of landfall) that have damaged the coastal areas during the twentieth century.

20. Draw the Earth and label the following oceanic climate patterns on your sketch including: the **equatorial region,** the **tropical regions,** the **subtropical regions,** the **temperate regions,** the **subpolar regions,** and the **polar regions.**

21. Differentiate between **sea ice, shelf ice,** and **icebergs** and describe the formation of each.

22. List the atmospheric gases that contribute to the **greenhouse effect.**

23. Outline the Earth's **heat budget.**

24. Detail potential changes in the Earth's climate as a result of increased global warming.

25. Suggest ways in which you personally can decrease your contribution to global atmospheric greenhouse gas production.

26. Describe the ocean's role in minimizing the effect of increased global atmospheric carbon dioxide.

Overview

This chapter explores the coupling of the atmosphere and the ocean as a single system. The chapter opens with a discussion of the effects of uneven distribution of solar energy and the resultant uneven heating of the Earth's surface. The Coriolis Effect is presented and examples of how the Coriolis Effect operates are included. The background information at the beginning of the chapter is applied later in the chapter in a discussion about atmospheric circulation cells. Atmospheric phenomena that are related to the oceans are presented including wind patterns, storms, and tropical cyclones. A discussion of the global climate pattern of the oceans follows. The chapter concludes with a discussion about the global greenhouse effect and possible solutions to increasing atmospheric concentrations of greenhouse gases.

Headings covered in this chapter include:
Earth's Seasons
Uneven Solar Heating Effects
    Distribution of Solar Energy
    Oceanic Heat Flow
Atmospheric Physical Properties
    Composition
    Temperature
    Density
    Water Vapor Content
    Pressure
    Movement
Coriolis Effect Influence On Moving Objects
    Example 1: Perspective and Frames of Reference on a Merry-Go-Round
    Example 2: A Tale of Two Missiles
Global Atmospheric Circulation
    Circulation Cells
    Pressure
    Wind Belts
    Boundaries
    Circulation Cells: Idealized or Real?
Oceanic Weather and Climate Patterns
    Weather versus Climate
    Winds
    Sea and Land Breezes
    Storms and Fronts
    Tropical Cyclones
    Ocean's Climate Patterns
Sea Ice and Iceberg Formation
    Formation of Sea Ice
    Formation of Icebergs
Atmospheric Greenhouse Effect
    Earth's Heat Budget
    Which Gases Contribute to the Greenhouse Effect?
    What Changes Will Occur as a Result of Increased Global Warming?
    What Should Be Done to Reduce Greenhouse Gases?
    The IPCC and the Kyoto Protocol

Air-Sea Interaction

Teacher's Resources

There are a wide assortment of good films/videos and CD-ROMs on the ocean and global weather, including:

Films/Videotapes
- Air-Sea Interaction (Encyclopedia Britannica), 15 minutes
- Atmospheric Science Series: Global Winds (Coronet), 12 minutes
- Danger's Edge (The Weather Channel), 25 minutes (subject: hurricanes)
- Hurricane Force: A Coastal Perspective and Anatomy of a Hurricane (University of California), 34 minutes
- Nature of Sea Water (Local Naval District, Film MN-103-17), 29 minutes
- The Gulf Stream (Bullfrog Films), 28 minutes (emphasizes oceanic climate belts).
- Underwater Sound – Basic Principles (Local Naval District, Film MN-10287), 29 minutes

CD-ROMs
- Everything Weather (The Weather Channel)
- Embracing Earth: Global Change (InterNetwork MEDIA)
- GeoMedia (InterNetwork MEDIA)
- TOPEX/POSEIDON: Perspectives on an Ocean Planet (Jet Propulsion Laboratory)
- NSCAT Winds of Change (Jet Propulsion Laboratory)
- Sea Ice in the Polar Regions & The Arctic Observatory (NASA)
- The Atmosphere (Videodiscovery, Inc).

Answers to End-of-Chapter Questions and Exercises

1. Describe the effect on Earth as a result of Earth's axis of rotation being angled 23.5 degrees from perpendicular relative to the ecliptic. What would happen if the Earth were not tilted on its axis?

Because the Earth is titled 23.5° from perpendicular relative to the ecliptic as it moves around the Sun, the Sun shines directly on the Southern Hemisphere between the latitudes between the latitudes of 0° and 23.5° for half of a year and on the Northern Hemisphere at the same latitude for the other half of a year. This produces the Earth's seasons. At the Northern Hemisphere summer and winter solstices, the Sun is at its most northerly and southerly positions relative to the Earth's surface (the Tropic of Cancer is 23.5°N and the Tropic of Capricorn is 23.5°S latitude, respectively). At these times, the portions of the Earth's surface below the Antarctic Circle (66.5°S) and above the Arctic Circle (66.5°N) receive no solar radiation from the Sun. It should be noted that when these areas are not receiving sunlight, the opposite pole is receiving continuous sunlight with no night.

2. Along the Arctic Circle, how would the Sun appear during the summer solstice? During the winter Solstice?

At regions above the Arctic Circle (66.5°N or higher latitude) during the Northern Hemisphere summer solstice, there would be continual daylight (midnight sun). During the Northern Hemisphere winter solstice, there would be perpetual darkness (no sunrise). At regions above the Antarctic Circle (66.5°S latitude or higher), during the Northern Hemisphere summer solstice, there would be continual darkness (no sunrise). While during the Northern Hemisphere winter solstice, there would be perpetual daylight (midnight sun).

3. Since there is an annual net heat loss at high latitudes and a net annual heat gain at low latitudes, why does the temperature difference between these regions not increase?

Heat is transferred from the low latitudes to the high latitudes by atmospheric winds and ocean currents.

4. Describe the physical properties of the atmosphere, including its composition, temperature, density, water vapor content, pressure, and movement.

The relationship between temperature, density, water vapor content, and pressure in the atmosphere is complex. The *composition* of the atmosphere (dry air) is:
- Nitrogen (N_2)=78.1%
- Oxygen (O_2)=20.9%
- Argon (Ar)=0.9%
- Carbon dioxide (CO_2)=0.035%
- All others=trace

Within the troposphere, the *temperature* of the atmosphere gets cooler with increasing distance form the Earth's surface. The atmosphere's *density* is strongly related to temperature (among other properties) such as warm air is less dense (so it rises) and that cool air has a greater density (so it sinks). The *water vapor content* of the atmosphere changes with temperature: warm air can hold more water vapor and is typically moist, while cool air is typically dry. Atmospheric *pressure* is related to the weight of the air column above (static case) or, for moving air (dynamic case), sinking air (movement toward the surface) causes high pressure at the surface and rising air (movement away from the surface) causes low pressure at the surface. In terms of *movement*, air always moves from high pressure to low pressure regions.

5. Describe the Coriolis effect in the Northern and Southern Hemispheres and include a discussion of why the effect increases with increased latitude.

The Coriolis effect causes objects in motion in the Northern Hemisphere to veer right of their intended course while objects in the motion in the Southern Hemisphere tend to veer to the left. The Coriolis effect is a result of the fact that points at different latitudes on the Earth rotate at different velocities ranging form 0 kilometers per hour at the poles to 1600 kilometers (1000 miles) per hour at the Equator. Since the rate of change of rotational velocity per degree of latitude is greater at higher latitudes, the effect is greater there. For instance, the change in the rate of Earth's rotation is 200 kilometers (124 miles) per hour from the Equator to 30 degrees latitude, while over the same number of degrees of latitude from 60 degrees latitude to the pole the change is 800 kilometers (500 miles) per hour.

Air-Sea Interaction

6. Sketch the pattern of surface wind belts on Earth, showing atmospheric circulation cells, zones of high and low pressure, the names of the wind belts, and the names of the boundaries between wind belts.

The sketch should resemble Figure 6-10.

7. Why are there high-pressure caps at each pole and a low-pressure belt in the equatorial region?

The different pressures observed in these two regions results primarily from temperature differences in the columns of air overlying each of these regions. The air over the Equator and at 60 degrees north or south latitude is rising due to being heated, while cold air descends over the poles and at 30 degrees north or south latitude.

8. Discuss why are the idealized belts of high and low atmospheric pressures shown in Figure 6-10 are modified (see Figure 6-11).

The idealized circulation cells are modified because the continents have a lower heat capacity than the oceans. Therefore, the continents will heat up to higher temperatures in the summer and cool to lower temperatures during the winter than will the oceans. This heating and cooling produces summer low-pressure cells and winter high-pressure cells over the continents that modify the idealized high and low pressure belts described by Figure 6-10.

9. What is the difference between weather and climate? If it rains in a particular area during the day, does that mean that the area has a wet climate? Explain.

Weather describes the conditions of the atmosphere at a given time and place, whereas climate is the long-term average of weather. If it rains in a particular area during the day, it does not necessarily mean that the area has a wet climate. For instance, if it rains one day in an area that is characterized as having an arid climate, the climate does not change – it just happened to have rain in its weather that day.

10. Describe the difference between cyclonic and anticyclonic flow, and show the how the Coriolis effect is important in producing both a clockwise and a counterclockwise flow pattern.

As air moves away from high-pressure cells and toward low-pressure cells, the Coriolis effect modifies the direction of air movement. In the Northern Hemisphere, this results in a counter-clockwise flow of air around low-pressure cells (called cyclonic flow) and a clockwise flow of air around high-pressure cells (called anticyclonic flow) (refer to Figure 6-12). Note that in the Southern Hemisphere, the directions of air flow are reversed.

11. How do sea breezes and land breezes form? During a hot summer day, which one would be most common and why?

Sea breezes and land breezes are caused by differential heating of land and ocean surfaces and are common in coastal areas. When an equal amount of solar energy is applied to both land and ocean, the land heats up about five times more due its lower heat capacity. The land heats the air around it, and during the afternoon, the warm, low-density air over the land rises. This rising air creates a low-pressure region over the land and causes the cooler air over the ocean to be pulled toward the lab, creating what is called a sea breeze. This condition is most pronounced on a hot summer day. At night, the land surface cools about five times more rapidly than the ocean and cools the air around it. This cool, high-density air sinks, creates a high-pressure region, and causes the wind to blow from the land. This is known as a land breeze, which is commonly well developed in the late evening and early morning hours.

12. Name the polar and tropical air masses that affect U.S. weather. Describe the pattern of movement across the continent and patterns of precipitation associated with warm and cold fronts.

The major polar air masses that affect weather across the United States are the polar maritime air masses of the North Pacific and North Atlantic oceans as well as the polar continental air mass that originates over Canada. Tropical maritime air masses originate from the tropical Pacific and Atlantic oceans as well as the Caribbean Sea. A tropical continental air mass that originates over Mexico also affects United States weather.

       Warm and cold fronts are influenced by the prevailing westerlies and generally move across the United States from west to east. In either case where a warm or cold front is produced, the less dense, warmer air always rises above the denser cold air. The rising air cools, and the water vapor in it condenses and falls as precipitation. A cold front is usually steeper, and the temperature difference across it is greater than a warm front. Therefore, rainfall along a cold front is usually heavier and briefer than rainfall along a warm front.

13. What are the conditions needed for the formation of a tropical cyclone? Why do most mid-latitude areas only rarely experience a hurricane? Why are there no hurricanes at the Equator?

The conditions needed for the formation of a tropical cyclone are:
- Warm ocean water greater than 25°C (77°F) that supplies the heat energy to the atmosphere by evaporation.
- Warm moist air that supplies additional heat as the water vapor in the air condenses.
- The Coriolis effect that causes the hurricane to spin (that's why there are no hurricanes on the Equator where the Coriolis effect is minimal). The air flowing toward the low-pressure center of a hurricane veers to its right in the Northern Hemisphere and to the left in the Southern Hemisphere, producing counterclockwise and clockwise rotation, respectively.

These conditions are found during the late summer and early fall, when the tropical and subtropical oceans are at their maximum temperature.

       The reason why most mid-latitude areas only rarely experience a hurricane is because ocean water temperature rarely gets warm enough to keep a hurricane going (however, there have been some notable exceptions to his when strong hurricanes reach the mid-latitudes). Once a hurricane travels over land or cool water, its energy source has been cut off, and it usually rapidly decreases in strength.

       There are no hurricanes at the Equator because the Coriolis effect is minimal there, preventing the storm from spinning.

14. Describe the major types of destruction caused by hurricanes. Of those, which one causes the majority of fatalities and destruction?

Destruction from hurricanes is caused by high wind speeds and because of flooding due to intense rainfall. The majority of a hurricane's fatalities and destruction is caused by a phenomenon called *storm surge*. A storm surge occurs when a hill of water that is created by winds moving toward the eye of the storm comes ashore. In severe hurricanes, storm surges can be up to 12 meters (40 feet) in height. Storm surge increases when storm landfall coincides with a spring tide (full moon or new moon) and occurs at

Air-Sea Interaction

high tide.

15. How are the ocean's climate belts (Figure 6-20) related to the broad patterns of air circulation described in Figure 6-10? What are some areas where the two are not closely related?

Equatorial: At the Equator, there is a great amount of atmospheric heating by radiation; the air is moving primarily in a vertical direction as it rises. The rising air is very humid, and when it cools by expansion daily rainfall keeps the salinity of the equatorial surface water lower than the salinity of the subtropical surface ocean. The lack of horizontal air motion at the Equator was termed the "doldrums" by sailors.

Tropical: A strong flow of northeasterly and southeasterly Trade Winds in the Northern Hemisphere and Southern Hemisphere, respectively, push the equatorial currents and produce moderately rough seas. Near the ends of the summer season in both hemispheres, hurricanes and typhoons move across this region as they carry heat from the equatorial low-pressure system into higher latitudes. There is low precipitation level in the higher latitude portion of these belts and the amount of precipitation increases toward the Equator.

Subtropical: Centered in the descending air masses at about 30 degrees north and south latitude, there are weak winds and ocean currents. This descending dry air evaporates large quantities of ocean water producing the highest surface salinities in the open ocean. Strong boundary currents do move along the western margin of the ocean basins at these latitudes carrying an intense flow of low latitude warn water into the cooler high latitude portions of the oceans.

Temperate: Westerly Wind belts drive ocean currents form west to east across this belt of the ocean where winter storms can be severe and accompanied by high precipitation rates as the cold polar air masses meet the warmer air masses represented by the westerly winds. The largest wind-generated waves are found in this region-particularly in the Southern Hemisphere.

Subpolar: The sea is covered in the winter by sea ice that melts away during the summer, and the ocean surface temperature remains about 5°C (41°F).

Polar: The water temperature remains near freezing throughout the year and the surface is covered by sea ice year-round. There is no night during the summer and no daylight during the winter in these regions of the Arctic and Southern Oceans.

16. What cause the sinking of RMS *Titanic*? What international organization formed after the sinking of the *Titanic* to prevent other such disasters?

On the evening of April 14, 1912, the RMS *Titanic* sideswiped a huge iceberg in the North Atlantic and sustained a 100-meter (330-foot) slash in the hull. Her compartments began to fill with water, causing the ship to tip towards the front and resulting in more compartments filling with water. Within two-and-a-half hours after impacting the iceberg, the ship broke in half and sank.

This tragedy brought about the passage of more stringent safety rules for ships and the formation of the International Ice Patrol, initiated immediately after the disaster. Today, the United States Coast Guard performs this function.

17. Describe the fundamental difference between solar radiation absorbed at the Earth's surface and the radiation that is primarily responsible for heating Earth's atmosphere.

The atmosphere is particularly transparent to visible radiation directed at Earth from the Sun and absorbs very little of it. It is absorbed at the Earth's surface by oceans and continents and radiated back toward space as infrared radiation. This form of radiation is readily absorbed by the water vapor and carbon dioxide in the atmosphere, so it is primarily this radiation from Earth that heats the atmosphere.

18. Discuss the greenhouse gases in terms of their relative concentrations and relative contributions to any increased greenhouse effect.

A comparison of greenhouses gases on a per molecule basis gives the following relationship: methane (CH_4): nitrous oxide (N_2O), ozone (O_3), CFC-11 (chloroflourocarbon-11) and CFC-12 (chloroflurocarbon-12) respectively: 25; 200; 2000; 12,000; and 15,000 times more effective than carbon dioxide (CO_2) at absorbing infrared radiation. However, based on their relative abundance in the atmosphere, CO_2, CH_4, N_2O, O_3, CFC-11, and CFC12 contribute to the current greenhouse effect in the following percentages, respectively: 60; 15; 5; 8; 4; and 8 (refer to Table 6-6).

19. Describe the iron hypothesis, and discuss the relative merits and dangers of undertaking a project that could cause dramatic changes in the global environment.

The iron hypothesis is an experimental technique for increasing primary productivity (thereby reducing the atmospheric carbon dioxide concentration) by fertilizing the ocean with finely ground iron. Preliminary results indicate that the iron hypothesis has promise; it could be attempted on a larger scale than in the trials. However, it should be noted that global engineering could produce more harm than benefit. It is unknown at this time what other kind of effects are likely in the ocean and the atmosphere is fertilizing the oceans with iron is done on a large scale.

20. What physical conditions produce a SOFAR, or sound channel, below the ocean's surface? How is the SOFAR channel being used to determine if global warming has occurred in the oceans?

The major variables that influence the speed of sound in the ocean are temperature and pressure. The velocity of sound increases in each. From the surface of the ocean to the bottom there is a steady increase in pressure that makes sound travel faster with increased depth. Surface temperature is higher in the vast majority of the ocean than at deep water. The decrease in surface temperature with depth is not a linear relationship, but occurs most rapidly at the thermocline (at depths between about 100 and 1000 meters). Due to the rapid decrease in water temperature at the thermocline, it more than offsets the increases pressure and produces a layer of low velocity sound transmission associated with the thermocline. Sound travels faster through ocean water above and below this low velocity channel, which causes sound to be trapped in it due to refraction. Sound can be transmitted for great distances within the SOFAR channel.

Regular pulses of low-frequency sound transmitted across an entire ocean basin through the SOFAR channel are being used to determine if the ocean is experiencing any changes in density due to global warming. Repeating the experiment in the future would show that the transmission of sound across an ocean would take measurably less time if the ocean were warming because sound travels faster in warmer water.

CHAPTER

7

Ocean Circulation

Learning Objectives

The instructional objectives are performance-based and detail specific learning outcomes for Chapter 7. The test items contained in the Test Bank are keyed to the learning objectives and key questions. The order of the objectives mirrors the content presentation in Chapter 7.

Upon completion of this chapter, the student should be able to:

1. Distinguish between **wind-driven** (or **surface**) and **density-driven** (or **deep**) ocean currents.

2. Describe methods used to measure the flow rate of surface currents including:
    a. direct methods of flow measurement.
    b. indirect methods such as internal density distribution/pressure gradient measurements, radar altimeter, and Doppler flow meter.

3. Detail how deep current flow rates are estimated.

4. Define **gyre** and describe its formation.

5. List the five subtropical gyres and describe their location.

6. Explain the formation of **equatorial currents**.

7. Discuss the relationship between the Coriolis effect and **western boundary currents** in gyres.

8. Give the physical characteristics of western boundary currents.

9. Give the physical characteristics of **eastern boundary currents**.

10. Differentiate between **northern boundary currents** and **southern boundary currents** describing the location and direction of flow for each in both hemispheres.

11. Distinguish between equatorial currents and **equatorial countercurrents**.

12. Discuss the formation of the **subpolar gyres** and describe their location.

13. Describe the **Ekman spiral** and detail its implications for ocean water circulation.

14. Give the direction of **Ekman transport** in the northern and southern hemispheres.

15. Define **geostrophic current** and give an example.

16. Discuss the factors that contribute to **western intensification** of subtropical gyres.

17. Differentiate between **upwelling** and **downwelling** and relate these phenomena to surface water productivity in these areas.

18. Describe the causes of upwelling and list the places where upwelling would occur.

19. List, describe the location, and give the physical characteristics (temperature, size, etc.) of the major surface ocean currents including:
    a. **Antarctic Circumpolar Current (West Wind Drift).**
    b. **East Wind Drift.**
    c. **Atlantic Equatorial Countercurrent.**
    d. **South Equatorial Current.**
    e. **Brazil Current.**
    f. **Benguela Current.**
    g. **Gulf Stream.**
    h. **North Equatorial Current.**
    i. **Antilles Current.**
    j. **Caribbean Current.**
    k. **Florida Current.**
    l. **Labrador Current.**
    m. **Irminger Current.**
    n. **Norwegian Current.**
    o. **North Atlantic Current.**
    p. **Canary Current.**
    q. **Kurishio Current.**
    r. **North Pacific Current.**
    s. **California Current.**
    t. **Alaskan Current.**
    u. **East Australian Current.**
    v. **Peru Current.**
    w. **Agulhas Current.**
    x. **West Australian Current.**
    y. **Leeuwin Current.**

20. Discuss the El Niño-Southern Oscillation (ENSO) in the Pacific Ocean detailing the effects of ENSO on global weather patterns.

21. Describe the effects of El Niños and La Niñas on regional weather in the United States.

22. Detail the relationship between global wind belts in tropical areas and seasonal variation in precipitation and temperature patterns (**monsoons**).

23. Explain how water density drives **thermohaline circulation.**

Ocean Circulation

24. List the source and location and describe the process of bottom water (deep water) formation.

25. Outline the **conveyer-belt circulation** model for ocean water.

Overview

This chapter explores ocean circulation; currents are presented as the horizontal or vertical movement of ocean water. The chapter begins with a section discussing the measurement of ocean water. Surface currents are presented in detail, focusing on their wind-driven transport mechanism and the organization of surface currents into gyres. Important aspects of upwelling and downwelling are presented, including how these processes are accomplished by various methods. A description of surface current flow within each major basin and a tour of the ocean basins follow. A model of deep-ocean water circulation is presented as part of a discussion of deep ocean currents.

Headings covered in this chapter include:
Measuring Ocean Currents
       Surface Current Measurement
       Deep Current Measurement
Surface Ocean Currents
       Equatorial Currents, Boundary Currents, and Gyres
       Equatorial Countercurrents
       Ekman Spiral and Ekman Transport
       Geostrophic Currents
       Western Intensification
       Ocean Currents and Climates
Upwelling and Downwelling
       Diverging Surface Water
       Converging Surface Water
       Coastal Upwelling and Downwelling
       Other Upwelling
Surface Currents of the Oceans
       Antarctic Circulation
       Atlantic Ocean Circulation
       Pacific Ocean Circulation
       El Niño-Southern Oscillation (ENSO)
       Indian Ocean Circulation
Deep Currents
       Origins of Thermohaline Circulation
       Sources of Deep Water
       Worldwide Deep-Water Circulation
Special Features:
       Box 7-1:The Oceanography of Everyday Things: Running Shoes as Drift Meters: Just Do It.
       Box 7-2: The Voyage of the Fram: A 1000-Mile Journey Locked In Ice.
       Box 7-3: Historical Feature: Benjamin Franklin: The World's Most Famous Physical Oceanographer.
       Box 7-4: Research Methods In Oceanography: El Niño and the Incredible Shrinking Marine Iguanas of the Galápogos Islands.

Teacher's Resources

There are a wide assortment of good films/videos and CD-ROMs on oceanic circulation including:

Films/Videotapes
- The Gulf Stream (Bullfrog Films), 28 minutes
- The Ocean Currents (McGraw-Hill), 17 minutes
- The Upwelling Phenomenon (Counselor Films, Inc.), 15 minutes
- Vermilion Sea Expeditions: Hydrographic Work (University of California), 13 minutes

CD-ROMs
- The El Niño CD-ROM (REMedia)
- The Monsoon and Data Assimilation CD-ROM (The Data Assimilation Office (DAO) at NASA's Goddard Space Flight Center)
- Ocean Expeditions: El Niño (Planet Earth Science, Inc.)
- TOPEX/POSEIDON: Visit to an Ocean Planet (Jet Propulsion Laboratory)

Answers to End-of-Chapter Questions and Exercises

1. Compare the forces that are directly responsible for creating horizontal and deep vertical circulation in the oceans. What is the ultimate source of energy that drives both circulation systems?

Horizontal ocean currents derive their energy directly from the wind. Vertical circulation is driven by density changes in surface water. This circulation is initiated by the creation of dense surface water in the high latitudes of the Atlantic Ocean where water temperatures are low and salinity is increased during the winter months due to ice formation. The Sun is the ultimate source of energy for both circulation systems.

2. Describe the different ways in which currents are measured.

Surface currents can be measured either directly or indirectly:
- *Direct current measurement* is accomplished by releasing a device that is transported by the current and is tracked through time or by lowering into the water from a stationary position a current-measuring device capable of measuring flow rates (usually with a propeller).
- *Indirect current measurement* is completed in one of three ways: by determining the internal distribution of density and the corresponding pressure gradient across an area of the ocean; by using radar altimeters mounted on satellites to determine the shape of the ocean surface (dynamic topography), from which current flow is inferred; or by using low-frequency sound signals sent through the ocean to determine differences in pressure, which indicate current movement.

Deep currents can be measured by using various drift devices, by detecting the presence of a telltale chemical tracer, or by measuring the distinctive temperature and salinity of a deep-water mass.

3. What would the pattern of ocean surface currents look like if there were no continents on Earth?

If there were no continents on Earth, the ocean surface currents (which are caused by surface winds) would be identical to the pattern of world wind belts (refer to Figure 6-10).

Ocean Circulation

4. On a base map of the world, plot and label the major currents involved in the surface circulation gyres of the oceans. Use colors to represent warm versus cool currents and indicate which currents are western intensified. On an overlay, superimpose the major wind belts of the world on the gyres and describe the relationship between wind belts and currents.

The map should resemble Figure 7-4, with the westerly boundary currents of all subtropical gyres marked as western intensified. The overlay should show that there is a correlation between ocean surface currents and the major wind belts of the world (refer to Figure 6-10); this makes sense because the surface currents are wind-induced.

5. What atmospheric pressure is associated with the centers of subtropical gyres? With subpolar gyres? Explain why the subtropical gyres in the Northern hemisphere move in a clockwise fashion while the subpolar gyres rotate in a counterclockwise pattern.

The center of subtropical gyres is along the 30° latitude, this is a region of descending air and high atmospheric pressure. The center of subpolar gyres is along the 60° latitude, this is a region of rising air and low atmospheric pressure.

In the Northern Hemisphere, differences in pressure cause a clockwise flow of air around high-pressure cells (anticyclonic flow; associated with subtropical gyres). Conversely, a counter-clockwise flow of air occurs around low-pressure cells (cyclonic flow; associated with subpolar gyres). This movement of air drives the surface currents. As mentioned in Chapter 6, the screwdriver analogy applies here: to tighten a screw (equivalent to high pressure), the screwdriver is turned clockwise; to loosen a screw (equivalent to low pressure), the screwdriver is turned counter-clockwise. Try experimenting with this using the surface currents map (Figure 7-4).

6. Diagram and discuss how Ekman transport produces the "hill" of water within subtropical gyres that causes geostrophic current flow. As a starting place on the diagram, use the wind belts (the trade winds and the prevailing westerlies).

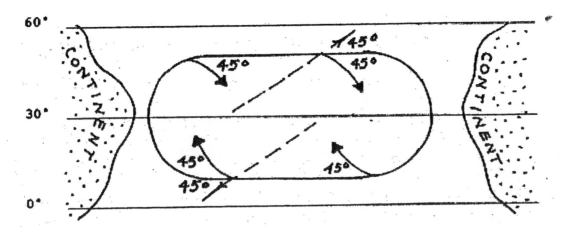

In the Northern Hemisphere, the trade winds and the prevailing westerlies (dashed lines in the figure above) create a westerly and easterly current, respectively, flowing at 45° to the right of the winds. The Coriolis effect creates a clockwise flow as continents interrupt the currents. Ekman transport (solid lines with closed arrows in the figure above) shows a net transport of water at an angle of 45° to the right of the surface current (in the Northern Hemisphere), pushing water toward the center of the rotating gyre.

7. Describe the voyage of the *Fran*, and how it helped prove that there was no continent beneath the Artic ice pack.

The *Fram* was intentionally locked in the Arctic ice pack in 1893, where it drifted with the ice for almost three years and was carried to past the North Pole. The fact that she drifted over 1600 kilometers (1000 miles) proved that the ice was not grounded and that there was no continent beneath the ice pack.

8. What causes the apex of the geostrophic "hills" to be offset to the west of the center of the ocean gyre system?

The offset of the geostrophic "hills" to the west of center in ocean gyres is a result of an equilibrium reached among a number of forces, but the primary factor is the increasing strength of the Coriolis effect with latitude.

9. Draw or describe several different oceanographic conditions that produce upwelling.

- *Current divergence (equatorial upwelling)* is caused when surface waters move away from an area on the ocean's surface.
- *Ekman transport (coastal upwelling)* occurs where surface water is moved away from shore.
- *Offshore winds* move water away from shore.
- *Sea floor obstructions* restrict the flow of water and cause it to rise to the surface.
- *Coastline geometry* produces upwelling where a sharp bend in the coastline causes deep water to surface.
- *High latitude regions* have upwelling because there is no pycnocline to present vertical water movement.

10. During flood stage, the largest river in the world – the mighty Amazon River – dumps 200,000 cubic meters of water into the Atlantic Ocean each second. Compare its flow rate with the volume of water transported by the West Wind Drift and the Gulf Stream. How many times larger than the Amazon is each of these two ocean currents?

The Amazon River's flow rate at flood stage of 200,000 cubic meters of water per second equals 0.2 Sverdrups (remember that 1 Sverdrup=1 million cubic meters per second).

	Amazon River	**Gulf Stream**	**West Wind Drift**
Flow Rate (Sverdrups)	0.2	90	190
Magnitude (X larger than Amazon)	_____	450	950

11. Observing the flow of Atlantic Ocean currents in Figure 7-14, offer an explanation as to why the Brazil Current has a lower velocity and volume of transport than the Gulf Stream.

As the South Equatorial Current approaches the eastern tip of Brazil, it is split. Much of the flow crossed the Equator and enters the North Atlantic Gyre as the Caribbean Current. With only a portion of the equatorial flow turning south as he Brazil Current, it volume, and therefore its strength, is relatively small compared to that of the Gulf Stream, which is the beneficiary of the volume of water lost to the northern

Ocean Circulation

gyre. The fact that South American is considerably east of North America also contributes to this difference in strength.

12. Why did Benjamin Franklin want to know about the surface current pattern in the North Atlantic?

Benjamin Franklin, deputy postmaster of the Atlantic colonies, 1753-1774, became interested in the North Atlantic Ocean circulation patterns when he was puzzled by the fact that it took mail ships coming from Europe two more weeks to reach New England by a northerly route than it did ships that came a more southerly route. Franklin talked to Nantucket sea captains about why this occurred and was told about the strong Gulf Stream current. Franklin became the first person to publish a map of the Gulf Stream, which was the cause of the delay in mail ships when they traveled against it.

13. Explain why Gulf Stream eddies that develop northeast of the Gulf Stream rotate clockwise and have warm-water cores, whereas those that develop to the southwest rotate counterclockwise and have cold-water cores.

Since eddies are formed by the pinching off of meanders, the water is following a clockwise path in the meanders on the northwest side of the Gulf Stream and a counterclockwise path on the southeast side. This pattern of movement is maintained in the pinched-off meanders.

14. Describe the changes in oceanographic phenomena including Walker Circulation, the Pacific Warm Pool, trade winds, equatorial countercurrent flow, upwelling/downwelling, and the abundance of marine life that occur during an El Niño event. What are some global effects of El Niño?

During El Niño events, the Walker Circulation between the southeastern Pacific high-pressure cell and the Indonesian low-pressure call is weakened. Since this circulation reinforces the equatorial trade winds, they weaken and may even reverse themselves. With no trade winds pushing equatorial water into the dome of warm water (the Pacific Warm Pool) that forms near Indonesia, this water pushes east along the Equator aided by a strengthened equatorial countercurrent. The Pacific Warm Pool spreads along the Equator and even as far as the coasts of North and South America. Its arrival is manifest as high sea surface temperature anomalies in eastern Pacific waters. This wedge of warm water causes the thermocline to be abnormally deep and suppresses upwelling. In some cases, the sloshing of warm water against the western coast of South America causes downwelling. The lack of upwelling limits primary productivity in surface waters, causing marine life to be much less abundant.

       In severe El Niños, worldwide weather patterns are disrupted, that could cause local weather to be wetter, drier, hotter, or colder than normal, depending upon the areas. Typically, severe El Niño events cause flooding, coastal erosion, and impacts on marine life along the eastern Pacific, and droughts and wildfires on the western Pacific and Indian Oceans. Refer to Figure 7-21 for other global effects.

15. How often do El Niño events occur? Using Figure 7-20, determine how many years since 1950 have been El Niño years. Has the pattern of El Niño events occurred at regular intervals?

El Niño events have occurred irregularly at intervals of 2 to 10 years. Since 1950, there have been 13 El Niño events of varying strength, the strongest of which occurred in 1982-1983. Figure 7-20 shows that the pattern of El Niño events does not occur at regular intervals.

16. How is La Niña different from El Niño? Describe the pattern of La Niña events in relation to El Niños since 1950 (see Figure 7-20).

La Niña is a cooling of surface ocean temperatures in the eastern Pacific that commonly occurs following an El Niño. La Niña is characterized by trade winds that are very strong and surface waters in the equatorial South Pacific that are cooler than usual. Figure 7-20 shows that since 1950, conditions in the tropical Pacific have oscillated between La Niña and El Niño events, and that "normal conditions" have occurred rarely.

17. Describe the relationship between atmospheric pressure, winds, and surface currents during the monsoons of the Indian Ocean.

During the winter, the typical northeastern trade winds are called northeast monsoons. The rapid cooling of air over the Asian mainland during the winter strengthens them. This creates a high-pressure cell, that forces atmospheric masses off the continent and out over the ocean, where the air pressure is lower.

During the summer, the Asian mainland warms faster than the oceanic water. This results in a summer low-pressure cell developing over the continent, allowing high-pressure air to reverse direction and move from the Indian Ocean onto the Asian landmass. This produces the southeast monsoon that may be thought of as a continuation of the southeast trade winds across the Equator. During this season, the North Equatorial Current disappears and is replaced by the Southeast Monsoon Current. It flows from west to east across the northern Indian Ocean. In September or October, the northeast trade winds are reestablished, and the North Equatorial Current reappears.

18. Discuss the origin of thermohaline vertical circulation. Why do deep currents form only in high-latitude regions?

In low latitudes the temperature of the water is too high to become dense enough to sink, even when high salinity values develop, as they do in the subtropics. As a result, deep currents only form in high latitudes. Even in high latitude regions where the surface water temperatures are always low, sinking may only take place during the winter when sea ice formation increases surface water salinity.

19. Name the two major deep-water masses and give the location of their formation at the ocean's surface.

North Atlantic Deep Water forms in the Norwegian Sea and off the tip of Greenland in the North Atlantic Ocean. *Antarctic Bottom Water* forms primarily as a result of the mixing of water in the Weddell Sea with water from the West Wind Drift.

20. The Antarctic Intermediate Water can be identified throughout much of the South Atlantic based on its temperature, salinity, and dissolved oxygen content. Why is it colder and less salty – and contains more oxygen – than the surface-water mass above it and the North Atlantic Deep Water below it?

The Antarctic Intermediate Water forms at the surface and sinks at the Antarctic Convergence, and because it has recently left the surface of the ocean where the water is cold and has a relatively low salinity, it has a high capacity for holding atmospheric oxygen and a high level of diatom productivity around the Antarctic. Thus, it has a lower temperature and salinity and a higher dissolved oxygen concentration that the surface mass above it and the North Atlantic Deep Water mass beneath it.

CHAPTER

8
Waves and Water Dynamics

Learning Objectives

The instructional objectives are performance-based and detail specific learning outcomes for Chapter 8. The test items contained in the Test Bank are keyed to the learning objectives and key questions. The order of the objectives mirrors the content presentation in Chapter 8.

Upon completion of this chapter, the student should be able to:

1. List the factors that produce waves.

2. Differentiate between **ocean waves, atmospheric waves,** and **internal waves**.

3. Distinguish between **splash waves, seismic sea waves (tsunami),** and **tides**.

4. Describe the differences in the direction of water movement among **longitudinal, transverse,** and **orbital waves**.

5. Define the following wave characteristics, and where applicable, give the equation used to calculate the trait including:
    a. **crest**
    b. **trough**
    c. **wave height (H)**
    d. **wavelength (L)**
    e. **wave steepness**
    f. **wave period (T)**
    g. **frequency (f)**

6. Explain the **circular orbital motion** of ocean water in relation to the movement of the waveform.

7. List the factors that affect the speed of **deep-water waves**.

8. Give the equation for calculating the **wave speed (S)** of deep-water waves.

9. List the factors that affect the speed of **shallow-water waves**.

10. Give the equation for calculating the wave speed (S) of shallow-water waves.

11. Discuss the development of wind-generated waves including:

a. **capillary waves**
b. **gravity waves**
c. **"sea"**
d. **swell**

12. List the three factors that affect wave energy.

13. Describe the **Beaufort Wind Scale** and its relationship to the appearance of the ocean surface.

14. Differentiate between **wave trains, wave dispersion**, and **decay distance** in fully developed seas.

15. Distinguish between the effects of **constructive interference, destructive interference, and mixed interference** on waves.

16. Define the **surf zone**.

17. Discuss the changes that waves undergo as they move from deep water to shallow water and move toward the shoreline.

18. Distinguish between a **spilling breaker**, a **plunging breaker**, and **surging breaker**.

19. Describe the differences between **wave refraction** and **wave reflection**.

20. Define **tsunami** and describe the forces that produce these waves.

21. Discuss the effects of tsunami on coastal areas and describe locations worldwide where tsunami occur.

22. List historical tsunami events and give their locations.

23. Discuss the Pacific Tsunami Warning Center (PTWC) and how **tsunami watches** and **tsunami warnings** are issued.

24. Describe the LIMPET 500 and the potential for harnessing wave energy to generate electricity.

Overview

This chapter explores wave and water dynamics and begins with an introduction to waves and their movement by examining the forces that produce waves. Wave characteristics are presented, including aspects of circular orbital motion and the differences between deep-water and shallow-water waves. A description of wind-generated ocean waves, where the terms "sea" and swell are defined. The unusual oceanographic conditions that generate rouge waves are also discussed. Once waves reach shallow water, they become breaking waves and may undergo physical changes that are described under the headings surf, wave refraction, and wave reflection. Tsunami, a special type of long-wavelength wave, can produce severe coastal damage. Descriptions of some historically important tsunami are included, as well as a discussion of the Pacific's tsunami warning system. The chapter concludes with a consideration of power generated by wave energy.

Waves and Water Dynamics

Headings covered in this chapter include:
What Causes Waves?
How Do Waves Move?
Wave Characteristics
     Circular Orbital Motion
     Deep-Water Waves
     Shallow-Water Waves
     Transitional Waves
Wind-Generated Waves
     Factors Affecting Wave Energy
     "Sea"
     Swell
Surf Zone
     Breakers and Surfing
     Wave Refraction
     Wave Reflection
Tsunami
     Coastal Effects
     Historical Tsunami Examples
     Tsunami Warning System
Wave Generated Power
     LIMPET 500
Special Features:
     Box 8-1:The Oceanography of Everyday Things: Rouge Waves: Ships Beware!
     Box 8-2: Historical Feature: The Biggest Wave in Recorded History: Lituya Bay, Alaska (1958)

Teacher's Resources

There is a wide assortment of good films/videos on ocean waves including:

Films/Videotapes
- Oceanographic Studies off Georges Bank (NOAA, Film p-1056-25), 15 minutes
- Waves Across the Pacific (McGraw-Hill), 30 minutes
- Waves on Water (Revised Edition) (Encyclopedia Britannica), 16 minutes

Answers to End-of-Chapter Questions and Exercises

1. Discuss several different ways in which waves form. How are most ocean waves generated?

All waves begin as disturbances (releases of energy). This can be accomplished by a variety of mechanisms, including wind, the movement of fluids of different densities, mass movement into the ocean, underwater sea floor movements, the gravitation pull of the Moon and the Sun, and by human activities. Most ocean waves are wind-generated.

2. Why is the development of internal waves likely within the pycnocline?

Internal waves develop along density interfaces within the ocean. The greatest rate of density change in most parts of the ocean is found within the pycnocline, which is caused by a rapid change in temperature with depth (thermocline). Internal waves are often found within the thermocline (which is associated with the pycnocline).

3. Discuss longitudinal, transverse, and orbital wave phenomena, including the states of matter which each can transmit energy.

Longitudinal waves: Particles move back and forth in the direction of energy transmission, and these waves can transmit matter through solids, liquids, or gases.

    Transverse waves: Particles move back and forth in a direction at right angles to the direction of energy transmission, and these waves can transmit energy through solids.

    Orbital waves: Particles move in circular orbits passing through the top half of the orbit in the direction of energy transmission. They develop when energy is being transmitted along a density interface between two fluids such as the low-density atmosphere and the denser ocean water.

4. Draw a diagram of a simple progressive wave. From memory, label the crest, trough, wavelength, wave height, and still water level.

The drawing should look life Figure 8-3(b).

5. Can a wave with a wavelength of 14 meters ever be more than 2 meters high? Why or why not?

A wave with a wavelength of 14 meters could never be more than 2 meters high because its wave steepness would be too great and it would break. In fact, if any wave ever has a wave steepness that exceeds a 1:7 ration, it would break.

6. What physical feature of a wave is related to the depth of the wave base? On the diagram that you drew for Question 5, add the wave base. What is the difference between the wave base and still water level?

Wave base is at a depth equal to ½ the wavelength, measured from still water level. Wave base is deeper than still water level. Wave base is at a depth of ½ the wavelength and still water level (also known as zero energy level) is halfway between the crest and the trough.

7. Explain why the following statements for deep-water waves are either true of false.
   a. The longer the wave, the deeper the wave base.
   b. The greater the wave height, the deeper the wave base.
   c. The longer the wave, the faster the wave travels.
   d. The greater the wave height, the faster the wave travels.
   e. The faster the wave, the greater the wave height.

   a. The longer the wave, the deeper the wave base: True, because wave base is at a depth of ½ the wavelength.
   b. The greater the wave height, the deeper the wave base: False, because wave base is a function of wavelength only.
   c. The longer the wave, the faster the wave travels: True, because wavelength influences wave speed, where longer waves travel faster.

Waves and Water Dynamics

    d. The greater the wave height, the faster the wave travels: False, because wave height is independent of wave speed (big waves are not necessarily fast waves).
    e. The faster the wave, the greater the wave height: False, because wave speed is independent of wave height (fast waves are not necessarily big waves).

8. Calculate the speed (S) in meters per second for deep-water waves with the following characteristics:
    a. $L=351$ meters, $T=15$ seconds
    b. $T=12$ seconds
    c. $F=0.125$ wave per second

The following answers were determined using the most straightforward equations, but note that other equations may be used to determine deep-water wave speed, all of which will arrive at the correct answer.

    a. $S=L/T=(351$ meters$)/(15$ seconds$)=23.4$ meters per second

    b. $S=1.56T=(1.56)(12$ seconds$)=18.7$ meters per second

    c. $T=1/f=1/(0.125$ seconds$)=8$ seconds;

       $S=1.56T=(1.56)(8$ seconds$)=12.5$ meters per second

9. Using the information about giant waves experienced by the USS *Ramapo*, what were the waves' wavelength and speed?

The waves had a period (T) of 14.8 seconds, thus the wave speed of these deep-water waves can be determined as follows:
$S=1.56T=(1.56)(14.8$ seconds$)=23.1$ meters per second.
Note that 23.1 meters per second = 83.1 kilometers (51.6 miles) per hour.
Now that wave speed is known, wavelength can be calculated:
$S=L/T$, so $L=S \times T$
$L=(23.1$ meters per second$)(14.8$ seconds$)=342$ meters (1121 feet).

10. Define swell. Does swell necessarily imply a particular wave size? Why or why not?

Swell describes uniform, symmetrical waves that have traveled out of the area of origination. Although swell can often have a large wave height, swell does not necessarily imply a particular wave size. This is because swell describes any waves that have traveled out of their area of origination, independent of the factors that influence wave size (wind speed, duration, and fetch).

11. Waves from separate sea areas move away as swell and produce interference patterns when they come together. If Sea A has wave heights of 1.5 meters (5 feet) and Sea B has wave heights of 3.5

12. meters (11.5 feet), what would be the heights of waves resulting from constructive interference and destructive interference? Illustrate you answer (refer to Figure 8-13).

Constructive interference would produce waves 5 meters (16.4 feet) high (see the figure below, left) and destructive interference would produce waves 2 meters (6.6 feet) high (see figure below, right).

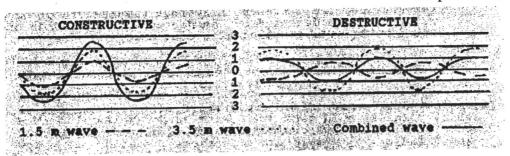

13. Describe the physical changes that occur to a wave's wave speed (*S*), wavelength (*L*), height (*H*), and wave steepness (*H/L*) as a wave moves across shoaling water to break on the shore.

As the orbiting articles begin to touch or feel the bottom when the water depth becomes less than ½ *L*, the waves will slow down and their speed (*S*) will be reduced. Since the leading wave will be in shallower water than the wave behind it, it will be slowed more and the trailing wave will decrease the distance between its crest and the crest of the wave ahead, reducing the wavelength (*L*). Since there is the same volume of water in each waveform, it will have to increase its height (*H*) as its length decreases. Since wave height has increased and wavelength has decreases, the wave steepness (*H/L*) increases until it exceeds the 1:7 ratio and the wave breaks.

14. Describe the three different types of breakers and indicate the slope of the beach that produces the three different types. How is the energy of the wave distributed differently within the surf zone by the three different types of breakers?

Spilling breakers result forma relatively gentle slope of the ocean bottom, which more gradually extracts energy from the wave, producing a turbulent mass of air and water that runs down the front slope of the wave. The wave energy in spilling breakers is spread over a large distance within the surf zone.

 Plunging breakers have a curling crest that moves over an air pocket. This results because the curling particles literally outrun the wave, and there is nothing beneath them to support their motion. Plunging breakers form on moderately steep beach slopes and expend their energy over a shorter distance of the surf zone.

 Surging breakers build up and break right at the shoreline in areas that have an abrupt beach slope. Consequently, the wave energy is compressed into an even shorter distance.

15. Using examples, explain how wave refraction is different from wave reflection.

Wave refraction is the bending of wave energy, such as how waves bend around an island or how waves bend as they approach the shore at an angle. *Wave reflection* is the bouncing back of wave energy once it hits any solid object such as a jetty, coastal cliff, or other solid structure.

16. Using orthogonal lines, illustrate how wave energy is distributed along a shoreline with headlands and bays. Identify areas of high and low energy release.

The illustration should resemble Figure 8-18.

17. Define the terms *node* and *antinode* as they relate to standing waves.

Waves and Water Dynamics

A *node* is a point on a standing wave where vertical motion is lacking or minimal. If this condition extends across the surface of an oscillating body of water, the line of no vertical motion is the nodal line. An *antinode* is a zone of maximum vertical particle movement in standing waves where crest and trough formation alternate.

18. How large was the largest wave ever recorded? Where did it occur, and how did it form?

The largest wave ever authentically recorded was a 530-meter (1740-foot) high splash wave produced by an earthquake-initiated landslide that occurred in Lituya Bay, Alaska, on July 09, 1958.

19. While stopping in a surf shop, you overhear some surfing enthusiasts mention that they would really like to ride the curling wave of a tidal wave at least once in their life, because it is a single wave of enormous height. What would you say to these surfers?

Responses to this question will vary, but it is important to point out that a tidal wave (more accurately known as a seismic sea wave or a tsunami) does not express itself at the shore as a giant breaking wave. Rather, it is a series of surges and withdrawals of water that vary in height but can change the average sea level by many meters.

20. Explain what it would look like at the shoreline if the trough of a tsunami arrives first? What is the impending danger?

If the trough of the tsunami arrives at a shore first, the water will suddenly withdraw and look as if an extreme low tide is occurring. The impending danger is that within the next few minutes, a strong surge of water will arrive at shore, followed by a series of withdrawals and surges many minutes apart.

21. What ocean depth would be required for a tsunami with a wavelength of 220 kilometers (136 miles) to travel as a deep-water wave. Is it possible that such a wave could become a deep-water wave any place in the world ocean? Explain.

The ocean would have to be at least ½ L or 110 kilometers (68 miles deep). Since the deepest part of the ocean is just over 11 kilometers (about 7 miles) deep, there is no place in the ocean where a tsunami of this wavelength would be considered a deep-water wave.

22. Explain how the tsunami warning system in the Pacific Ocean works. Why must the tsunami be verified at the closet tide recording station?

Since tsunami have small wave heights and are difficult to predict in the open ocean, the Pacific Tsunami Warning center (PTWC) uses seismic waves to predict the occurrence of large waves. When a seismic disturbance occurs beneath the ocean surface that is large enough to be considered tsunamigenic, a tsunami watch is issued. At this point, a tsunami may or may not have occurred, but certainly the potential for one exists, so a station close to where the tsunami originated must verify the tsunami. Since the PTWC is linked to over 50 tide-measuring stations throughout the Pacific, the closest recording station to the earthquake is closely monitored for any indication of unusual wave activity. If unusual wave activity is verified, the tsunami watch is upgraded to a warning. Once a tsunami is detected, warnings are sent to all of the coastal regions that might encounter a destructive wave, along with an estimated time of arrival. This warning, usually just a few hours in advance of a tsunami, allows for the evacuation of people from low-lying areas and the removal of ships from harbors before the wave arrives.

However, if the disturbance is nearby, there is not enough time for a warning to be issued because a tsunami travels so rapidly.

23. Discuss some environmental problems that might result from developing facilities for conversion of wave energy to electrical energy.

If a stretch of shore is deprived of wave energy that is needed to transport sediment along the shore, the sediment will not be moved. As a result, a different portion of the shore will be deprived of its supply of sediment, which protects the shore from erosion. This portion of the shore, if exposed to wave energy, will begin to be eroded because the energy that was once used to transport sediment in the longshore current is now available to erode the exposed bedrock.

CHAPTER

9
Tides

Learning Objectives

The instructional objectives are performance-based and detail specific learning outcomes for Chapter 9. The test items contained in the Test Bank are keyed to the learning objectives and key questions. The order of the objectives mirrors the content presentation in Chapter 9.

Upon completion of this chapter, the student should be able to:

1. Define **tide**.

2. Distinguish between **gravitation force, centripetal force, resultant forces**, and **tide-generating forces** in the context of the Earth-Moon-Sun system and tidal generation.

3. Describe the **barycenter** in the Earth-Moon system.

4. Differentiate between the **zenith** and the **nadir** in terms of gravitational forces in the Earth-Moon system.

5. Distinguish between a **lunar day** and a **solar day** and discuss the impact on timing of the tidal cycle.

6. Explain how **lunar tidal bulges** and **solar tidal bulges** are formed and discuss their effect on the tidal cycle.

7. Diagram the monthly tidal cycle detailing the relative position of the Earth, the Moon, and the Sun to produce a **new moon, quarter moon**, and a **full moon**. Include in your drawing the tidal range corresponding to each lunar phase (**spring tide** and **neap tide**).

8. Define **syzygy** and **quadrature**.

9. List and describe the phases of the moon in a lunar month including:
   a. **waxing crescent**
   b. **waxing gibbous**
   c. **full moon**
   d. **waning gibbous**
   e. **waning crescent**
   f. **new moon**

10. Differentiate between **declination** and the **ecliptic** with respect to the arrangement of the Earth, the Moon, and the Sun.

11. Illustrate the relative position of the Earth and the Sun at **perihelion** and **aphelion**.

12. Discuss the effect of **perigee** and **apogee** on tidal range including the implications of **proxigean tides** for coastal areas.

13. Distinguish between an **amphidromic point** and a **cotidal point** in the tide.

14. Detail the effects of the continents on the movement of the tidal bulges around the Earth.

15. Compare and contrast **diurnal, semidiurnal,** and **mixed tidal patterns** and describe where you would be most likely to find each tidal pattern.

16. Explain the extreme **tidal bore** in the Bay of Fundy.

17. Discuss the formation, velocity, and direction of coastal tidal currents including **rotary currents** and **reversing currents**.

18. Differentiate between a **flood current** and an **ebb current** and describe where these coastal currents form.

19. Explain the tidal forces that produce a **whirlpool** and give the locations of some infamous whirlpools.

20. List the advantages and disadvantages of using tidal power to generate electricity.

Overview

This chapter includes a discussion of the tide-generating forces from the idealized theory of tides. The tidal effects of both the Moon and the Sun are considered, leading to an idealized monthly tidal cycle. Other factors that influence tides on Earth are also presented in accordance with the dynamic theory of tides, from which a prediction of the tides can be based. Tidal phenomena in the ocean are discussed, including tidal patterns, tides in the Bay of Fundy, and coastal tidal currents. A feature box on grunion — the only fish that comes completely out of water to spawn, corresponding precisely with the tidal cycle — ties in an interesting interdisciplinary topic related to tidal phenomena. The chapter closes with a discussion of tidal force generated electricity.

Headings covered in this chapter include:
What Causes the Tides?
    Tide-Generating Forces
    Tidal Bulges: The Moon's Effect
    Tidal Bulges: The Sun's Effect
    Earth's Rotation and the Tides
How Do Tides Vary During a Monthly Tidal Cycle?

Tides

Teacher's Resources

There is a wide assortment of good films/videos on tides including:

Films/Videotapes
- Fish, Moon, and Tides: The Grunion Story (Academy Films), 14 minutes
- Ocean Tides: Bay of Fundy (Encyclopedia Britannica), 14 minutes
- Tides and Currents (NOAA, Film P-1056-24_, 15 minutes
- Tides of the Ocean (Academy Films), 16 minutes

Answers to End-of-Chapter Questions and Exercises

1. Explain why the Sun's influence on Earth's tides is only 46% that of the Moon's, even though the Sun is so much more massive than the Moon.

The Sun has a much greater mass than the Moon, so it generates a greater gravitational attraction (as mass increases, then gravity increases). Remember that the Sun is much farther away from the Earth and that as distance increases, the gravitational force greatly decreases. Even though the Sun has a much greater mass, it is much farther away, so its influence on Earth tides is much less (about half of the Moon's).

Approaching the question from a more mathematical perspective, the tide-generating influence of a body on Earth is proportional to its mass and inversely proportional to the cube of the distance from Earth. The Moon has a mass of 7.3×10^{19} tons, while the Sun's mass is 2.0×10^{27} tons. Taking a proportion gives:

$$(2.0 \times 10^{27})/(7.3 \times 10^{19}) = 2.74 \times 10^{7}, \text{ which is } 27.4 \text{ million}$$

Therefore, the Sun is over *27 million* times as effective ingenerating Earth Tides as the Moon based on mass.

However, comparing the *distances* of the Sun and Moon from Earth, we find the Moon to be 384,835 kilometers average distance from Earth while the Sun is 149,758,000 kilometers average distance from Earth. Taking a proportion of these two values gives:

$$(149,758,000)/(384,835) = 389.1$$

This shows that the Sun is 389.1 times farther from Earth than the Moon. The cube of 389.1 is 58,931,347 or almost *59 million*. Comparing the two tide-producing factors gives:

$$(27 \text{ million})/(59 \text{ million}) = 0.46 \text{ X } 100\% = 46\%$$

Therefore the Sun is only 46% as effective as the Moon in generating Earth tides.

2. Why is a lunar day 24 hours and 50 minutes long, while a solar day is 24 hours long?

The solar day is defined as the time that elapses between successive passages over a given meridian on the Earth's surface, which takes 24 hours. The lunar day is defined as the time that elapses between successive passages of the Moon over a given meridian on the Earth's surface, which is 24 hours and 50 minutes of solar time. The difference between the two involves the Moon's movement relative to the Earth. Since the Moon moves from west to east relative to the Earth's surface in its orbital path and requires 29.53 days to complete an orbit, the Moon moves through an angle of 12.2° each solar day or 24 hours. Earth must rotate through 372.2° (360° +12.2°) each lunar day. The time required for Earth to rotate the additional 12.2° is 50 minutes.

3. Which is more technically correct: The tide comes in and goes out: or Earth rotates in and out of tidal bulges. Why?

From our perspective on Earth, the tide appears to come in and go out, but it is technically more correct to speak of the Earth rotating into and out of the tidal bulges. This is because the tidal bulges are in fixed positions relative to the positions of the Moon and the Sun, and the Earth's rotation carries parts of the Earth into and out of the tidal bulges.

4. From memory, draw the positions of the Earth-Moon-Sun system during a complete monthly tidal cycle. Indicate the tide conditions experienced on Earth, the phases of the Moon, the time between those phases, and syzygy and quadrature.

Refer to Figure 9-9.

5. Explain why the maximum tidal range (spring tide) occurs during new moon and full moon phases and the minimum tidal range (neap tide) at first-quarter and third-quarter moons.

During new and full moon phases, the Sun and Moon are very nearly aligned with the Earth and the crests and troughs of the lunar and solar bulges overlap to produce constructive interference. This results in a larger set of tidal bulges because the magnitude of the displacements of the crests above and the troughs below the still water level are added together, thus creating a greater tidal range (spring tide conditions).

During quadratures (first and third quarter moon phases), the Sun and the Moon are at right angles to one another relative to Earth. This results in destructive interference between the lunar and solar tidal bulges because the magnitude of the lunar tidal crest and trough are reduced by an amount equal to

Tides

the solar tide trough and crest, respectively (refer to Figure 9-9). This minimum tidal range is known as neap tide.

6. If Earth did not have the Moon orbiting it, would there still be tides? Why or why not?

If Earth did not have the Moon orbiting it, there would still be tides on Earth caused by the Sun. However, the tides would be smaller than they are now and they would not alternate between spring and neap tide conditions.

7. Assume that there are two moons in orbit around Earth that are on the same orbital plane but always on opposite sides of Earth and that each moon is the same size and mass of our Moon. How would this affect the tidal range during spring and neap conditions?

If there were two moons in orbit around the Earth, the size of the lunar tidal bulges would be doubled. Because the lunar bulges are already the primary factor that influence tide on Earth, the tidal range would be greater during both spring and neap tide conditions.

8. What is declination? Discuss the degree of declination of the Moon and Sun relative to Earth's Equator. What are the effects of declination of the Moon and Sun on the tides?

Declination is the angular distance of the Sun or Moon above or below the Earth's equatorial plane. The Sun's declination from the plane of the Earth's Equator is equal to an angle of 23.5° from perpendicular. The maximum declination of the Sun is always 23.5°, and its period is one year.

The maximum declination of the Moon from the Earth's Equatorial plane is 28.5° from perpendicular. During the period of the Moon's orbit (29.53 days), the declination of the Moon will move from its maximum value in one hemisphere across the equator to a maximum value in the other hemisphere and back. The period of the Moon's declination is the same as that of its orbit.

As the Earth rotates through the tidal bulges with a declination relative to the Equator, any location north or south of the Equator will pass through one bulge nearer its center than when it passes through the other. Therefore the two high tides experienced, and the two low tides, will not have the same tidal height. These differences are called *diurnal inequalities*.

9. Diagram the Earth-Moon system's orbit about the Sun. Label the positions on the orbit at which the Moon and Sun are closet to and farthest from Earth, stating the terms used to identify them. Discuss the effects of the Moon's and Earth's positions on Earth's tides.

Refer to Figure 9-12. The Moon is closet to Earth during perigee (375,200 kilometers) and farther away at apogee (405,800 kilometers). Greater tidal ranges are experienced during perigean tides.

The Sun is closest to Earth during perihelion (148,500,000 kilometers) and farther away during aphelion (152,200,000 kilometers). Greater tidal ranges are experienced during perihelion tides.

The period of the Moon's changing distance is 27.5 days while that of the Sun is one year, so perigean tides are experienced about once a month while perihelion rides occur only once a year.

10. Observe the Moon from a reference location every night at about the same time for two weeks. Keep track of your observations about the shape (phase) of the Moon and its position in the sky. Then, compare these to reported tides in your area, How do the two compare?

Chapter 9 – Instructor's Manual

Answers will vary depending on when the observations begin. Best results are achieved by beginning immediately after sunset. During this two-week time span, for example, the phase of the Moon changes from new to first quarter to full, rising about 50 minutes later each night and moving more easterly in the sky. Correspondingly, the tides alternate between spring tide, neap tide, and back to spring tide conditions over the two-week span.

11. Are tides considered deep-water waves anywhere in the ocean? Why or why not?

Nowhere in the ocean are tides considered deep-water waves because the ocean basins are so shallow relative to the long wavelength of the wave crests created by tidal phenomena.

12. Describe the number of high and low tides in a lunar day, the period, and any inequality of the following tidal patters: diurnal, semidiurnal, and mixed.

Diurnal tidal pattern—One high tide and one low tide per lunar day. Period: 24 hours and 50 minutes. There is no diurnal inequality because there is only one high tide and one low tide daily.
 Semidiurnal tidal pattern—Two high tides and two low tides per lunar day. Period: 12 hours and 25 minutes. There is no significant diurnal inequality.
 Mixed tidal pattern—Two high tides and two low tides per lunar day. Period: Throughout most of the month, the period will be 12 hours and 25 minutes, but there may be a few days when it is 24 hours and 50 minutes. The diurnal inequality is usually very significant, that causes the two high tides to be of different heights and the two low tides to be of differing heights as well.

13. Discuss factors that help produce the world's greatest tidal range in the Bay of Fundy.

Because the period of free oscillation in the Bay of Fundy is nearly the same as the tidal period resonance that is produced, a very large tidal range occurs at the northern end of Minas Basin due to constructive interference. The bay also narrows and becomes progressively shallower toward its northern end, which amplifies tidal effects. In addition, the Bay of Fundy is a right-curving bay, so the Coriolis effect in the Northern Hemisphere adds to the tidal range.

14. Discuss the difference between rotary and reversing tidal currents.

As the tidal current rotates through the open ocean, it follows a circular path as illustrated in Figure 9-14. This current is not very noticeable because there are no restrictions to its flow. Near the shore where the ocean floor shoals on approach to the continents, tidal current flow becomes a reversing current – flowing in and out (flood and ebb currents). These reversing currents can be very intense due to restrictions imposed on their flow by coastal topography.

15. Of flood current, ebb current, high slack water, and low slack water, when is the best time to enter a bay by boat? When is the best time to navigate in a shallow, rocky bay?

Generally, the best time to enter a bay by boat is during flood current because the boat will be carried into the bay by the incoming tidal current. The best tine to navigate in a shallow, rocky harbor is during high slack water, when submerged obstacles are in the deepest water (refer to Figure 9-18).

Tides

16. Describe the spawning cycle of grunion, indicating the relationship between tidal phenomena, where grunion lay their eggs, and the movement of sand on the beach.

The grunion spawning cycle is closely related to the rise and fall of the tides. Shortly after the maximum spring tide has occurred, these small silver fish come ashore to bury their fertilized eggs in the sand. During the summer months, the higher high tide occurs at night. As the high tides become higher each night while the maximum spring-tide range approaches, sand is eroded from the beach (refer to Figure 9B). After the maximum height of the spring tide has occurred, the higher high tide that occurs each night will be a little lower than the pervious night. During the decreasing tidal heights produced as neap-tide conditions approach, sand is deposited on the beach, The grunion depend on this pattern of beach sand deposition and erosion for spawning success.

17. Discuss at least two positive and two negative factors related to tidal power generation.

Responses to this question will vary. Positive factors include the fact that tidal power is a renewable energy resource and there is a reduced pollution threat relative to other power sources. Negative factors include high initial coasts, maximum generating potential does not always correspond to maximum power consumption, and the interference with maritime use in the area where the tidal power plant is located.

18. Explain how a tidal power plant works, using as an example an estuary that has a mixed tidal pattern. Why does the potential for usable tidal energy increase with an increase in tidal range?

A tidal power plant works by trapping seawater in an estuary during high tide and using that water to turn turbines and generate electricity as the water moves out to sea at low tide. A power plant situated at the entrance of an estuary would be able to allow water to enter the estuary during an incoming high tide (for a mixed tidal pattern, this occurs twice daily) and use the water for electricity generation as it flows out through the power plant. Factors that increase the usable tide-generating potential of an estuary include a large surface area of an estuary (more water), a large tidal range (higher potential energy), and a narrow mouth to the sea (greater ability to channel the water).

CHAPTER
10
The Coast: Beaches and Shoreline Processes

Learning Objectives

The instructional objectives are performance-based and detail specific learning outcomes for Chapter 10. The test items contained in the Test Bank are keyed to the learning objectives and the Key Questions at the beginning of the chapter. The order of the objectives mirrors the content presentation in Chapter 10.

Upon completion of this chapter, the student should be able to:

1. Distinguish between a **coast** and a **coastline**.

2. Draw and label a the features on a beach profile including:
   a. **backshore**
   b. **foreshore**
   c. **shoreline**
   d. **nearshore**
   e. **offshore zone**
   f. **beach**
   g. **beach face**
   h. **longshore bars**
   i. **longshore trough**

3. Describe beach composition including the physical and geologic factors that produce beaches of differing composition.

4. Discuss the factors that move sand and sediment perpendicular to the shoreline.

5. Differentiate between **swash** and **backwash**.

6. Compare and contrast the appearance and composition of **summertime** and **wintertime** beaches including a discussion of the relative location and the seasonal movement of sediments.

7. Discuss the factors that move sand and sediment parallel to the shoreline.

8. Distinguish between **longshore current** and **longshore drift** and discuss the impact of these processes on a sandy beach shoreline.

9. Make a distinction between a **rip current** and **undertow**.

The Coast: Beaches and Shoreline Processes

10. List and describe the formation of features that characterize an **erosional shoreline** including;
    a. **headlands**
    b. **wave-cut cliffs**
    c. **sea caves**
    d. **sea arches**
    e. **sea stacks**
    f. **marine terraces**
11. List and describe the formation of features that characterize a **depositional shoreline** including:
    a. **spit**
    b. **bay-mouth bar (bay barrier)**
    c. **tombolo**
    d. **barrier island**
    e. **delta**

12. Illustrate the physiographic features of a temperate barrier island including the locations of:
    a. **ocean beach**
    b. **dunes**
    c. **barrier flat**
    d. **low salt marsh**
    e. **high salt marsh**

13. Explain the movement of sand or sediment in **beach compartments**.

14. Detail the relationship between **beach starvation** and human activity on a sandy or muddy coastline.

15. List and describe the features of **submerged shorelines** including:
    a. **drowned beach**
    b. **submerged dune topography**
    c. **drowned river valley**

16. Describe mechanisms for sea level changes in the past, present, and future.

17. Summarize the characteristics of the U.S. Atlantic coastline.

18. Summarize the characteristics of the U. S. Gulf of Mexico coastline.

19. Summarize the characteristics of the U. S. Pacific coastline.

20. Describe the structures erected by man to stabilize the coast including:
    a. **groin**
    b. **jetty**
    c. **breakwater**
    d. **seawall**

21. Discuss alternatives to hard stabilization and their potential impact on coastal erosion and sediment transport.

Overview

Chapter 10 is an overview of coastal landforms and the processes that shape coastlines. The chapter opens with an introduction to coastal regions and a presentation of technical vocabulary relating to beaches. Beach composition is discussed, and descriptions of sediment transporting mechanisms that move sediments parallel and perpendicular to the coastline are presented. Erosional- and depositional-type shores are compared including a presentation of the features that characterize each type of shoreline. A description of emerging and submerging shorelines follows, including an analysis of shoreline movements that produce a change in relative sea level. Characteristics of the United States coasts are considered with an emphasis on the processes affecting the Atlantic, the Gulf of Mexico, and the Pacific coasts. The chapter concludes with consideration of the various types of coastline hard stabilization including other alternatives.

Headings covered in this chapter include:
Coastal Region
    Beach Terminology
    Beach Composition
Movement of Sand on the Beach
    Movement Perpendicular to Shoreline
    Movement Parallel to Shoreline
Features of Erosional and Depositional Shores
    Features of Erosional Shores
    Features of Depositional Shores
    Features of Barrier Islands
Emerging and Submerging Shorelines
    Features of Emerging Shorelines
    Features of Submerging Shorelines
    Isostatic Adjustment
    Eustatic Sea Level Changes
    Sea Level Changes During Ice Ages
    Global Warming and Sea Level Change
Characteristics of U.S. Coasts
    The Atlantic Coast
    The Gulf Coast
    The Pacific Coast
Effects of Hard Stabilization
    Groins and Groin Fields
    Jetties
    Breakwaters
    Seawalls
Hard Stabilization Alternatives
    Construction Restrictions
    Beach Replenishment
    Relocation
Special Features:

The Coast: Beaches and Shoreline Processes

 Box 10-1: The Oceanography of Everyday Things: Warning: Rip Currents...Do You Know What To Do?
 Box 10-2: The Oceanography of Everyday Things: The Move of the Century: Relocating the Cape Hatteras Lighthouse

Teacher's Resources

There is a wide assortment of good films/videos on coastlines and coastal processes including:

Films/Videotapes
- Galveston Island Barrier Sands (Modern Talking Picture Service), 28 minutes
- Marine Erosion Processes—Cliffed Coasts (A. F. Films), 11 minutes
- The Beach: A River of Sand (Encyclopedia Britannica), 20 minutes
- The Beaches Are Moving (Environmental Media/North Carolina Public TV), 60 minutes
- Will Venice Survive Its Rescue? (NOVA), 60 minutes

Answers to End-of-Chapter Questions and Exercises

1. To help reinforce your knowledge of beach terminology, construct and label your own diagram similar to Figure 10-1.

Refer to Figure 10-1.

2. Describe differences between summertime and wintertime beaches. Explain why these differences occur.

During the summertime, there is light wave activity (characterized by lower energy waves), the swash zone from the breaking waves rushes up to the beach face and much of the water soaks into the beach sediment. As a result, there is a reduced amount of backwash. The swash dominates the sediment transport system. Since the swash moves the sediment up the beach face, it causes a net movement of sand up the beach face towards the berm. This results in sand deposition on the berm, producing a wide and well-developed berm that characterizes the summertime beach.
 During the winter, heavy wave activity from storms produces higher energy waves. The beach sediment is water saturated from pervious waves, so very little of the swash soaks into the beach. The amount of backwash is greatly increased, carrying a large amount of sediment with it as it drains down the beach face. This effect is magnified by the fact that the incoming swash comes on top of the previous wave's backwash, effectively preventing sediment in the incoming swash from deposition on the beach face or berm. Backwash dominates the wintertime sediment transport system, producing a much narrower berm and a flattened beach face.

3. What variables affect the speed of longshore currents?

The speed of the longshore currents increases with increasing beach slope, angle of the breakers and the shore, wave height, and decreasing wave period.

4. What is longshore drift, and how is it related to longshore current?

Longshore drift is the movement of sediment carried along the shore by longshore currents. As water from breaking waves in the surf zone washes onto the shore ad runs back down the beach face to the ocean, sediment is carried along with it. The longshore current water and the sediment carried by longshore drift follows a zigzag path along the shoreline.

5. How is the flow of water in a stream similar to longshore current? How are the two different?

In a stream, both water and sediments are transported within its banks from upstream to downstream ends. This is similar to a longshore current: it too carries water and sediment within the surf zone from upstream and downstream ends. Differences between streams and longshore currents include the fact that longshore currents involve transport in a zigzag fashion (streams have either turbulent or laminar flow conditions) and that the longshore current direction can change with the changing direction of breaking waves (streams always flow in the same direction, downhill).

6. Why does the direction of longshore current sometimes reverse direction? Along both U.S. coasts, what is the primary direction of annual longshore current?

The direction of longshore current sometimes reverses in flow direction because waves approach the beach from different angles. Along both the east and west U.S. coasts, the primary direction of annual longshore drift is from north to south. This direction will reverse if storms bring waves in from the south.

7. Describe the formation of rip currents. What is the best strategy to ensure that you won't drown if you are caught in a rip current?

A rip current is a surface current that typically occurs perpendicular to the coast and moves in the opposite direction of the breaking waves. Rip currents form where water builds up along the shore from breaking waves and flows back in a narrow flow toward the open ocean through topographic lows in the longshore bars. Swimmers who realize that they are caught in a rip current can escape by swimming parallel to shore for a short distance.

8. Discuss the formation of such erosional features as wave-cut cliffs, sea caves, sea arches, sea stacks, and marine terraces.

If waves release their energy along the base of a coastal cliff, they erode the cliff by abrasion with the force of water aided by sediment carried within the water, creating a *wave-cut cliff*. *Sea caves* typically begin along a weakness in the cliff (such as a fracture) and are further enlarged by wave erosion. If a headland juts into the ocean, waves refract around it and concentrate their energy release there. Waves may erode completely through the headland to create an opening through the rock called a *sea arch*. Continued erosion of the sea arch will case the sea arch roof to collapse, separating the seaward side of the arch from the headland and forming a column of rock called a *sea stack*.

9. Describe the origin of these depositional features: spit, bay barrier, tombolo, and barrier island.

A *spit* is a beach extension that protrudes into the open water of the bay. It will usually have a curved end due to the flow of tidal currents in and out of the bay, and it will often be elongated in the predominate direction of longshore drift. A *bay barrier* (*bay-mouth bar*) is a depositional feature that extends completely across the bay mouth and usually results from the depositional extension of a spit. A *tombolo*

The Coast: Beaches and Shoreline Processes

is a depositional feature that connects an island with another island or the mainland. It forms in the wave shadow of the island, and it is an extension of a beach deposit away from the landmass to which it is attached. *Barrier islands* are depositional features separated from the mainland by a lagoon. They may only be a few hundred meters wide but tens of kilometers in length (see Figure 10-7).

10. Describe the response of a barrier island to a rise in sea level. Why do some barrier islands develop peat deposits running through them from the ocean beach to the salt marsh?

Barrier islands are often associated with subsiding shores, but they are thought to move similar to a tractor's tread (rolling itself and moving toward the mainland) in response to a relative rise in sea level. Evidence for such migration can be seen in peat deposits, which are the remnants of old marshes that lie beneath the barrier islands. As barrier islands migrate toward the continents, islands override the marshes so that peat deposits are exposed on the ocean beach (see Figure 10-10).

11. Discuss why some rivers have deltas and others do not. What are the factors that determine whether a "bird's-foot" delta (like the Mississippi Delta) or a smoothly curved delta (like the Nile Delta) will form?

Since the last rise in sea level from melting glaciers, the ocean has invaded many rivers to the extent that they now stop flowing with sufficient with sufficient velocity to carry sediment from the estuary heads many miles inland from the open ocean. These rivers will not create deltas until they have filled their estuaries with sediment. Once the river's estuaries are filled and they deposit sediment on the continental shelf, they only build deltas if the sediment deposition rate is greater than the rate at which the longshore current can redistribute river sediment. If the longshore drift can carry away only a portion of the sediment deposits, then a curved delta front, similar to the Nile River Delta, will form. If the sediment deposition rate greatly exceeds the rate of sediment redistribution by the longshore current, a "bird's-foot" delta, similar to the Mississippi River Delta, will form.

12. Describe all parts of a beach compartment. What will happens when dams are built across all of the rivers that supply sand to the beach?

Beach compartments have three components: a series of rivers that supply sand to a beach; the beach itself where sand is moving due to longshore transport; and submarine canyons that lie offshore where sand is drained away from the beach. When dams are built across all of the rivers that supply sediment to beach compartments, it deprives the beach of sand that it would normally receive. The longshore transport process continues to operate in the absence of river sediment input, resulting in narrower beaches as the sand is moved from the beach offshore to the submarine canyon. If all of the streams supplying sediment to longshore transport are dammed, the beaches will nearly disappear.

13. Compare the causes and effects of tectonic versus eustatic changes in sea level.

Tectonic changes in sea level result from uplift or subsidence of a continent along a shoreline segment as a result of processes related to global plate tectonics. Tectonic uplift is occurring along the west coast of the United States as a result of the collision of the North American Plate with the Pacific, Juan de Fuca, and Gorda Plates. Along the east coast, tectonic events of a more passive nature are causing the shoreline to subside due to thermal contraction as the continent moves farther from the Mid-Atlantic Ridge. Contributing to this subsidence is the increasing sediment load deposited at continental margins.

   Eustatic sea level changes are a worldwide phenomenon resulting from changes in the holding capacity of the ocean basins or the amount of water in them. The most readily identifiable cause of eustatic sea level changes is the formation and melting of continental glaciers. Other types of eustatic sea level change include those due to thermal expansion or contraction of water due to global warming or cooling and from changes in the shape of the seafloor due to increased or decreased rates of seafloor spreading.

No matter what produced the sea level change, similar deposits are left as evidence. For relative rises in sea level, drowned river mouths and drowned beaches and dune topography are left as evidence. For relative drops in sea level, marine terraces and stranded beach deposits are left as evidence.

14. List the two basic processes by which coasts advance seaward, and list their counterparts that lead to coastal retreat.

Coasts may advance seaward as a result of uplift or deposition. Retreating coasts can result from subsidence or erosion.

15. List and discuss for factors that influence the classification of a coast as either erosional or depositional.

Whether the dominant process along a coast is erosion or deposition depends on the combined effect of many variables. These variables include: degree of exposure to ocean waves, tidal range, composition of coastal bedrock, tectonic subsidence or emergence, isostatic subsidence or emergence, and eustatic sea level change.

16. Describe tectonic and depositional processes causing subsidence along the Atlantic Coast.

The Atlantic Coast is subsiding due to tectonic processes associated with thermal contraction of the lithosphere as the edge of the continent moves farther away form the Mid-Atlantic Ridge. This same process causes the oceans to deepen with increased distance from spreading centers. In addition, the sediment load that the thick wedge of sediment underlying the continental margin represents is pushing the lithosphere down into the asthenosphere. Although both of these processes are in effect, it may be uplift occurring north of Cape Hatteras is a result of isostatic rebound following the removal of the continental ice sheet that once extended as far south as New York and New Jersey.

17. Compare the Atlantic Coast, Gulf Coast, and Pacific Coast by describing the conditions and features of emergence-submergence and erosion-deposition that are characteristic of each.

Atlantic Coast: This subsiding coast is composed principally of relatively soft sedimentary rock with the exception of some position of the Maine coast composed of crystalline rocks. The tidal range varies from less than 1 meter (3.3 feet) at the southern tip of Florida to between 2 and 4 meters (6.5 and 13.1 feet) along the Maine coast. The entire coast is openly exposed to storm waves from the Atlantic Ocean, but the most energetic waves strike the coast north of Cape Hatteras when nor-easters blow out of the North Atlantic. South of New York, barrier islands are well developed and indicative of the tectonic subsidence that is occurring. To the north, some uplift may be resulting from the isostatic rebound that is continuing following the melting of the continental glacier that once extended as far south as New York City.

Gulf Coast: The Gulf coast is undergoing tectonic subsidence throughout its length, but locally this is more than compensated for by sediment deposition in the Mississippi River Delta. The degree of exposure here is not great because the Gulf of Mexico is a relatively small body of water, so except when a hurricane passes through, the waves are generally small. The tidal range is also small. Erosion is still not a major problem, except in the Louisiana marshes, because of the low level of wave energy released against the soft sediments that comprise most of the exposed bedrock. Barrier islands along most of the coast attest to the fact that subsidence is a dominant process along the Gulf coast.

Pacific Coast: Tectonic uplift is the dominant characteristic of the Pacific coast. Tides are for the most part between 1 and 2 meters (3.3 to 6.5 feet) although they average between 2 and 4 meters (6.5 and 13.1 feet) along the Washington coast. Relatively soft sedimentary rock comprises most of the bedrock along the coast. Locally along the California and Oregon coasts, crystalline granite and volcanic rock are found. Essentially the entire length of the coast is openly exposed to high-energy storm waves that move in from the North Pacific in winter. Particularly in southern California, there is a problem with a decrease in the amount of sediment in the longshore drift as a result of the damming of many mountain streams for flood control. Construction of boat harbors and marinas has resulted in interference with the movement of available sediment in the longshore drift that moves from north to south along this coast most of the time. Some beaches lose their sand during the winter when heavy surf leaves behind only cobbles and pebbles. The sand moves back along the shore with decreased wave energy in the summer. Along some lengths of the shore, a continual battle is going on between the seaward advance of the shore by uplift and retreat of the shoreline through erosion.

18. List the types of hard stabilization and describe what each is intended to do.

- *Groins* are barriers to sediment flow built perpendicular to a coastline. They are constructed of many kinds of material, but they are usually made of large blocky material called riprap. Sometime, groins are even constructed of sturdy wood pilings (similar to a fence built out into the ocean). A groin is constructed with the express purpose of trapping sand. A groin interrupts the flow of longshore drift and will cause sediment to be deposited in its upstream side as the current is slowed and experiences a decreased ability to carry sediment. Downstream from the groin, waves begin to erode sediment from the beach because the wave's energy that was once used to transport sediment along the length of the shore is now available to pick up and transport other sediment. Until the sediment moves around the groin, erosion downstream of the groin will continue.
- A *jetty* is similar to a groin in that it is a structure that is built perpendicular to the shore, and it is also usually constructed of riprap. Jetties are built to protect harbor entrances from wave action and they secondarily trap sand. Jetties are often built in closely spaced pairs, and they are usually longer than groins. As a result, they usually cause more pronounced upstream sediment deposition and downstream sediment erosion.
- *Breakwaters* are hard stabilization built parallel to the shoreline that often protects a harbor or creates boat anchorage. From the experience at Santa Barbara and Santa Monica, California, breakwaters cause a build-up of sand inshore of them and unwanted erosion downstream from them.
- *Seawalls* are built parallel to the shore along a beach to protect the coastline from high water and wave energy. Once waves begin breaking against a seawall, the turbulence generated by the abrupt release of wave energy quickly erodes the sediment on its seaward side, causing it to collapse in the surf. Where they have been used to protect barrier island property, the seaward slope of the island beach has steepened, increasing the erosion rate. Seawalls destroy recreational beaches.

19. Draw an aerial view of a shoreline to show the effect on erosion and deposition caused by constructing a groin, a jetty, a breakwater, and a seawall within the coastal environment.

Answers will vary, but the illustration should resemble Figure 10-19 (groin), Figure 10-21 (jetties and groins), Figures 10-22 and 10-23 (breakwaters), and Figure 10-24 (seawall). Deposition occurs upstream of groins and jetties (inshore of breakwaters) while erosion occurs downstream of these structures. Reflection of wave energy from seawalls causes the seaward slope of the beach to increase, increasing the rate of beach erosion.

20. Describe alternatives to hard stabilization.

There are several alternatives to hard stabilization: restriction of building in flood-prone, erosional coastal areas; beach replacement (beach nourishment); and relocation. In some coastal areas, residents are prohibited from rebuilding following a natural disaster in the hope of reducing future losses (financial and environmental). Beach replenishment involves the replacement of lost sand to beach, and this process can be expensive as it most be done on a continual basis. Offshore sand is either dredged and deposited on the beach or pumped into the longshore drift for deposition. The average coast of beach replenishment is around $5.00 to $10.00 per cubic yard of sand (0.76 cubic meters). In some cases, relocation of a valuable structure to an area that is not subject to erosion. The most notable example of relocation was moving the Cape Hatteras Lighthouse 884 meters (2900 feet) in 1999 at a cost in excess of 12 million dollars.

11

The Coastal Ocean

Learning Objectives

The instructional objectives are performance-based and detail specific learning outcomes for Chapter 11. The test items contained in the Test Bank are keyed to the learning objectives and the Key Questions at the beginning of the chapter. The order of the objectives mirrors the content presentation in Chapter 11.

Upon completion of this chapter, the student should be able to:

1. List in chronological order the historical events relating to the ownership of marine resources including:
   a. *Mare liberum*
   b. *De dominio maris*
   c. United Nations Conference on the Law of the Sea

2. Define an **Exclusive Economic Zone (EEZ)**.

3. Differentiate between **coastal waters** and the **open ocean**.

4. Distinguish between a **halocline** and a **thermocline**.

5. Describe the creation of **coastal geostrophic currents** and give an example of such a current in United States coastal waters.

6. Define **estuary** and give an example.

7. Discuss the origins of estuaries including:
   a. **coastal plain estuary**.
   b. **fjord**.
   c. **bar-built estuary**.
   d. **tectonic estuary**.

8. Describe the water mixing patterns in the following types of estuaries:
   a. **vertically mixed estuary.**
   b. **slightly stratified estuary.**
   c. **highly stratified estuary.**
   d. **salt wedge estuary.**

9. Compare and contrast the physical characteristics of the *Columbia River Estuary* and the *Chesapeake*

Bay Estuary.

10. Explain the physical and chemical parameters that determine the type(s) of coastal **wetlands** in a give area.

11. Describe the physical parameters and the biological components of the following coastal ecosystems:
    a. **mangrove swamps.**
    b. **salt marshes.**

12. Characterize the changes the size and environmental quality of United States wetlands and discuss similar global trends.

13. Distinguish between a **wetland**, an **estuary**, and a **lagoon** and give an example of each.

14. Diagram the circulation patterns in the Mediterranean Sea and explain the implications of climate on the salinity and temperature patterns within Mediterranean water masses.

15. Define **pollution.**

16. Explain how the EPA uses a **standard laboratory bioassay** to assess potential harm from pollutants.

17. Discuss the implications of ocean waste disposal for coastal areas.

18. List and define the main types of marine pollutants including:
    a. **petroleum.**
    b. **hydrocarbons.**
    c. **sewage sludge.**
    d. **dichlorophenyltrichloroethane (DDT).**
    e. **polychlorinated biphenyls (PCBs).**
    f. **mercury.**
    g. **trash.**
    h. **non-point-source pollution.**
    i. **plastics.**

19. Detail the historical oil spills in United States coastal waters.

20. Describe the biological effects of oil spills in marine environments.

21. Discuss ways in which oil spills can be cleaned up or contained in coastal areas.

22. Differentiate between **primary sewage treatment** and **secondary sewage treatment.**

23. Define **bioremediation** and describe its use in treating oil and hydrocarbon wastes.

24. Explain the impact of the Clean Water Act of 1972 on coastal waters.

25. Give examples of persistent organic pollutants in marine environments and describe their initial source(s) prior to disposal.

The Coastal Ocean

26. Explain the relationship between environmental DDT levels and the decline in marine bird populations.

27. Describe **Minamata Disease** and its relationship to mercury contamination in marine ecosystems.

28. Distinguish between **bioaccumulation** and **biomagnification** and discuss the implications of these phenomena in marine ecosystems.

29. Detail the possible sources of **non-point-source pollution** in marine waters.

30. Outline the effects of plastic trash in coastal waters on living organisms. Propose possible solutions for the problem.

Overview

Chapter 11 is an overview of the ocean in coastal regions. Due to the proximity to land and the shallow nature of coastal waters, they are subject to a relatively great rate of change and broad ranges of physical features in comparison to the open ocean. The chapter begins with a presentation of the historical agreements that govern the use of marine resources. The Law of the Sea and global ocean policy for coastal and open ocean waters is discussed. Physical oceanographic features affecting coastal waters such as salinity and temperature are examined. Estuaries, coastal wetlands, and lagoons are defined and discussed with an emphasis on the classification of estuaries as a function of origin and the type of mixing. The Mediterranean Sea serves as a case of a large body of coastal water with restricted communication with the open ocean. The chapter concludes with an examination of coastal water pollution including the types of pollutants commonly found in coastal waters.

Headings covered in this chapter include:
Laws that Govern Ocean Ownership
    Mare Liberum and the Territorial Sea
    Law of the Sea
Characteristics of Coastal Waters
    Salinity
    Temperature
    Coastal Geostrophic Currents
Types of Coastal Waters
    Estuaries
        Water Mixing in Estuaries
        Estuaries and Human Activities
        Columbia River Estuary
        Chesapeake Bay Estuary
    Coastal Wetlands
        Coastal Wetland Characteristics
        Serious Loss of Valuable Wetlands
    Lagoons
        Laguna Madre
    Marginal Seas
        Case Study: Mediterranean Sea

Mediterranean Circulation
Pollution in Coastal Waters
    Definition of Marine Pollution
    Standard Laboratory Bioassay
    Ocean Waste Disposal Issues
Types of Marine Pollution
    Petroleum
    Sewage Sludge
    DDT and PCBs
    Mercury and Minamata Disease
    Non-Point-Source Pollution and Trash
Special Features:
    Box 11-1: Historical Feature: The Exxon Valdez: Not the Worst Spill Ever
    Box 11-2: The Oceanography of Everyday Things: From A to Z in Plastics: The Miracle
Substance?

Teacher's Resources

There are a wide assortment of good films/videos and C-ROMs on coastal waters and estuaries including:

Films/Videotapes
- Are You Swimming in a Sewer? (NOVA/Coronet), 58 minutes
- Estuary (Bullfrog Films), 12 minutes
- The Science Show: Ocean Resources (Films for the Humanities and Sciences), 23 minutes
- Oceanographic Mediterranèene (Society from French-American Cultural Service and Educational Aids), 32 minutes
- The Global Environment: The Troubled Sea (Coronet), 20 minutes
- The Ring of Truth: Clues (Phillip Morrison/PBS), 60 minutes (examines evidence for the drying of the Mediterranean Sea).
- The Salt Marsh: A Question of Values (Encyclopedia Britannica), 21 minutes
- Trashing the Oceans (NOAA), 8 minutes
- The Ocean Sink (The Blue Revolution Series), 29 minutes (subject: ocean pollution)

CD-ROMs
- The Digital Field Trip to the Wetlands (Tasa Graphic Arts, Inc.)

Answers to End-of-Chapter Questions and Exercises

1. Discuss the possible reasons why less developed nations believe that the open ocean is the common heritage of all, whereas the more developed nations believe that the open ocean's resources belong to those who recover them.

Less developed nations are dependent on the developed nations for economic survival, so a significant piece of the profits from the resources of the open ocean would give them an increased level of independence as they try to improve the standard of living for their populations. If developed nations supply the capital and technology, taking all the risk involved in trying to exploit the mineral resources of the open ocean, they should also receive the profit potential commensurate with taking such risks.

The Coastal Ocean

Sharing the profit with those who do not share in the risk is an unfamiliar and unwise idea to investors of risk capital.

2. For coastal oceans where deep mixing does not occur, discuss the effect that offshore winds and fresh water runoff will have on salinity distribution. How will the winter and summer seasons affect the temperature distribution in the water column?

In coastal waters, salinity is increased by evaporation resulting from offshore winds, and decreased due to freshwater input from runoff and precipitation. If no mixing occurs, these changes will be restricted to the surface water, and a significant halocline (layer of rapidly changing salinity with depth) will develop. Surface coastal water temperatures will decrease during the winter and increase during the summer. This seasonal temperature pattern in areas with not mixing produces seasonal thermoclines (a layer of rapidly changing temperature with depth) (refer to Figure 11-2).

3. How does coastal runoff of low-salinity water produce a coastal geostrophic current?

Water coming from coastal runoff will not mix with seawater due to its low salinity and corresponding lower density. Instead, this freshwater will pile up into a low mound of water along the coast. The water at the surface of the accumulation will run downhill toward the open ocean under the influence of gravity. As it moves offshore, the Coriolis force will curve it to the right in the Northern Hemisphere and to the left in the Southern Hemisphere. This produces flow along the coastline. (see Figure 11-4).

4. Based in their origin, draw and describe the four major classes of estuaries.

Drawings of the four major classes of estuaries as a function of origin (coastal plain, fjord, bar-built estuary, and tectonic estuary) should resemble Figure 11-5).

5. Describe the difference between vertically mixed and slat wedge estuaries in terms of salinity distribution, depth, and volume of river flow. Which displays the more classical estuarine circulation pattern?

Differences between vertically mixed and salt wedge estuaries are shown in the following table:

Type of Estuary	Salinity Distribution	Depth	Volume of River Flow
Vertically mixed	same top to bottom (no halocline)	shallow	small
Salt wedge	freshwater top, saltwater wedge below (well-defined halocline)	deep	large

Vertically mixed estuaries occur where small volumes of water are emptied into shallow estuaries by streams. At any location in the estuary the water is a uniform salinity throughout the water column. There is no halocline developed as the flow within the estuary moves toward the mouth of the estuary mixing uniformly with marine water.

Salt wedge estuaries develop when large volume rivers flow into deep estuaries. The surface of the estuary will be covered by freshwater, producing a significant halocline within the estuary. The halocline develops at increasingly shallower depths toward the estuary mouth.

The classic estuarine circulation of freshwater flowing toward the ocean at the surface and a subsurface flow of salt water toward the head of the estuary is more accurately represented by the circulation pattern found in a salt wedge estuary (refer to Figure 11-4).

6. Discuss factors that cause the surface salinity of Chesapeake Bay to be greater along its east side, and why periods of summer anoxia in deep water are becoming increasingly severe with time.

The surface water salinity is normally greater on the east side of the Chesapeake Bay for two reasons. First, the greatest amount of surface freshwater runoff into the bay is from rivers that drain the Appalachian Mountains to the west of the bay. Second, as marine water enters the bay from the south, the Coriolis force moves it toward the eastern bay margin.

With maximum spring river flow, a strong halocline (and corresponding pycnocline) develops, preventing the mixing of fresh surface water and saltier deep water. Beneath the pycnocline (which can be as shallow as 5 meters or 16 feet), waters may become anoxic from May through August as dead organic matter decays in deep water. Since the 1950s, the bay has experiences intense pressure from human activities. Studies suggest that increased nutrient inputs from sewage and agricultural fertilizers have been added to the bay as a result of anthropogenic activities. The increased nutrients have resulted in an increased microscopic algal biomass (algal blooms), increasing the deposition of organic matter of the bottom. Increased biological oxygen demand from decomposition increases the possibility of deep water anoxia occurring.

7. Name the two types of coastal wetland environments and the latitude ranges where each will likely develop. How do wetlands contribute to the biology of the oceans and the cleansing of polluted river water?

The two types of coastal wetlands are *salt marshes* and *mangrove swamps*. Salt marshes are common to latitudes of 65° in areas where killing frosts occur. Marshes develop in coastal areas with low wave energy in areas with silt and clay sediments. Mangroves are restricted to areas between 30°N to 30°S in areas with no killing frosts and low wave energy. Once mangrove swamps begin to develop in areas formally covered by a salt marsh, they will usually replace the marsh.

Over half if the commercial fisheries along the United States coastline depend on wetlands as nursery areas. Fishes such as flounder and bluefish use wetlands as feeding grounds and they over winter in these protected areas. The fisheries for oysters, clams, scallops, smelt, and eels are located in marshes. Clay-sized particles typical of sediment in marshes are able to remove appreciable amounts of inorganic nitrogen and metal compounds from polluted water by absorption.

8. What factors lead to a wide seasonal range of salinity in Laguna Madre?

Laguna Madre is a 160-kilometer (100-mile) long, narrow body of water separating Padre Island from the south Texas coast. It has very shallow connections with the Gulf of Mexico on both ends, resulting in a low exchange rate between the waters of the Gulf and the lagoon. The lagoon is also very shallow, and this allows for large ranges in temperature and salinity to develop seasonally. Temperatures become very high in the summer and low in the winter. Salinity can range from 2 parts per thousand (0.2%) to 100 parts per thousand (10%) as a result of alternating periods of rain caused by local thunderstorms (adds freshwater, decreases salinity) with hot, dry weather (increases evaporation, increases salinity).

The Coastal Ocean

9. Describe the circulation between the Atlantic Ocean and the Mediterranean Sea, and explain how and why it differs from estuarine circulation.

A high rate of evaporation that greatly exceeds the rate of precipitation in the Mediterranean region creates a water level at the eastern end of the Mediterranean Sea that is 15 centimeters (6 inches) less than that near the straits of Gibraltar. This creates a gravity flow at the surface from the Atlantic Ocean into the Mediterranean Sea. As this water moves east across the Mediterranean, its salinity is increased from about 36.5 parts per thousand to near 39.1 parts per thousand near Cypress. Here it sinks because of its high density to become Mediterranean Intermediate Water and flows back toward Gibraltar at depths from 200 to 600 meters (660 to 1970 feet). This subsurface flow enters the Atlantic Ocean at a salinity of 37.3 parts per thousand. In estuaries where these is a surface flow of fresh water toward the ocean and a subsurface flow of marine water into the estuary, the climate is characterized by an excess of runoff and precipitation of fresh water compared to that lost to evaporation. The reverse is true of the Mediterranean region.

10. Without consulting the textbook, define pollution. Then consider these items and determine if each one is a pollutant based on your definition (and refine you definition as necessary):
    • Dead seaweed on the beach
    • Natural oil seeps
    • A small amount of sewage
    • Warm water dumped into the ocean

Responses may vary. All responses should provide a justification whether they are forms of pollution or not. Based in the definition of pollution by the World Health Organization, the first two are probably not pollution, and the last two probably are.

11. Why would many marine pollution experts consider oil among the *least* damaging pollutants in the ocean?

Many marine pollution experts consider oil to be among the least damaging marine pollution because oil-a hydrocarbon-is a naturally occurring source of energy that is biodegradable. In fact, natural undersea oil seeps have occurred for millions of years, and the ocean ecosystem seems to be unaffected (or even, since oil is a source of energy, *enhanced*) by their presence.

12. Describe the effects of oil spills on species diversity and recovery of bottom-dwelling organisms based on the experience at Wild Harbor.

At Wild Harbor, there was nearly a total initial killing of all intertidal and subtidal organisms in heavily oiled areas. During the first year, 99.9% of organisms found within the area were a single species of polychaete worm, *Capitella capitana*. It was well into the third year before an appreciable increase in species diversity occurred.

13. Compare oil spills that wash ashore to those that do not, such as the *Argo Merchant*, in terms of destruction to marine life.

Oil spills that wash ashore are probably more destructive to marine life than those that do not because at shore, oil becomes trapped in sediment grains and is not readily available to the processes of evaporation and bacterial decomposition. In addition, oil that washes ashore is more likely to damage a high percentage of particular environment-say salt marsh-than oil that remains floating on the open ocean.

14. Discuss techniques used to clean oil spills. Why is it important to begin cleanup immediately?

Once an oil spill occurs in the ocean, lower-density oil initially floats on top of the higher density water. Skimming the surface with specially designed skimmers can collect the floating oil or it can be soaked into absorbent materials. However, the collected oil (or oiled materials) must still be disposed of elsewhere. Additionally, cleanup must begin immediately after the spill or the oil will begin to disperse and come ashore or form tar balls and sink. Because oil is a natural energy source, it is naturally biodegraded by microorganisms such as bacteria and fungi. The method of using these organisms to help clean spills is called bioremediation. Bioremediation has proven to be one of the most successful methods for coping with the deleterious effects of oil spills.

15. When and where was the world's largest oil spill? How many times larger was it than the *Exxon Valdez* oil spill?

The largest oil spill on record occurred because of intentional dumping by the Iraqi army during their invasion of Kuwait during the 1991 Persian Gulf War. By the time the Iraqi were driven out of Kuwait ad the leaking oil wells and sabotaged production facilities were brought under control, more than 908 million liters (240 million gallons) of oil had spilled into the Persian Gulf. The amount of oil from this spill was over 20 times larger than the spill from the *Exxon Valdez*, which is currently the largest oil spill in history in United States waters.

16. How would dumping sewage in deep water off the East Coast help reduce the negative effects to the ocean bottom?

If the sludge is dropped in deeper water with a layer of rapidly changing density (pycnocline) between the warmer surface water and the colder deep water, internal waves moving along the density gradient will keep the sludge in suspension until it is moved laterally up to 100 times its sinking rate. This will make the sludge available to detritus-feeding zooplankton and reduce the sludge concentration on the ocean bottom.

17. Discuss the animal populations that clearly suffered from the effects of DDT and the way in which this negative effect was manifested.

Birds are the animals that have clearly suffered the most from the effects of DDT in the environment. Most notably, ospreys of Long Island Sound, New York, and brown pelicans of Anacapa Island, California, produced thin eggshells after ingesting DDT. It resulted in most of their eggs being broken by the weight of the parents during incubation.

18. What causes Minamata disease? What are the symptoms of the disease in humans?

Minamata disease is a form of mercury poisoning caused by contact with or ingestion of high levels of the metal mercury. Symptoms include neurological disorders that affect the human nervous system.

The Coastal Ocean

19. What is non-point-source pollution and how does it get to the ocean? What other ways does trash get into the ocean?

Non-point-source pollution is any type of pollution entering the ocean from sources other than underwater pipelines. Mostly, non-point-source pollution arrives at the ocean via runoff from storm drains. Trash can enter the ocean from non-point-source pollution or from either legal or illegal ocean dumping.

20. What properties contributed to plastics being considered a miracle substance? How do those same properties cause them to be unusually persistent and damaging in the marine environment?

The properties of plastics that contribute to them being considered a miracle substance are that plastic products are lightweight, strong, durable, and inexpensive. The same properties cause them to be unusually persistent and damaging in the marine environment:

- Their lightweight property causes them to float and be concentrated at the surface.
- Their high strength results in entanglement of marine organisms.
- Their durability means that they don't biodegrade easily, causing them to last almost indefinitely.
- Their inexpensive cost allows them to be mass-produced and used in almost everything.

CHAPTER
12
Marine Life and the Marine Environment

Learning Objectives

The instructional objectives are performance-based and detail specific learning outcomes for Chapter 12. The test items contained in the Test Bank are keyed to the learning objectives and the Key Questions at the beginning of the chapter. The order of the objectives mirrors the content presentation in Chapter 12.

Upon completion of this chapter, the student should be able to:

1. Describe the classification of living organisms including the following **taxonomic** distinctions:
    A. **domain**
        (1). **Archaea**
        (2). **Bacteria**
        (3). **Eukarya**
    B. **kingdom**
        (1). **Monera**
        (2). **Protista (Protoctista)**
        (3). **Fungi**
        (4). **Plantae**
        (5). **Animalia**
    C. **phylum** (= **division** for organisms with cell walls)
    D. **class**
    E. **order**
    F. **family**
    G. **genus**
    H. **species**

2. Describe the classification of marine organisms as a function of their habitat including:
    A. **plankton**
        (1). classified according to nutrition and cell type
            (a). **phytoplankton**
            (b). **zooplankton**
            (c). **bacterioplankton**
        (2). classified according to size
            (a). **macroplankton**
            (b). **picoplankton**
            (c). **holoplankton**
            (d). **meroplankton**
    B. **Nekton**

Marine Life and the Marine Environment

   C. Benthos

3. Discuss the distribution of marine life in the zonation of the oceanic water column including:
   A. **pelagic environment**
   B. **benthic environment**

4. Outline the physical and physiologic adaptations of organisms to life in the marine environment including:
   A. strategies for body support
   B. strategies to prevent sinking
      (1). surface area to volume ratio
      (2). increasing surface area by adding appendages, spines, projections, etc
   C. streamlined body shape

5. Compare and contrast thermal tolerance in marine organisms including **stenothermal** and **eurythermal** organisms.

6. Compare and contrast **euryhaline** and **stenohaline** organisms. Give an example of a euryhaline and stenohaline marine/estuarine organism and describe the environment in which it would live.

7. Distinguish between **diffusion** and **osmosis**. How does the type of environment (living versus nonliving) and the state of matter affect these processes?

8. Distinguish between **hypertonic, hypotonic,** and **isotonic** solutions in terms of net water movement. What are the implications for living cells placed in each of these environments?

9. Discuss the strategies employed by marine and freshwater fish to maintain salt and water balance.

10. Detail the strategies employed by marine organisms to accomplish gas exchange.

11. Explain the relationship between the transparency of water and the kinds of color patterns exhibited by open ocean organisms. How do the strategies of **countershading, disruptive coloration,** and **transparency** affect predation?

12. Describe the relationship between depth and atmospheric pressure in the ocean.

13. The ocean environment is divided into two distinct zones - open water (**pelagic**) and bottom (**benthic**).

14. The pelagic environment is divided into two provinces - the **neritic** (coastal) **province** and the **oceanic province**. The oceanic province is further subdivided as a function of depth:
    A. **epipelagic zone**
    B. **mesopelagic zone**
    C. **bathypelagic zone**
    D. **abyssopelagic zone**

15. Distinguish among the following oceanic zones as a function of light availability:

    A. **euphotic (photic) zone**
    B. **disphotic zone**
    C. **aphotic zone**

Overview

Chapter 12 is the first of four chapters focusing on biological oceanography, and it serves as an introduction to the marine environment. The classification of living things is presented, followed by a discussion of the general classification of marine organisms. This is a functional classification based in where they live (habitat) and the type of movement (motility) exhibited. There are three distinct groups of organisms: plankton (organisms that can not swim against a current), nekton (swimmers), and benthos (bottom dwellers). The general distribution of life in the oceans is considered, including some examples of unique adaptations to ocean living. The chapter concludes with a section detailing organisms living in the two different marine environmental zones, surface (pelagic) and bottom (benthic), ocean waters.

Headings covered in this chapter include:
Classification of Living Things
        Three Domains of Life
        Five Kingdoms of Organisms
        Taxonomic Classification
Classification of Marine Organisms
        Plankton (Floaters)
        Nekton (Swimmers)
        Benthos (Bottom Dwellers)
Distribution of Life in the Ocean
        Why Are There So Few Marine Species?
Adaptations of Organisms to the Marine Environment
        Physical Support
        Viscosity and Streamlining
        Temperature
        Salinity
        Dissolved Gases
        Water's High Transparency
        Pressure
Marine Environment Divisions
        Pelagic Environment (Open Ocean)
        Benthic Environment (Sea Bottom)
Special Features:
        Box 12-1:Historical Feature: Alexander Agassiz: Advancements in Ocean Sampling
        Box 12-2: Research Methods in Oceanography: A False Bottom: The Deep Scattering Layer
(DSL)
        Box 12-3: Historical Feature: Diving into the Marine Environment

Teacher's Resources

There is a wide assortment of good films/videos on marine life including:

Marine Life and the Marine Environment

Films/Videotapes
- Adaptations to a Marine Environment (McGraw-Hill), 16 minutes
- Life in the Sea (Encyclopedia Britannica), 11 minutes
- Marine Ecology (McGraw-Hill), 28 minutes
- Mysteries of the Deep (Walt Disney Productions), 24 minutes
- Survival in the Sea: Where Land and Water Meet (Indiana University), 30 minutes

Answers to End-of-Chapter Questions and Exercises

1. List the three major domains of life and the five kingdoms of organisms. Describe the fundamental criteria used in assigning organisms to these divisions.
All living organisms can be divided into tone of three major domains (branches) of life: *Archaea*, *Bacteria*, and *Eukarya*.
- *Archaea* is a group of simple microscopic bacteria-like organisms that are believed to be the closest ancestors of primitive cells. They are often found living in extreme environmental conditions (temperature, pressure, salinity, etc.) that may be similar to the conditions of the primitive Earth. This group includes the methane producers and sulfur-oxidizing organisms found in hydrothermal vents.
- *Bacteria* include simple single-celled organisms that have cell walls and lack a defined nucleus. Members of this group include cyanobacteria (blue-green algae), purple bacteria, green non-sulfur bacteria, and many of the disease-causing bacteria.
- *Eukarya* contain all organisms containing cells with membrane-bound organelles and a nucleus defined by a membrane. Protists, fungi, plants, and animals are all members of this domain.

Within the three domains of living organisms, five distinct kingdoms of life are recognized. These kingdoms are separated using the level of cellular complexity and cellular structures shared by the members of the kingdoms: Monera, Protista (Protoctista), Fungi, Plantae, and Animalia.
- *Kingdom Monera* includes all of the simple, single-celled microscopic organisms in the domains *Archaea* and *Bacteria*. Theses organisms have cells that lack specialized organelles (compartments) delineated by membranes, and no membrane-bound organelles.
- *Kingdom Protista (Protoctista)* includes all of the simple unicellular organisms with membrane-bound nuclei and organelles, and many multicellular, photosynthetic organisms that have an independent unicellular phase in the life cycle (macroalgae).
- *Kingdom Fungi* includes complex multicellular heterotrophic organisms that have cell walls including fungi and molds.
- *Kingdom Plantae* includes complex multicellular photosynthetic organisms that have cells with cell walls; plants.
- *Kingdom Animalia* includes complex multicellular heterotrophic organisms that lack cells walls (plasma membranes only); animals.

2. Describe the lifestyles of plankton, nekton, and benthos. Why is it true that plankton account for a much larger percentage of the ocean's biomass than benthos and nekton?

- *Plankton* are organisms that can not swim against a current and drift in the ocean. Wind and water currents determine their movement.
- *Nekton* are organisms that are active swimmers such as fish and marine mammals. They can determine their position in the water column and on the ocean's surface because of their larger size and increased mobility (efficient locomotion).

- *Benthos* are organisms that live on the ocean's bottom.

Since larger animals east smaller animals and only a small percentage of the energy (10%) obtained by one population is passed on to the population that feeds on it, the percentage of ocean biomass represented by populations of large animals is necessarily less than that represented by smaller organisms. Because phytoplankton either directly or indirectly provide essentially all of the energy for all the oceans' populations, they therefore must also represent by far the largest part of the biomass in t he ocean.

3. List the subdivisions of plankton and benthos and the criteria used for assigning individual species to each.

Plankton
- Phytoplankton – photosynthetic, plant-like plankton
- Zooplankton – heterotrophic, animal-like plankton
- Bacterioplankton – unicellular, bacteria-like plankton
- Macroplankton – large plankton such as jellyfish
- Microplankton – small plankton that can be caught in a fine-meshed silk net
- Picoplankton – plankton that are smaller than 2 µm in diameter
- Holoplankton – organisms that spend their entire life cycle as plankton
- Meroplankton – organisms that spend only the larval stage as plankton and then become either nekton or benthos.

Benthos
- Infauna – sediment-dwelling benthos
- Epifauna – bottom-dwelling benthos
- Nektobenthos – animals that live on the bottom but are capable of swimming in the water above the bottom.

4. List the relative number of species of animals found in the terrestrial, pelagic, and benthic environments, and discusses the factors that may account for this distribution.

Of the more than 1.75 million known species of organisms that live on Earth, only about 14% (250,000) inhabit the oceans. Of the marine species, 98% are benthic and only about 2% (about 5,000 species) are pelagic. New species evolve more rapidly in a variable environment (as well as high rates of reproduction). The ocean's low temperature and environmental stability would not be as likely to produce as many species as the more varied ocean floor, and the considerably more variable and much warmer continental terrestrial environments.

5. Discuss the major differences between marine algae and land plants, and explain the reasons why there is a greater complexity of land plants.

The predominant populations of marine photosynthetic organisms are microscopic single-celled algae; more complex photosynthetic multicellular organisms are distributed throughout terrestrial environments. Marine algae are adequately supplied with water and buoyancy and frictional resistance to sinking provide structural support. As a result, no complex structures are needed to help these marine organisms meet their need for water and support. In contrast, land plants live in an environment where water is limited and there is no aqueous medium for support. Complex root structures are needed to obtain water and nutrients from the soil substrate, an outer layer of bark in needed to maintain water balance, and specialized conductive tissues are needed to transport water and nutrients throughout the plant.

6. Determine the surface to volume ratio of an organism whose liner dimensions is (1) 1 centimeter (0.4 inch), (b) 3 centimeters (1.1 inches), and (c) 5 centimeters (2 inches). Which one is better able to resist inking, and why? Discuss some adaptations other than size that are used by organisms to increase their resistance to sinking.

One of the strategies used by pelagic marine organisms is frictional resistance. The greater surface are to volume ration an organism possesses, the greater the amount of frictional resistance to sinking it will have per unit of body mass and the slower it will sink.

The surface area of an object increases as the square of its linear dimension, and the volume (which is proportional to mass) increases with the cube of the liner dimension. As illustrated in the table below, an organism with an average linear dimension of 1 centimeter will have a surface to volume ratio three times that of an organism with an average linear dimension of 5 centimeters (refer to Figure 12-8). As a result, the smaller the organism is, the higher its surface area to volume ration. This increased ration means that organism resists sinking better than larger organisms.

In addition to small size, many small pelagic planktonic organisms increase their surface area (and increase frictional drag) using spiny appendages, needle-like extension and ornamentation, or a ring-like body structure to remain in the photic zone. Other organisms use a tiny oil droplet to increase buoyancy.

Linear Dimension	Surface Area	Volume (Mass)	Surface Area/Volume Ratio
1 cm	6 cm^2	1 cm^3	6.0
3 cm	54 cm^2	27 cm^3	2.0
5 cm	150 cm^2	125 cm^3	1.2

7. Discuss some adaptations other than size that are used by organisms to increase their resistance to sinking.

Organisms use several strategies to prevent sinking that are not related to size. Organisms can increase their drag in the water using adaptive body shapes that increase fictional resistance. Organisms can also decrease their density relative to seawater. This is accomplished in several ways. The Portuguese Man-O-War has a gas bladder that it uses as a floatation device. Other organisms have evolved "sail-like" structures such as appendages that are perpendicular to the water surface. Pelagic large macroalgae have gas-filled bladders (pneumocysts) that keep these organisms near the surface where light is available for photosynthesis. The majority of bony fishes have internal gas bladders that they use to adjust water column position. Other organisms increase fat and/or oil concentrations in their bodies to decrease their density. Sharks have large fatty livers that increase their buoyancy. Some organisms, squid and dinoflagellates for example, exchange heavier ions (such as sodium, molecular weight 23) for lighter ions (ammonium, molecular weight 18). The exchanged ions have the same electrical charge so that salt and water balance is not affected.

8. Changes in water temperature significantly affect the density, viscosity of water, and ability of water to hold gases in solution. Discuss how decreased water temperature changes these variables and how these changes affect marine life.

As temperature decreases, *density* increases making it easier for plankton to float and more difficult for active swimmers to move through the water. Similarly, *viscosity* increases, making it easier for plankton to float and more difficulty for active swimmers to move through the water. Additionally, gas solubility increases as water temperature decreases. As water temperature drops, dissolved oxygen and carbon dioxide concentrations increase, and the ability of the ocean to support greater biomass also increases.

9. List the differences between cold- and warm-water species in the marine environment.

• In warmer waters, floating organisms are physically smaller than organisms in colder waters. This is probably related to the lower viscosity and density of seawater in low-latitude waters. Smaller tropical species can expose more surface area per unit of body mass.

• Warm-water species are characterized by ornate appendages/plumage to increase surface area. The extra ornamentation is notable absent in cold-water species (refer to Figures 12-7 and 12-8).

• Warmer temperatures increase biological activity rates that more than double with an increase of 10°C (18°F). Tropical organisms apparently grow faster, have a shorter life expectancy, and reproduce earlier and more frequently than their cold-water counterparts.

• Tropical populations have increased species diversity in comparison to cooler water marine populations. However, total planktonic biomass in colder, higher-latitude environments in much greater than at tropical latitudes.

10. What do the prefixes *eury-* and *steno-* mean? Define the terms *eurythermal/stenothermal* and *euryhaline/stenohaline*. Where in the marine environment will organisms displaying a well-developed degree of each characteristic be found?

The prefixes *eury-* means "broad or wide" and *steno-* means "narrow". The term *eurythermal* refers to an organism that is able to withstand wide temperature variations. In contrast, the term *stenothermal* refers to organisms that tolerate a narrow temperature range. Similarly, *euryhaline* organisms can tolerate wide fluctuations in environmental salt concentration. *Stenohaline* organisms are adapted to a narrow range of environmental salinities.

Eurythermal and euryhaline organisms are likely to be found in shallow coastal waters and estuaries where greater temperature and salinity fluctuations occur. Stenothermal and stenohaline organisms are more likely to be distributed in areas where narrow fluctuations in temperature and salinity are found, such as in deep water areas of the open ocean.

11. Describe the process of osmosis. How is it different from diffusion? What three things can occur simultaneously across the cell membrane during osmosis?

Osmosis is the movement of a substance in solution from an area of higher concentration to an area of lower concentration across a selectively permeable membrane. Diffusion is the spontaneous movement of a substance from an area of higher concentration to an area of lower concentration. Osmosis occurs only in the liquid state of matter, and usually occurs only in living cells. In contrast, diffusion occurs in all three states of matter (solid, liquid, gaseous) and occurs in both living and non-living matter. The three simultaneous processes that occur across the cell membrane during osmosis are:

(1). Water molecules move through the semi-permeable membrane toward an area of lower concentration.

(2). Water-soluble nutrient molecules or ions move from where they are more concentrated into the cell where they are used to maintain cell function.

Marine Life and the Marine Environment

(3). Water-soluble waste molecules move from the cell into the surrounding seawater.

12. What is the problem requiring osmotic regulation faced by hypotonic fish in the ocean? How have these animals adapted to meet this problem?

Hypotonic fish living in the ocean have body fluids with lower salinity and osmotic pressure than the salinity and osmotic pressure of the ocean water. As a result, their body fluids have a higher concentration of water than the surrounding ocean water, and they tend to lose water from their bodies by osmosis. To replace the lost water, they drink large quantities of ocean water, remove the salt though special cells, and thereby create a supply of replacement water. To conserve their body water, they excrete small volumes of very concentrated urine.

13. How does water temperature affect the water's ability to hold gases? How do marine organisms extract the dissolved oxygen from seawater?

Reducing the temperature of sweater increases its capacity to hold gases in solution (cold water holds more dissolved gas in solution). To extract dissolved oxygen from seawater, most marine animals have specially designed fibrous respiratory organs called gills that serve to exchange oxygen and carbon dioxide directly with seawater.

14. How does the depth of the deep scattering layer vary over the course of a day? Why does it do this? Which organisms comprise the DSL?

The deep scattering layer is a sonar reflecting surface that undergoes a daily vertical migration in response to light intensity between the depths of 100 to 200 meters (330 to 660 feet) about midnight and 900 meters (2950 feet) at noon. It is possible that the organisms moving in response to the changes in light intensity are small crustaceans such as copepods or euphausids. Contributing a great deal to the reflecting of sound waves may be small lantern fish that feed on these crustaceans. One reason for this is that lantern fish have swim bladders that help them maintain neutral buoyancy in the water column. These swim bladders contain gas that has a very low density in comparison to seawater and is quit effective at sound reflection.

15. Construct a table listing the subdivisions of the pelagic and benthic environments and the physical factors used in assigning their boundaries.

Benthic: The Bottom Environment	*Supralittoral* (Splash zone)—Above the spring high tide and covered by water only during storms and unusually high tides.	
	Littoral (Intertidal)—Between normal spring high and low tides.	
	Sublittoral (Continental shelf)—Extends from low tide shoreline to depth of 200 meters or to the edge of the continental shelf. Sediment is relatively coarse.	*Inner*—Above the euphotic zone and contains attached plants.
		Outer—Below the euphotic zone to the edge of the continental shelf or to a depth of 200 meters.
	Bathyal (Continental slope)—From 200 to 4000 meters depth, which includes most of the continental slope. Sediment is finer than on the sublittoral due to lower velocity currents. Regions of the deep ocean basin that extend up into this depth range will have a significant percentage of $CaCO_3$ deposited on them, and calcareous oozes are common.	
	Abyssal (Deep ocean basins)—From 4000 to 6000 meters depth. Sediment will be mostly abyssal clay because the bottom is beneath the $CaCO_3$ compensation depth.	
	Hadal (Trenches)—Below a depth of 6000 meters. Restricted to ocean trenches.	
Pelagic: The Water Environment	*Neritic*—The water overlying depths from the shoreline to 200 meters. This is essentially the nutrient-rich water overlying the continental shelf.	
	Oceanic—The water overlying depths greater than 200 meters. This is essentially the water column lying beyond the continental shelf and overlying the deep ocean basins.	*Epipelagic*—From the surface to a depth of 200 meters. Within this segment is the bottom limit of the euphotic zone (about 150 meters). Therefore, all plant life in the Oceanic province is restricted to this region. There is a relatively high concentration of oxygen and low concentration of plant nutrients. The seasonal thermocline, mixed layer and surface water masses are confined to the epipelagic.
		Mesopelagic—From 200 to 1000 meters. Dissolved oxygen begins to decrease at 200 meters and reaches a minimum near the base of the mesopelagic while the concentration of plant nutrients begins to increase at about 200 meters and reaches a maximum near 1000 meters. The intermediate water masses move within the mesopelagic zone and the permanent thermocline extends across its range. The base of the disphotic zone corresponds well with the base of the mesopelagic zone, and the deep scattering layer moves up and down within this water column in response to changing light intensity.
		Bathypelagic—From 1000 to 4000 meters depth. The aphotic zone begins at 1000 meters, and the deep-water masses move horizontally through the bathypelagic carrying oxygen that increases in concentration from the top to the bottom of the zone.
		Abyssopelagic—From 4000 meters to the ocean bottom. Oxygen concentration continues to increase with increasing depth as bottom water carries oxygen to the ocean floor from the high-latitude ocean surface where it forms. It moves in a direction opposite that of the deep-water masses above it.

Biological Productivity and Energy Transfer

Learning Objectives

The instructional objectives are performance-based and detail specific learning outcomes for Chapter 13. The test items contained in the Test Bank are keyed to the learning objectives and the Key Questions at the beginning of the chapter. The order of the objectives mirrors the content presentation in Chapter 13.

Upon completion of this chapter, the student should be able to:

1. Define **biomass** in the context of the marine environment.

2. Define **primary productivity** and distinguish between **photosynthesis** and **chemosynthesis** with respect to primary productivity. Name locations in the ocean in which you would expect to find photosynthetic and chemosynthetic organisms.

3. Differentiate between **gross primary productivity** and **net primary productivity**. How do the metabolic processes of photosynthesis and cellular respiration relate to gross and net primary productivity?

4. Outline the methods used to estimate primary productivity in marine environments including:
    A. **plankton nets**
    B. **Gran method** (= light and dark bottles)
    C. **SeaWiFS (Sea-viewing Wide Field-of-View Sensor)**

5. Name the nutrients that limit primary productivity in marine environments.

6. Describe the sources of nutrient input into ocean systems including:
    A. coastal run-off
    B. river input
    C. upwelling

7. Define the **compensation depth for photosynthesis** and describe how it is measured.

8. Explain the relationship between the compensation depth, the euphotic zone, and the depth to which solar radiation penetrates the ocean. How do these relationships change in coastal waters as opposed to waters of the epipelagic open ocean?

9. Provide and explanation as to why marine life is more abundant in coastal waters as compared to the

10. open ocean. List all factors (biological, chemical, geologic, and physical) that affect species diversity, biomass, and the distribution of life in the ocean.

11. Detail the **electromagnetic spectrum** for **visible light** and explain the relationship between wavelength and energy. Discuss the implications of this relationship for light penetration in marine environments.

12. Describe the measurement of water clarity in aquatic systems. What is the relationship between clarity and turbidity? How are these concepts related to primary productivity?

13. Discuss the relationship between the color of ocean water and the productivity level of that area.

14. Define **eutrophic**. How is eutrophication related to nutrient input? To primary productivity?

15. List the photosynthetic organisms commonly found in marine environments, their taxonomic classification, and their preferred habitat including:
    A. sea grasses (Kingdom Plantae, Division Angiospermae (or Anthophyta)) – textbook uses Spermatophyta
    B. cord grass, *Spartina alterniflora* (Kingdom Plantae, Division Angiospermae (or Anthophyta))
    C. mangroves, *Rhizophora* and *Avicennia* (Kingdom Plantae, Division Angiospermae (or Anthophyta))
    D. brown algae (Kingdom Protista, Division of Phaeophyta)
    E. green algae (Kingdom Protista, Division Chlorophyta)
    F. red algae (Kingdom Protista, Division Rhodophyta)
    G. golden algae (Kingdom Protista, Division Chrysophyta)
    H. diatoms (Kingdom Protista, Division Bacillariophyta)
    I. coccolithophorids (Kingdom Protista, Division Haptophyta)
    J. dinoflagellates (Kingdom Protista, Division Dinoflagellata or Pyrrophyta)

16. Describe the formation of a **harmful algal bloom (HAB)**. List the causative organisms and the environmental factors that contribute to the development of HABs.

17. Compare and contrast the productivity of polar, temperate, and tropical oceans. Describe the physical, chemical, and geologic factors that contribute to productivity differences as a function of latitude. Apply what you have learned in previous chapters.

18. Define **entropy** as it applies to marine systems.

19. Distinguish between a **community** and an **ecosystem**. Give an example of each that you would find in a marine environment.

20. Differentiate between **autotrophic** and **heterotrophic** modes of nutrition. Give an example of a marine organism that would employ each nutritional strategy.

21. Define each of the following terms that describe the position of an organism in the food chain (**trophic level**) and an example of a marine organism that fits the category including:
    A. **producer**
    B. **consumer**

Biological Productivity and Energy Transfer
  C. **decomposer**

22. Distinguish among the following types of consumers in terms of the food they eat and their position on the food chain and give an example of a marine organism that would fit into each category including:
  A. **herbivore**
  B. **carnivore**
  C. **omnivore**
  D. **bacteriovore**

23. Define **detritus** and describe how detritus fits into the energy flow in a marine ecosystem.

24. Describe the **biogeochemical cycling** of the following nutrients in the ocean:
  A. carbon
  B. nitrogen
  C. phosphorus
  D. silica

25. Describe the various feeding strategies employed by marine organisms including:
  A. **suspension (filter) feeding**
  B. **deposit feeding**
  C. **carnivorous feeding**

26. Know the relationship between trophic level (caloric content) and the trophic transfer efficiency (**gross ecological efficiency**). What are the biological implications of a 90% energy loss between adjacent trophic levels?

27. Distinguish between a **food chain**, a **food web**, and a **biomass pyramid**.

28. Describe the role of microorganisms in the marine environment.

29. Differentiate among the following types of **symbiotic** relationships and give an example of each including:
  A. **commensalism**
  B. **mutualism**
  C. **parasitism**

29. Define **fisheries**.

30. Define **maximum sustainable yield (MSY)**. Discuss how MSY is determined and the implications of yield exceeding MSY, **overfishing**.

32. Define **by-catch** and describe how the amount of by-catch relates to the type of fishing gear used and the area fished.

33. Discuss the impact of an addendum to the **Marine Mammals Act** in 1992 on dolphin populations and tuna fishing. How has "dolphin-safe" tuna labeling impacted accidental dolphin mortality rates in the tuna industry?

34. Distinguish between **purse seines** and **drift nets (gill nets)**. Discuss the amount of by-catch resulting from the use of these nets.

35. Detail the regulation and management of commercial fish species including:
    A. regulation of fishing vessels
    B. gear regulation
    C. limits (weight, size, and sex)
    D. limiting season to ensure successful reproduction
    E. regulating licenses
    F. enforcement

31. Outline how consumer choices affect commercial fisheries. Make recommendations regarding how consumer choice can impact fisheries management and harvest of target species.

Overview

Chapter 13 begins with a description of various aspects of primary productivity, focusing on the two factors that limit productivity rates: solar input and nutrient concentration. Chemosynthetic productivity is also examined. A discussion of the physical oceanographic conditions that allow productivity to be maximized in the oceans near continental margins follows with an examination of light transmission in ocean water. Photosynthetic marine organisms are described including seed plants (Anthophyta), macroscopic algae ("seaweeds"), and microscopic algae (diatoms, coccolithophorids, and dinoflagellates). Productivity in polar, tropical, and temperate oceans is explored through a comparison of regional controlling factors (the availability of solar radiation and development of thermal stratification, which limits nutrient concentrations). Energy transfer is examined in terms of mass and other energy forms, with an emphasis on biogeochemical cycles, oceanic trophic levels, and biomass pyramids. The chapter finishes with a discussion of ecosystems and fisheries.

Headings covered in this chapter include:
Primary Productivity
    Photosynthetic Productivity
    Measurement of Primary Productivity
    Factors Affecting Primary Productivity
        Available Nutrients
        Available Solar Radiation
    Ocean Margins
        Upwelling and Nutrient Supply
    Light Transmission in Ocean Water
Photosynthetic Marine Organisms
    Seed-Bearing Plants (Anthophyta)
    Macroscopic (Large) Algae
    Microscopic (Small) Algae
    Photosynthetic Bacteria
Regional Productivity
    Productivity in Polar Oceans
    Productivity in Tropical Oceans
    Productivity in Temperate Oceans
Energy Flow and Nutrient Cycling
    Energy Flow in Marine Ecosystems

Biological Productivity and Energy Transfer
　　　Biogeochemical Cycling

Oceanic Feeding Relationships
　　　Feeding Strategies
　　　Trophic Levels
　　　Transfer Efficiency
　　　Food Chains, Food Webs, and the Biomass Pyramid
　　　Symbiosis
Issues Affecting Marine Fisheries
　　　Marine Ecosystems and Fisheries
　　　Overfishing
　　　Incidental Catch
　　　Fisheries Management
　　　Seafood Choices
Special Features:
　　　Box 13-1: The Oceanography of Everyday Things: Red Tides: Was Alfred Hitchcock's The Birds Based on Fact?
　　　Box 13-2: Research Methods in Oceanography: Pfiesteria: A Morphing Peril to Fish and Humans
　　　Box 13-3: The Oceanography of Everyday Things: Ocean Eutrophication and the Dead Zone
　　　Box 13-4: Research Methods In Oceanography: A Case Study in Fisheries Management: The Peruvian Anchoveta Fishery

Teacher's Resources

There are several good films/videos and CD-ROMs available on marine primary productivity including:

Films/Videotapes
- Plankton and the Open Sea, 2nd edition (Encyclopedia Britannica), 22 minutes
- Sargasso Sea: Ocean Desert (Films for the Humanities and Sciences), 9 minutes
- Seasons in the Sea (National Geographic), 55 minutes (subject: the kelp forest)
- The Sea (Encyclopedia Britannica), 26 minutes
- Where the Bay becomes the Sea (Bullfrog Films), 30 minutes

CD-ROMs
- The Digital Field Trip to the Wetlands (Tasa Graphic Arts, Inc.)

Answers to End-of-Chapter Questions and Exercises

1. Discuss chemosynthesis as a method of primary productivity. How does it differ from photosynthesis?

Chemosynthesis differs from photosynthesis in that the energy that goes into the product of the reaction comes from the release of energy from chemical bonds rather than solar radiation. Chemosynthesis can occur in the absence of sunlight such as in communities associated with hydrothermal vents along the mid-ocean ridge. Here the energy of hydrogen sulfide bonds (H_2S) is released through oxidation to free (S) or sulfate (SO_4). The bacteria that serve as food for filter-feeding benthos, and the chemosynthetic worms associated with these vents, produce their own food through chemosynthesis.

2. How does gross primary productivity differ from net primary production? What are the two components of gross primary production, and how are they different?

The total amount of organic matter produced by photosynthesis per unit of time is the *gross primary production* of the oceans. Algae use some of this organic matter for their own maintenance through respiration. The difference between the total amount of fixed organic carbon and the organic carbon lost through respiratory activity is *net primary production*. This organic carbon is converted to biomass. The difference between gross and net primary productivity is similar to the difference between gross pay (earnings before taxes) versus net pay (the amount of take home pay after taxes are deducted).
  Gross primary productivity has two components, new production and regenerated production. *New production* is the portion of primary production supported through the input of nutrients from outside local ecosystems by processes such as upwelling. The higher the ratio of new production to gross primary production in an ecosystem, the greater its ability to support animal populations that are depended upon for fisheries, such as pelagic fishes and benthic scallops. *Regenerated production* results from nutrients being recycled within the ecosystem.

3. An important variable determining the distribution of life in the oceans is the availability of nutrients. How are the following variables related: proximity to the continents, availability of nutrients, and the concentration of life in the oceans?

Since the continents are the ultimate source of inorganic nutrients for plants, the waters neat the continents are richer in nutrients than the surface water of the ocean far from land. The greatest concentration of life in the oceans is found in the shallow water near the continents.

4. Another important determinant of productivity is the availability of solar radiation. Why is biological productivity relatively low in the tropical open ocean, where the penetration of sunlight is greatest?

Even though there is a thicker column of sunlit water in the open ocean far from the continents than in the turbid water near their shores, photosynthesis is greatly restricted in the clear open ocean water by the lack of nutrients in surface waters.

5. Discuss the characteristics of the costal ocean where unusually high concentrations of marine life are found.

Conditions that result in unusually high concentrations of marine life in some coastal regions are the result of coastal upwelling. Particularly where the surface water is moved offshore by Ekman transport, water from beneath the photosynthetic zone will rise to replace it. Since there is no plant or algal life growing in these deeper waters, they are rich in plant and algal nutrients and serve to continuously supply nutrients to the sunlit surface waters.

6. Why does everything in the ocean at depths below the shallowest surface water take on a blue-green appearance?

The blue-green appearance of objects below the ocean surface is caused by the fact that red wavelengths of light are selectively absorbed within the upper 10 meters (33 feet) of the water. Unless divers bring their own light source, everything has a blue-green tint below this depth.

Biological Productivity and Energy Transfer

7. What factors create the color difference between coastal waters and the less productive open-ocean water? What color is each?

Coastal waters are almost always greenish in color because they contain more suspended particulate matter (turbidity) due to runoff from the land. This disperses solar radiation in such a way that the wavelengths most scattered are those for greenish or yellowish light. This condition is also partly the result of yellow-green microscopic marine algae in these coastal waters. In the open ocean, where the particulate matter is relatively scarce and marine life exists in low concentration, the water appears blue. This is due to the scattering of blue wavelengths of light caused by the extremely small size hydrogen bonding of the water molecules. Green color in the water usually indicates the presence of a large phytoplankton population, such as the large biomass of plant life in a continental tropical rainforest. The deep indigo blue of the open oceans, particularly in the tropics, usually indicates an area that lacks abundant life.

8. Compare the macroscopic algae in terms of color, maximum depth to which they grow, common species, and size.

Phaeophyta (Brown Algae): The dominant color is brown to black. The may grow attached to ocean bottoms at depths of 30 meters (100 feet) or more. The brown algae range in size form the small genus *Ralfsia* that is a common encrusting form on intertidal rocks to the 30-meter (100-foot) long *Pelagophycus* (bull kelp). In the Sargasso Sea, a free-floating brown alga gives the area its name, *Sargassum*.

Chlorophyta (Green Algae): The dominant color is green, and green algae are found in the shallow intertidal zone only. The majority of species are less than 30 centimeters (12 inches) in maximum dimension. *Ulva*, sea lettuce, is common in tidal pools in colder waters while *Codium*, sponge weed, is widely distributed in warm water coastal areas.

Rhodophyta (Red Algae): The dominant color is pink to dark red. These algae can use short blue and green wavelengths of light for photosynthesis, they are the group of algae found growing attached to the ocean floor at the lower portion of the photic zone. They have been found at depths up to 268 meters (880 feet), and *Corallina* is common in rocky intertidal areas.

9. The golden algae include two classes of important phytoplankton. Compare their composition and structure of their tests and explain their importance in the geologic fossil record.

Diatoms secrete a siliceous cell wall composed of two halves (valves) that are an important constituent of siliceous sediment celled diatomaceous earth that is used in filtering devices, industrial abrasives, polishing agents, and numerous other applications. Diatomaceous earth accumulates on the sea floor beneath surface waters that are relatively low in temperature such as in high-latitude regions where equatorial upwelling occurs.

Coccolithophorids are covered with tiny calcareous plates (coccoliths) that are abundant in calcareous oozes found on the sea floor beneath warm surface waters (not to deep because the calcium carbonate goes into solution below the calcite compensation depth (CCD)).

10. How does paralytic shellfish poisoning (PSP) differ from amnesic shellfish poisoning? What types of microorganisms create each?

Paralytic shellfish poisoning (PSP) is caused by the dinoflagellate *Gonyaulax*, which is not poisonous to shellfish, but is concentrated in their tissues and is poisonous to humans who eat the shellfish, even after the shellfish are cooked. PSP affects the human nervous system and symptoms include incoherent speech, uncoordinated movement, dizziness, nausea, and even death.

Amnesic shellfish poisoning is caused by a diatom that produces domoic acid that accumulates in the tissues of unaffected organisms such as mussels and anchovies, but it can be poisonous to other organisms throughout the food web. Symptoms of amnesic shellfish poisoning in humans include permanent memory loss and, in severe cases, death.

11. Describe how a biological pump works. What percentage of organic material from the euphotic zone accumulates on the sea floor?

The process of removing organic matter form the euphotic zone and concentrating this material on the sea floor is called a *biological pump* because it removes ("pumps") carbon dioxide and nutrients from the upper ocean and concentrates them in deep-sea waters and sea floor sediments. Since the vast majority of organic matter is decomposed before it reaches the ocean floor, only about 1% of material from the euphotic zone accumulates on the deep-ocean floor.

12. Compare the biological productivity of polar, temperate, and tropical regions of the oceans. Consider seasonal changes, the development of a thermocline, the availability of nutrients, and solar radiation.

Polar regions: There is little seasonal variation in water temperature, which is always at or slightly above the freezing point. Since the surface water is so cold, there is little or no thermal stratification (no thermocline), and nutrient-rich water can readily move to the sunlit surface during the summer months to produce a sustained high level of biological productivity. Plant nutrients are usually available, and productivity is limited only by the availability of solar input. During the winter months, productivity ceases due to little or no solar radiation at high latitudes.

Tropical regions: There is very little seasonal variation in water temperature at low latitudes where the surface water temperatures are always high. The thermocline is permanent, and it prevents nutrient-rich colder water from moving to the surface restricting primary productivity. At low latitudes solar input never restricts primary production, and primary production is limited by nutrient availability. Primary productivity in the open ocean at tropical latitudes is very low, except in coastal and upwelling areas with nutrient input.

Temperate regions: There are pronounced seasonal variations at temperate latitudes, and this variation produces a more complex pattern of productivity than in either polar or tropical regions. During the winter, thermal stratification may be minimal, and the surface waters are rich in nutrients as a result of mixing between the deep and surface water layers. Productivity is low however due to the low angle at which the Sun's rays strike the ocean surface. Very little solar radiation penetrates the water column, producing a low photosynthetic rate. As the Sun rises higher in the sky during the spring sufficient sunlight penetrates the water column producing a spring phytoplankton bloom. The increased availability of solar radiation also results in the development of a thermocline that prevents the continued supply of nutrients from deep water, and productivity decreases until fall cooling begins to weaken the thermocline. Mixing again occurs, and a smaller fall phytoplankton bloom occurs. It is soon limited by decreased amounts of solar radiation because the Sun is lower in the sky and the day length decreases. To summarize, there is a high level of spring productivity that is limited by a reduced supply of nutrients and a fall increase in productivity that comes to an end because of the lack of solar radiation.

Biological Productivity and Energy Transfer

13. Generally, the productivity in tropical oceans is rather low. What are three environments that are exceptions to this, and what factors contribute to their higher productivity?

Equatorial upwelling: Where the trade winds drive westerly equatorial currents on either side of the Equator, surface water diverges as a result of Ekman transport. The surface water that moves toward

higher latitudes is replaced by nutrient-rich water that surfaces from depths of 200 meters (660 Feet). Equatorial upwelling is best developed in the eastern Pacific Ocean.
Coastal upwelling: Where the prevailing winds blow toward the Equator and along the western continental margins, surface waters are driven away from the coast. The displaced water is replaced by nutrient-rich water surfacing from depths of 200 to 900 meters (660 to 2950 feet). This nutrient-rich upwelling promotes high primary productivity in these areas, in turn, supports large fisheries. In the Pacific, such conditions exist along the southern coast of California and the southwestern coast of Peru; in the Atlantic, they exist along the northwestern coast of Morocco and the southwestern coast of Africa.
Coral reefs: Organisms that comprise and live among coral reefs are superbly adapted to low-nutrient conditions, in a similar manner to how some terrestrial organisms are adapted to a desert existence. Symbiotic algae livening within the tissues of coral and other species allow coral reefs to be highly productive ecosystems. Additionally, coral reefs tend to hold and concentrate the low levels of nutrients in the ecosystem.

14. Describe the flow of energy through the biotic community and include forms into which solar radiation is converted. How does this flow differ form the manner in which mass is moved through the ecosystem?

Most energy enters the biotic community as radiant energy supplied by the Sun. Pants convert the solar energy to chemical energy. The chemical energy is stored in the bonds of the organic molecules created during photosynthesis. Chemical energy is released through respiration to be converted into kinetic energy and heat energy until it becomes biologically useless in a state of entropy. This unidirectional flow prevents the recycling of energy within the system once it has been released from its chemical state. Mass moved through the ecosystem is different because the energy represented by the mass of organic matter that is decomposed to inorganic forms is recyclable through the biological uptake of photosynthesis and chemosynthesis.

15. What is the average efficiency of energy transfer between trophic levels? Use this efficiency to determine how much phytoplankton mass is required to add *1 gram* of new mass to a killer whale, which is a third-level carnivore. Include a diagram that shows the different trophic levels and the relative size and abundance of organisms at different levels. How would your answer change if the efficiency were half the average rate, or twice the average rate?

The efficiency of energy transfer between trophic levels averages 10% (0.10). To add 1 gram of new mass to a killer whale at the fourth trophic level requires:
$$1 \div 0.10 \div 0.10 \div 0.10 \div 0.10 = 10,000 \text{ grams of phytoplankton mass}$$
Diagrams of trophic levels will vary but should contain the elements illustrated in Figure 13-19.
   If the transfer efficiency were **half the average rate** of 10% (5% or 0.05), 1 gram of new mass on a killer whale would require:
$$1 \div 0.05 \div 0.05 \div 0.05 \div 0.05 = 160,00 \text{ grams of phytoplankton mass}$$
If the transfer efficiency were **twice the average rate** of 10% (20% or 0.20), 1 gram of new killer whale mass would require:

$$1 \div 0.20 \div 0.20 \div 0.20 \div 0.20 = 625 \text{ grams of phytoplankton mass}$$

16. Describe the advantage that a top carnivore gains by eating from a food web as compared to a single food chain.

An animal that feeds on many other organisms is less likely to be severely affected by the extinction (or population reduction) of one of the populations of animals it feeds on than would an animal that feeds primarily one population of organisms.

17. What are the three types of symbiosis, and how do they differ?

Commensalism occurs when a smaller or less dominant participant benefits without harm to the host species that provides the commensal with food or protection. *Mutualism* occurs when both species benefit. *Parasitism* occurs when one organism (parasite) benefits at the expense of the host organism.

18. When a species is overfished, what changes are there in the standing stock and the maximum sustainable yield? What are some problems with fisheries management?

When a fishery overfishes a species, the *standing stock* (the biomass in the ecosystem at that point in time) decreases and the *maximum sustainable yield* (the maximum fishery biomass that can be removed annually and sill be sustained by the fishery ecosystem) also decreases.

    Some problems with fishcrics management include difficulty enforcing fishing limits (especially for fish that inhabit waters of many different countries), failure to successfully regulate the number of fishing vessels (resulting in increased fishing effort), and a lack of protection for critical fish habitats. In addition, factors that determine the health of the fish stock have not been frequently assess, such as the natural relationships among organisms in marine food webs, the critical environmental factors for the health of the fishery, and the effects of removing so many organisms as fishery catch.

14

Animals of the Pelagic Environment

Learning Objectives

The instructional objectives are performance-based and detail specific learning outcomes for Chapter 14. The test items contained in the Test Bank are keyed to the learning objectives and the Key Questions at the beginning of the chapter. The order of the objectives mirrors the content presentation in Chapter 14.

Upon completion of this chapter, the student should be able to:

1. Define the term **biomass** in the context of the marine environment.

2. Discuss the strategies employed by pelagic animals that prevent sinking in the water column including:
    a. air chambers - gas bladder, swim bladder
    b. increase surface area – additional appendages, spines, and ornamentation
    c. fatty organs or fat deposits below the skin
    d. structural modifications for living as depth

3. Describe the zooplankton commonly found in the pelagic zone and discuss their role in pelagic food webs including:
    a. radiolarian (Kingdom Protista, Phylum Polycystina)
    b. foraminferans (Kingdom Protista, Phylum Foraminifera)
    c. copepods (Kingdom Animalia, Phylum Arthropoda, Class Crustacea)

4. Describe the macroscopic planktonic animals commonly found in the pelagic zone and discuss their role in pelagic food webs including:
    a. krill (Kingdom Animalia, Phylum Arthropoda, Class Crustacea)
    b. cnidarians - hydrozoans (Kingdom Animalia, Phylum Cnidaria, Class Hydrozoa), examples: Portuguese man-of-war (*Physalia*) and By-the-wind sailor (*Velella*)
    c. cnidarians - jellyfish (Kingdom Animalia, Phylum Cnidaria, Class Scyphozoa)
    d. tunicates - salps (Kingdom Animalia, Phylum Chordata, Subphylum Urochordata)
    e. ctenophores - comb jellies (Kingdom Animalia, Phylum Ctenophora), example: Sea gooseberry (*Pleurobrachia*)
    f. chaetognaths - arrowworms (Kingdom Animalia)

5. Describe the role of squid (Kingdom Animalia, Phylum Mollusca, Class Cephalopoda) in the pelagic ocean and give examples of specific pelagic genera.

6. List and describe the usual arrangement of fins in fishes including:
   a. dorsal fins
   b. caudal fins
   c. pelvic fins
   d. pectoral fins
   e. anal fins

7. Describe specialized pectoral fin modifications in fishes and provide specific examples of fishes with highly modified pectoral fins.

8. Differentiate between the musculature of fish that wait for their prey (**lungers**) as compared to fish that swim at a constant speed (**cruisers**).

9. Relate the body size of a fish to its potential swimming speed.

10. Compare and contrast **poikilothermic** versus **homeothermic** temperature patterns in fishes. Give examples of poikilothermic fishes and of fishes that approximate homeothermic regulation.

11. Discuss the available food sources for deep-water nekton. How does the body size and population density of deep-water nekton differ from that of coastal species?

12. Explain the function(s) of bioluminescence in deep-water nekton.

13. Suggest reasons why schooling behavior in fishes is highly adaptive.

14. List the physiological and physical characteristics shared by all marine mammals.

15. Describe the characteristics shared by the members of the Class Mammalia, Order Carnivora (Kingdom Animalia, Phylum Chordata) including sea otters and polar bears. Describe the geographic distribution of the Carnivora and their food preferences.

16. Describe the characteristics shared by the members of the Class Mammalia, Order Pinnipedia (Kingdom Animalia, Phylum Chordata) including sea lions, walruses, and true seals. Describe the geographic distribution of the Carnivora and their food preferences.

17. Describe the characteristics shared by the members of the Class Mammalia, Order Sirenia (Kingdom Animalia, Phylum Chordata) including manatees and dugongs. Describe the geographic distribution, food preference, and postulate as to why the number of these animals is declining.

18. Describe the characteristics common to members of the Class Mammalia, Order Cetacea (Kingdom Animalia, Phylum Chordata).

19. Discuss physiologic and anatomical modifications observed in Cetaceans for swimming and diving.

20. Distinguish between the Cetacean Suborder Odontoceti and Suborder Mysticeti. Provide examples of marine mammals that belong to each taxon.

Animals of the Pelagic Environment

21. Define the term **echolocation**. Discuss the **melon (spermaceti organ)** in toothed whales and describe its function.

22. Describe feeding styles among baleen whales.

23. Differentiate among the three major groups of baleen whales including:
    a. gray whale
    b. rorqual whales
    c. right whales

24. Describe the seasonal migration of the gray whale. How does latitude relate to the gray whale's activities (feeding versus reproduction)?

Overview

Chapter 14 presents adaptations and behavioral patterns of pelagic organisms. The chapter opens with a discussion of staying above the ocean floor and then develops into a discussion of finding prey and predator avoidance. Because marine mammals are some of the most charismatic and recognizable ocean inhabitants, the chapter includes a detailed presentation of the three different orders of marine mammals. The chapter concludes with a description of the migratory patterns of gray whales.

Headings covered in this chapter include:
Above the Ocean Floor
       Gas Containers
       Floating Organisms (Zooplankton)
       Swimming Organisms (Nekton)
Adaptations for Seeking Prey
       Mobility: Lungers versus Cruisers
       Speed and Body Size
       Cold-Blooded versus Warm-Blooded Organisms
       Circulatory System Modifications
       Adaptations of Deep-Water Nekton
Predator Avoidance Adaptations
       Schooling
       Other Adaptations
Marine Mammals
       Mammalian Characteristics
       Order Carnivora
       Order Sirenia
       Order Cetacea
               Modifications to Increase Swimming Speed
               Modifications to Allow Deep Diving
Migration: Why Do Gray Whales Migrate?

Special Features:

Box 14-1: The Oceanography of Everyday Things: Some Myths (and Facts) about Sharks
Box 14-2: The Oceanography of Everyday Things: Killer Whales: A Reputation Deserved?

Teacher's Resources

There are several good films/videos available about pelagic organisms and marine mammals including:

Films/Videotapes
- Life in the Sea (Encyclopedia Britannica), 11 minutes
- The Dolphins that joined the Navy (Local Navy District, Film MN-10199), 26 minutes
- The Sea Otter (Grover Productions), 17 minutes
- The Sea Otters of Amchitka (Thorne Films, Inc.), 45 minutes

Answers to End-of-Chapter Questions and Exercises

1. Discuss why the rigid gas chamber in cephalopods limits the depth to which they can descend. Why do fish with a swim bladder not have this limitation?

The cephalopods *Nautilus*, *Sepia*, and *Spirula* (see Figure 14-1) all have rigid chambered shells that contain gas at a pressure of 1 atmosphere (14.7 pounds per square inch). The maximum depth to which they can descend depends on the strength of the chambered shell. The shells of these cephalopods will collapse when the external pressure exceeds the strength of their shell. For example, the *Nautilus* will implode at a depth of about 500 meters (1640 feet). Animals with flexible air bladders, such as certain fish, do not suffer the threat of the swim bladder structurally collapsing because the bladder is flexible in contrast to the rigid cephalopod shell. These fish can also regulate the air pressure inside their air bladder.

2. Draw and describe several different types of microscopic zooplankton and macroscopic zooplankton.

Microscopic zooplankton: Three of the most important groups of microscopic zooplankton are the radiolarians, the foraminiferans, and the copepods. The radiolarians are single-celled, microscopic organisms that secrete shells of silica (refer to Figure 14-3). Their microscopic tests have intricate patterns and ornamentation including long projections. Foraminiferans are microscopic to small macroscopic in size single-celled heterotrophic protists, many of which are planktonic. Foraminiferans produce a hard sell of calcium carbonate in which the organism lives (see Figure 14-1). Many of their tests appear to be segmented or chambered, and all have a prominent opening at on end. Copepods are microscopic planktonic crustaceans (recall that the Class Crustacea includes shrimp, lobsters, and crabs). Like other crustaceans, copepods have a hard chitinous (polysaccharide) exoskeleton, a segmented body, and jointed appendages (refer to Figure 14-5).
Macroscopic zooplankton: Three of the most important groups of macroscopic zooplankton are krill, the Portuguese Man-O-War, and jellyfish. Krill are crustaceans that resemble tiny shrimp (see Figure 14-6), and they are relatives of the copepods. There are over 1500 species of krill, most of which are 5 centimeters (2 inches) or less in length. Krill are abundant in Antarctica and form a critical link in the Antarctic food web for many organisms from birds to whales. The Portuguese Man-O-War (*Physalia*) is a small colonial cnidarian (a hydrozoan) that has a gas float (pneumatophore) with a sail so that the wind

can push it through the water. The colony has long tentacled polyps that are used to capture prey. The tentacles have specialized stinging cells, cnidocytes, that contain harpoon-like structures (nematocysts), and they can penetrate the skin of the prey. The stinging cells contain a string neurotoxin that immobilizes the prey. Jellyfish are floating cnidarians (scyphozoans) exhibiting the medusa body form. They float near the ocean surface, and they swim by jetting water trapped under their bell-shaped body through muscular contractions. Around the bell's edge are light-sensitive and/or gravity-sensitive sensory receptors designed to help the animal determine which way is up. The ability to orient their bodies to the surface is critical because they feed on the high concentrations of plankton and small fish that live near the ocean surface.

3. Name and describe the different types of fins that fish exhibit. What are the five basic shapes of caudal fins, and what are their uses?

Most active swimming fish have two sets of paired fins used in maneuvers such as turning, braking, and balancing. These are the pelvic fins and pectoral fins (refer to Figure 14-9). When not in use, these fins can be folded against the body. Vertical fins, both dorsal and anal, serve primarily as stabilizers. The fin that provides most of the thrust for forward motion in high-speed fish is the caudal fin (tail fin). There are five basic shapes of caudal fins, as illustrated in Figure 14-10 and keyed by letter to the following description:
  A. The rounded fin is flexible and useful in accelerating and maneuvering at slow speeds.
  B. & C. The somewhat flexible truncate tail (B) and forked tail (C) are found on faster fish and still may be used for maneuvering.
  D. The lunate caudal fin is found on the fast-cruising fishes such as tuna, marlin, and swordfish; it is very rigid and useless for maneuvering, but very efficient at propelling the fish.
  E. The heterocercal fin is asymmetrical, with most of its mass and surface in the upper lobe. The heterocercal fin produces a significant lift as it is moved from side to side and is common in fish with no swim bladder such as sharks.

4. What are the major structural and physiological differences between fast-swimming cruisers and lungers that patiently lie in wait for their prey?

Lungers (such as grouper) have a truncate caudal fin with an aspect ratio of 3 and white muscle tissue that can sustain only the short swimming bursts required to capture passing prey.
Cruisers (such as tuna) have a lunate caudal fin with an aspect ratio of 10 and a large percentage of muscle tissue that is composed of red fiber. The red fiber with its high concentration of myoglobin can reach metabolic rates six times greater than white muscle fiber. Therefore, red muscle fiber does not fatigue as fast as white muscle fibers.

5. Are most fast swimming fish cold-blooded or warm-blooded? What circulatory system modifications do these fish have to minimize heat loss?

Most fast swimming fish, such as mackerel, sharks, and tuna, are warm-blooded (homeothermic). The higher body temperature of homeothermic cruisers increases the power output of their muscle tissue. These fish conserve the heat needed to maintain body temperature by a modification of their circulatory system: They have cutaneous veins and arteries running along the sides of their body. This allows blood leaving the muscle tissue to warm blood entering as both flows past each other in close proximity to the other through a fine network of blood vessels.

6. What are the two food sources of deep-water nekton? List several adaptations of deep-water nekton that allow them to survive in their environment.

The food source for deep-water nekton comes from one of two places: detritus, dead and decaying organic matter and waste products that slowly settle through the water column from the highly productive surface waters, or each other. There are a number of predatory species.

Deep-water nekton have many special adaptations to allow them to be efficient at finding and collecting food. These include:
- Good sensory devices such as long antennae or sensitive lateral lines that are used to detect the movement of other organisms within the water column.
- Many species have large and sensitive eyes that enable them to see potential prey. To avoid becoming prey, most species are dark colored so that they blend in with the environment.
- Other species are blind and rely on their other sense to obtain food. For instance, the sense of smell is well developed in some species, and that allows certain fish to track down prey items by following a scent trail.
- Well over half of deep-sea fish have bioluminescence capabilities (the ability to biochemically produce light) by using specially designed structures or cells called photophores.
- Large sharp teeth.
- Expandable bodies.
- Hinged jaws that can disarticulate.
- Huge mouths in proportion to their body size.

7. What are several benefits of schooling?

Although schooling is advantageous during spawning in that it ensures that males and females are in close proximity, most fish appear to school for the protection it provides from predators:
- If members of a species form schools, they reduce the percentage of ocean volume in which a cruising predator might find one of their species.
- Should a predator encounter a large school, it I less likely to consume the entire unit than if it encounters a small school or an individual.
- The school may appear as a single large and dangerous opponent to the potential predator and prevent some attacks.
- Predators may find the continually changing position and direction of the movement of fish within the school confusing, making attack particularly difficult for predators, who can only attack one fish at a time.

8. What common characteristics do all organisms in the Class Mammalia share?

All organisms in the Class Mammalia (including marine mammals) share these common characteristics:
- They are warm-blooded.
- They breathe air.
- They have hair (or fur) in at least some stage of their development.

- They bear live young (except for the few egg-laying Australian mammals from the Subclass Prototheria, which includes the duck-billed platypus and the spiny anteater).
- The females of each species have mammary glands, structures that give the class its name, that are used to produce milk for their young.

9. Describe marine mammals within the Order Carnivora, including their adaptations for living in the marine environment.

Marine mammals within the Order Carnivora include sea otters, polar bears, and the pinnipeds (walruses, seals, sea lions, and fur seals), all of which have prominent canine teeth. Sea otters have dense fur that insulates them from the cold water in which they live. Polar bears have fur with hollow hair shafts for insulation and webbed feet for swimming. Pinnipeds have sensitive whiskers and prominent skin-covered flippers that are used to propel them through the water.

10. How can true seals be differentiated from the eared seals (sea lions and fur seals)?

Seals, also called earless seals or true seals, differ from *sea lions* and *fur seals*, also called eared seals, by the following distinguishing characteristics:
- Seals lack the prominent earflap that is specific to sea lions and fur seals (compare Figures 14-16 (b) and (c)).
- Seals have smaller and less prominent front flippers (called fore flippers) than sea lions and fur seals.
- Seals have prominent claws that extend from their flippers that sea lions and fur seals lack (refer to Figures 14-16 and 14-17).
- Seals have a different hip structure than sea lions and fur seals. Seals cannot move their rear flippers underneath their bodies as sea lions and fur seals can (refer to Figure 14-17).
- Seals do not walk on land very well, and can only slither along on their bellies (like a caterpillar); sea lions and fur seals use their rear flippers under their bodies and their large front flippers to walk easily on land, can they can even ascend steep slopes, climb stairs, and do other acrobatic tricks.
- Seals propel themselves through the water by a back-and-forth motion of the rear flippers (similar to a wagging tail) in contrast to sea lions and fur seals that swim by flapping their large front flippers.

11. Describe the marine mammals within the Order Sirenia, including their distinguishing characteristics.

Marine representatives of the Order Sirenia include the *manatees* and *dugongs*, which are collectively referred to as "sea cows". The manatees are concentrated in coastal areas of the tropical Atlantic Ocean, while dugongs populate the tropical regions of the Indian and Western Pacific Oceans. Both of these animals have a paddle-like tail and rounded front flippers (see Figure 14-18 (a)). The land-dwelling ancestors of the sirenians were elephant-like, and extant sirenians today retain some of these unique characteristics, such as a large body size and the presence of toenails in manatees. The sirenians have sparse hairs covering their body but concentrated around the mouth.

12. How can dolphins be differentiated from porpoises?

Porpoises are generally smaller than *dolphins*, and they have a more "stout: (bulky and robust) body shape compared to the more elongated and streamlined dolphin body. Generally, porpoises have a blunt snout (called a rostrum) in contrast to dolphins, which have a longer rostrum. Porpoises have a smaller and more triangular (or, on one species, no) dorsal fin, whereas the dolphin's dorsal fin is sickle-shaped or falcate. The best way to tell the two apart is by their teeth. Dolphin teeth end in points in contrast to porpoise teeth that are blunt or flat (shovel-shaped) and resemble human incisors.

13. List the modifications that are thought to allow some cetaceans the ability to (a) increase their swimming speed, (b) dive to great depths without suffering the bends, and (c) stay submerged for long periods.

(a). Modifications that allow cetaceans to increase their swimming speed include:
- Few Hairs.
- Streamlining.
- A specialized skin structure that modifies the flow of water around their bodies and produces uniform flow conditions that reduce drag and turbulence.

(b). Modifications that allow cetaceans to dive to great depths without suffering the bends include:
- A collapsible rib cage, that collapses by the time cetaceans reach a depth of 70 meters (230 feet). There is no air in the lungs to be absorbed under high pressure and the bends, decompression sickness, can be avoided.
- Lungs within the rib cage also collapse, which removes all air from the alveoli where most gas absorption into the blood occurs.
- Insensitivity to nitrogen gas that causes the bends.

(c). Modifications that allow cetaceans to dive and stay submerged for long periods of time include:
- An ability to alternate between periods of normal breathing and cessation of breathing.
- At the surface, cetaceans take only 1 to 3 breathes per minute, and that results in inhaled breath remaining in the alveoli longer.
- The alveolar membrane, with its dense capillary beds, can extract up to 90% of the oxygen in the air.
- Some cetaceans have twice as many red blood cells and 9 times as much myoglobin in their muscle tissue as do terrestrial animals. Large supplies of O_2 can be stored in the blood's hemoglobin and myoglobin of muscle tissue.
- Muscles can continue to function using anaerobic glycolysis when the oxygen is used up.
- Additional oxygen conservation may be achieved by closing off the blood flow to most of the body's organs except the heart and brain (the Mammalian Diving Reflex). This can reduce the heart rate by 50%.

14. Describe the differences between cetaceans of the Suborder Odontoceti (toothed whales) from those of the Suborder Mysticeti (baleen whales). Be sure to include examples from each suborder.

Suborder Odontoceti (toothed whales) have prominent teeth and includes killer whales, sperm whales, porpoises, and dolphins. *Suborder Mysticeti* (baleen whales) includes the great whales (the largest whales) such as the blue whale, the finback whale, humpback whale, and the gray whale. The baleen whales have not teeth. Instead they have baleen, plates of fibrous material that hang from the whale's upper jaw on the inside of their mouths. Toothed whales have one external nasal opening (blowhole) in contrast to the baleen whales that have two external openings.

15. Describe the process by which the sperm whale produces echolocation clicks.

Animals of the Pelagic Environment

In the sperm whale's large head, air is forced from the trachea through the nasal passages and past the lips of the "monkey's muzzle". Contractions of muscles in these structures produce sound that travels toward the head and reflects off the front of the skull, which is bowl-shaped and resembles a radar dish. The sound passes through an organ called the spermaceti organ in which sound is concentrated by forming various shapes and sizes of lenses. IN essence, the organ acts as an acoustical lens that focuses the sound.

16. Discuss how sound reaches the inner ear of toothed whales.

All cetaceans have evolved structures that insulate the inner ear housing from the rest of the skull. In toothed whales, the inner ear is separated form the rest of the skull and surrounded by an extensive system of air sinuses (cavities). The sinuses are filled with an insulating emulsion of oil, mucous, and air and are surrounded by fibrous connective tissue and venous networks. In many toothed whales, it is believed that sound is picked up by the thin, flaring jawbone and passed to the inner ear via the connecting oil-filled body.

17. Describe the mechanism by which baleen whales feed.

The main obstacle that baleen whales face in obtaining food is how to concentrate their small prey items and how to separate these items from seawater. To accomplish these tasks, baleen whales use their rows of fibrous baleen in their mouths that hang from their upper jaw and act as an ideal strainer. To feed, baleen whales fill their mouths with water that includes their prey, allowing their pleated lower jaw to balloon in size. The whales force the water out between the baleen slats, trapping small fish, krill, and other plankton on the inside of their mouths. Mostly, baleen whales feed at or near the surface, sometimes working cooperatively in large groups. However, the gray whale has short baleen slats and feeds by filtering sediment from the shallow bottom of its North Pacific and Arctic feeding grounds, straining out a diet of benthic organisms.

18. Discuss the reasons why gray whales leave their cold-water feeding grounds during the winter season.

Initially, gray whales were thought to migrate so far because the physical environment of the cold-water feeding grounds that the adults are adapted to does not meet the needs of the young baleen whales. Recent research on the physiology of newborn gray whales indicates that gray whale calves have the ability to survive in much colder water, suggesting that the migration of the gray whales is a relict form the Ice Age when sea level was lower. At this time, the productive feeding grounds of the gray whales were above sea level. Hence gray whales could not feast on the abundant food and probably gave birth to smaller calves that could not survive in the colder water. This necessitated the migration to warmer water regions that continues to this day in spite of a more abundant food supply.

An alternative explanation for leaving colder waters to calve is to avoid killer whales. Killer whales are more numerous in colder waters, and they are a major threat to young whales. This may also help to explain why only those lagoons with shallow entrances in Mexico are used as calving areas. Killer whales have been seen near the lagoons and have also been observed to feed in water so shallow that they come completely out of the water.

CHAPTER
15
Animals of the Benthic Environment

Learning Objectives

The instructional objectives are performance-based and detail specific learning outcomes for Chapter 15. The test items contained in the Test Bank are keyed to the learning objectives and the Key Questions at the beginning of the chapter. The order of the objectives mirrors the content presentation in Chapter 15.

Upon completion of this chapter, the student should be able to:

1. Discuss the relationship between benthic **biomass** and depth of the ocean bottom, and the productivity of the euphotic zone above.

2. Define **epifauna** in benthic marine environments and provide an example of organisms that are part of the marine epifauna.

3. Apply the terminology and concepts mastered in previous chapters to describe the morphology of a rocky shore including the:
    - A. **spray (supralittoral) zone**
    - B. **intertidal (littoral) zone**
    - C. **high water intertidal zone**
    - D. **middle water intertidal zone**
    - E. **low water intertidal zone**

4. Describe the distribution of organisms within the intertidal zone. List the organisms commonly encountered in the spray zone and at differing heights in the intertidal zone. Discuss the physical and chemical factors that affect species distribution on the rocky shore.

5. Define the term **sessile** and give an example of a marine organism that exhibits this growth pattern.

6. Distinguish between a **cnidocyte** and a **nematocyst**. Give the function of these structures and name the Phylum characterized by the presence of cnidocytes.

7. Explain the relationship between particle size, water velocity, and wave energy. Where do you find rocky shores, sandy beaches, and mud flats with respect to coastal morphology and wave energy?

8. Describe survival strategies employed by organisms that live in sandy or muddy areas. Include a discussion of the feeding styles of sediment dwellers including: suspension (filter) feeding , deposit feeding and predation.

Animals of the Benthic Environment

9. List and describe the lifestyle of animals found in the sediment-covered intertidal and subtidal zones including:
    A. Phylum Mollusca, Class Bivalvia – clams, oysters, scallops – animals with a soft body and a mantle that secretes a shell
    B. Phylum Annelida, Class Polychaeta - fan worms, feather duster worms, lugworm – segmented bodies with paddle-like structures and bristles used for burrowing
    C. Phylum Arthropoda, Class Crustacea – external skeleton, segmented bodies, jointed appendages, examples: lobsters, crabs, shrimp, barnacles
    D. Phylum Echinodermata – spines cover the body, water vascular system with external tube feet, adults are radially symmetrical, examples: sea urchins, brittle stars, starfish

10. Define **meiofauna**, describe where meiofauna are found in the sediments, and give examples of organisms that comprise the meiofauna.

11. Describe fiddler crab (*Uca*) claw-waving behavior and the preferred habitat where fiddler crabs are found.

12. Discuss the distribution of organisms found in temperate subtidal (sublittoral) zones with rocky bottoms. Describe the kelp forest in the Pacific Northwest and the adaptations of kelp to life in a rocky area with high wave energy.

13. Explain the structure of a coral polyp (Phylum Cnidaria, Class Anthozoa) and describe the colonial nature of a coral reef structure.

14. Discuss the worldwide distribution of corals. Why are corals more common on the western side of an ocean basin? List the physical and chemical parameters required for coral growth.

15. Describe the endosymbiotic relationship between coral polyps and **zooxanthellae**. What happens to the coral if the zooxanthellae die?

16. Define **mixotroph** and apply the term in the context of a coral reef.

17. Explain the vertical and horizontal zonation of a coral reef from the windward side (high wave velocity area) to the reef crest to the reef flat in the lagoon. Describe the shape of corals that predominate in each zone and the other organisms that live in each zone.

18. List the biological functions that coral reefs serve in tropical marine environments. Why are they economically important?

19. Discuss anthropogenic impact on corals. How do coastal development, fishing, tourism, and farming/aquaculture affect coral reef health?

20. Detail the effect of *Acanthaster planci*, the Crown-of-Thorns sea star on Pacific coral reefs. Is this a recent phenomenon?

21. Describe the mechanisms by which coral reefs repair damaged areas.

22. Describe the physical and chemical environment of the deep ocean including the salinity, temperature, currents, sediment load, and pressure.

23. List the factors that limit benthic biomass in abyssal regions.

24. Relate oceanic plate movement to the distribution of **hydrothermal vent communities** in the deep ocean. When, where, and by whom were these communities first discovered?

25. Describe a **black smoker**. Relate the chemical concentration of the vent water to the color of the chimney "smoke".

26. Relate the presence of Archaea in hydrothermal vent communities to the food web. How is carbon fixed in the absence of sunlight?

27. Compare and contrast the geographic distribution and biological diversity of hydrothermal vent communities and **low-temperature seep communities**.

28. List and describe the following low-temperature seep communities including:
    A. hypersaline seep community
    B. hydrocarbon seep community
    C. subduction zone seep community

29. Define and describe the **deep biosphere**. What kinds of organisms inhabit this unique habitat?

Overview

Chapter 15 presents a survey of the distribution of life that exists on the ocean floor with an emphasis on the role that physical characteristics play in determining the distribution of benthic organisms. Ecosystems described in detail include rocky shores (intertidal zones), sediment-covered shores (sandy beaches), the shallow offshore ocean floor (including coral reefs), and the deep ocean floor (including hydrothermal vent communities).

Headings covered in this chapter include:
Distribution of Benthic Organisms
Rocky Shores
       Intertidal Zonation
       Supratidal (Spray) Zone
       High Tide Zone
       Middle Tide Zone
       Low Tide Zone
Sediment-Covered Shores
       Sediment Physical Environment
       Intertidal Zonation
       Sandy Beaches
       Mud Flats

Animals of the Benthic Environment

Teacher's Resources

There are several good films/videos and CD-ROMs available about benthic marine organisms and deep-ocean environments including:

Films/Videotapes
- Between the Tides (Contemporary Films), 22 minutes
- Coral Jungle (Doubleday Multimedia), 22 minutes
- 4000 Meters Under the Sea (NHK/Films for the Humanities and Sciences), 28 minutes (subject: hydrothermal vent biota)
- Jewels of the Caribbean (National Geographic), 50 minutes (subject: coral reefs)
- NOVA: City of Coral (WGBH/Peace River Films), 60 minutes
- The Intertidal Zone (Bullfrog Films), 17 minutes

CD-ROMs
- Coral Kingdom (Digital Studios)

Answers to End-of-Chapter Questions and Exercises

1. What are some of the adverse conditions on the intertidal zones? What are some organism's adaptations to those adverse conditions? Which conditions seem to be most important in controlling the distribution of life?

See Table 15-1 for a list of adverse conditions in the intertidal zone and some adaptations of organisms that live there.

     An organism's success is closely tied to its ability to cope with the physical water conditions, the ocean floor, and other members of the biological community. One of the most prominent variables affecting species diversification of benthic organisms may be temperature. As well, the distribution of benthic biomass closely mirrors the distribution of photosynthetic productivity in the surface waters. This suggests that life on the ocean floor is very much dependent upon the primary photosynthetic productivity within the ocean's surface waters.

2. Draw a diagram of the zones within the rocky shore intertidal region and list characteristic organisms of each zone.

Student drawings will vary, but the drawing should resemble Figure 15-2 (a) that illustrates the zones within the rocky shore intertidal region and characteristic organisms.

3. One of the most noticeable features of the middle tide zone long rocky coasts is a mussel bed. Describe general characteristics of mussels and include a discussion of other organisms that are associated with mussels.

Mussel beds of the genera *Mytilis* and *Modiolus* attach to the middle tide zone rocks by secreting hair-like byssal threads. The base of the mussel bed is often very abrupt. A common and visible member of the mussel bed is the goose barnacle, *Pollicipes*. The mussels are preyed upon by the sea stars, *Pisaster* and *Asterias*. Less visible algae, snails, hydroids, worms, clams, and crustaceans are also found in the mussel beds.

4. Describe how sandy and muddy shores differ in terms of energy level, particle size, sediment stability, and oxygen content.

This information is summarized in the table below:

	Sandy Shores	**Muddy Shores**
Energy Level	High	Low
Particle Size	Medium- to Coarse-Grained	Fine-Grained
Sediment Stability	Low	High
Oxygen Content	High	Low

Sediment salinity increases and permeability (the ability of a substance to pass fluid) decreases with decreased particle size. The higher sediment stability of mud flats results from the high cohesive attraction between clay particles and the lower energy longshore current in mud flat regions. The fact that sand-sized particles are rounder and clay-sized particles are flat results in the higher permeability of muddy sediment, large amounts of organic material must be anaerobically decomposed in these deposits. This often results in sediment from mad flats having a black color and a strong hydrogen sulfide odor.

5. How does the diversity of species on sediment-covered shores compare with that of the rocky shore? Suggest at least one reason why.

Animals of the Benthic Environment

There are more species living on rocky shores than sediment-covered shores. A possible reason for this is that there are more environmental niches on rocky shores than on sediment-covered shores. An environment that has many niches creates conditions that produce high species diversity.

6. In which intertidal zone of a steeply sloping, coarse sand beach would you find each of the following organisms: clams, beach hoppers, ghost shrimp, sand crabs, and heart urchins?

- Clams: Low through middle tide zones
- Beach hoppers: Supratidal zone
- Ghost shrimp: Middle and high tide zones
- Sand crabs: Low and middle tide zones
- Heart urchins: low tide zone

7. Discuss the dominant species of kelp, their epifauna, and animals that feed on kelp in Pacific coast kelp forests.

The dominant species of kelp found in Pacific coast kelp forests are *Macrocystis* (giant brown bladder kelp) and *Nereocystis*. Smaller varieties of reed and brown algae grow on the larger varieties along with hydroids and bryozoans. Nudibranchs feed on hydroids and bryozoans. Very few animals feed directly on living kelp plants. The sea harem *Alpysia*, and sea urchins do feed on living kelp.

8. Describe the environmental conditions required for development of coral reefs.

An environment suitable for coral reef growth must have a minimum average monthly temperature that exceeds 18°C (64°F) throughout the year. Reef building corals rely on photosynthetic endosymbiotic dinoflagellates (zooxanthellae) that live within their tissues. As a result of this relationship, corals survive only in sunlit waters. Strong water circulation assures and adequate supply of food and oxygen. The water must also have normal salinity and have relatively low turbidity (low amount of suspended sediment) that can smoother the coral. Additionally, corals need a hard substrate for attachment.

9. Describe the zones of the reef slope, the characteristic coral types, and the physical factors related to zonation.

Physical factors related to the zonation of coral reefs usually include wave energy, salinity, water depth, and temperature. Coral is usually massive in high-energy, near-surface portions of the reef. With increasing depth, wave energy and light energy decrease, producing corals that are more delicate. Corals will not survive at all below about 150 meters (492 feet).

   From the surface to a depth of 20 meters (66 feet), there is high-energy wave action and more than 60% of the surface light available. Massive branching corals and algae are found in this "buttress zone". Between the depths of 20 meters (66 feet) and 50 meters (164 feet), the light level drops to 20% of the surface light, and wave energy decreases. Massive head corals are common in this zone. Light levels drop to about 4% of surface light at 150 meters (492 feet). Wave energy is also minimal at this depth and delicate plate corals are common in this zone.

10. What is coral bleaching? How does it occur? What other diseases affect corals?

Coral bleaching is the loss of color in coral reef organisms that causes them to turn white. The cause of coral bleaching is due to the removal or expulsion of the coral's symbiotic partner, the zooxanthellae (endosymbiotic dinoflagellates), due to elevated seawater temperature or other environmental stresses. Other diseases that affect corals include white plague, black band disease, white band disease, white pox, and yellow band disease (yellow-blotch disease), patchy necrosis, and rapid wasting disease.

11. As one moves from the shoreline to the deep-ocean floor, what changes in the physical environment are experienced?

Moving from the shore along the ocean floor to the deep ocean basins, the physical environment changes considerably. The energy level decreases below wave base (variable, but generally shallow), light decreases gradually and is absent below 1000 meters (3300 feet), and the temperature drops to a fairly uniform 3°C (37.4°F). Pressure increases by 1 atmosphere (14.7 pounds per square inch) with each increase in depth of 10 meters (33 feet). Fine oozes and clays in the deep ocean basins replace coarse sediment near shore.

12. Where does the food come from to supply organisms living on the deep-ocean floor? How does this affect benthic biomass?

With the exception of chemosynthetic productivity that occurs around hydrothermal vents, all deep-ocean floor organisms receive their food from the surface waters above. Low food availability, not low temperature, low oxygen concentration, or high pressure, limits deep-sea benthic biomass.

13. Describe the characteristics of hydrothermal vents. What evidence suggests that hydrothermal vents have short life spans?

Hydrothermal vents occur along the crest of the mid-ocean ridge where the lithosphere is thin and volcanic activity is common. They exist in complete darkness at water depths ranging from 1525 meters (5000 feet) to 3600 meters (11,800 feet). Hydrothermal vents emit hot water up to 350°C (662°F) that is so rich in metal sulfides that it colors the water black, giving these features the name "black smokers". The chimneys associated with these vents were first observed in 1979 and are composed primarily of copper sulfides, zinc sulfides, and silver sulfides. Hydrothermal vents are often colonized by unusual life forms that comprise the hydrothermal vent Biocommunities.

      Evidence that suggests that hydrothermal vents have short life spans (a few years to a few decades) includes direct visitation to the sites that have been active only a few years ago but are no longer active. Other sites that have been visited at frequent intervals indicate an increase in volcanic activity.

14. What is the "dead whale hypothesis"? What other ideas have been suggested to explain how organisms from hydrothermal vent Biocommunities populate new vent sites?

The "dead whale hypothesis" suggests that when large animals such as whales die and sink to the deep ocean floor, they may provide a temporary stepping-stone for organisms that inhabit the hydrothermal vent fields separated by large distances. Decomposition of a whale carcass provides an energy source for these organisms that breed and release their larvae, some of which make it to the next hydrothermal vent site.

Animals of the Benthic Environment

Other researchers believe that deep ocean currents are strong enough to transport drifting larvae to new sites. Still others have suggested that the rift valleys of mid-ocean ridges may have acted as passageways along which drifting larvae of hydrothermal vent organisms have traversed to inhabit new vent fields. By whatever means these organisms travel, evidence indicates that they are able too colonize new hydrothermal vents soon after the vents are created.

15. What are the major differences between the conditions and biocommunities of the hydrothermal vents and the cold seeps? How are they similar?

In hydrothermal vent fields, water temperatures range as high as 12°C (54°F), while the temperatures at the cold water seeps are near ambient values of local water conditions (usually just a few degrees above freezing). Hydrothermal vents are found only in association with springs at the base of the Florida Escarpment, at hydrocarbon seeps, and at subduction zones where trench sediments have been folded. Additionally, the producers at hydrothermal vents are exclusively sulfur oxidizing bacteria, while at the cold seeps sulfur and methane oxidizing bacteria are important.

The overriding similarity of the communities found at the hydrothermal vents and cold water seeps is that the organisms are much larger than typical deep-sea species because of the large food supply that is locally available by chemosynthetic bacteria.

CHAPTER
1
Introduction to Planet "Earth"

Matching. Match the term or person with the appropriate phrase. You may use each answer once, more than once, or not at all.

_____ 1. Balboa
_____ 2. Eratosthenes
_____ 3. Magellan
_____ 4. Ptolemy
_____ 5. Vikings

A. made important observations about drift of sea ice
B. used ecological approach to solve fisheries problem
C. established temporary settlement in North America
D. incorrectly concluded that no life exists in deep ocean
E. first European explorer to Pacific Ocean
F. mapped the Mediterranean Sea for the Greeks
G. important observations on ocean chemistry
H. led voyage that first circumnavigated the globe
I. first determination of Earth's circumference
J. mapped world with Roman knowledge showing latitude and longitude
K. led voyage that first used the marine chronometer

Answers: 1-E, 2-I, 3-H, 4-J, 5-C
Key Questions: 4 & 5
Skill: knowledge
Difficulty: Level 1

Matching. Match the term or person with the appropriate phrase. You may use each answer once, more than once, or not at all.

_____ 6. core
_____ 7. crust
_____ 8. galaxy
_____ 9. mantle
_____ 10. nebula

A. Big Bang
B. composed of iron and nickel, liquid outer layer, and solid inner layer
C. gaseous and dusty space cloud
D. Milky Way
E. outermost portion of the Earth, basalt and granite
F. rich in ferromagnesian minerals, between crust and core
G. solar winds

Introduction to Planet "Earth"

True–False Questions.   Read each question carefully, write "True" if the statement is true, and write "False" if the statement is false.

11. Early Polynesians only traveled within sight of land.
Answer: False
Key Question: 3
Skill: knowledge
Difficulty: Level 1

12. Vikings led by Thor Heyerdahl established temporary colonies in North America.
Answer: False
Key Question: 4
Skill: knowledge
Difficulty: Level 1

13. Significant oceanographic knowledge was acquired during the Middle Ages.
Answer: False
Key Question: 5
Skill: knowledge
Difficulty: Level 1

14. The Ming Dynasty ships used magnetic compasses similar to those used today.
Answer: True
Key Question: 4
Skill: knowledge
Difficulty: Level 1

15. Christopher Columbus established trade routes from Europe around Africa to India.
Answer: False
Key Question: 5
Skill: knowledge
Difficulty: Level 1

16. The Earth's crust solidified around 4.5 billion years ago
Answer: True
Key Question: 10
Skill: knowledge
Difficulty: Level 1

17. When the Earth cooled, the layers of the earth separated on the basis of density differences.
Answer: True
Key Question: 10 & 11
Skill: knowledge
Difficulty: Level 1

18. Earth developed the first ocean by about 4 million years ago.
Answer: True
Key Question: 16
Skill: knowledge
Difficulty: Level 1

19. In general, the chemical composition of ocean water has remained constant through geologic time.
Answer: True
Key Question: 16
Skill: knowledge
Difficulty: Level 1

20. The mantle could not have produced enough water to fill the oceans.
Answer: False
Key Question: 16
Skill: knowledge
Difficulty: Level 1

21. The salinity of the oceans has been steadily increasing.
Answer: False
Key Question: 16
Skill: knowledge
Difficulty: Level 1

22. Free oxygen was present in the Earth's primordial atmosphere.
Answer: False
Key Question: 15
Skill: knowledge
Difficulty: Level 1

23. Production of the first free oxygen in the atmosphere caused organisms living at that time to flourish.
Answer: False
Key Question: 15
Skill: knowledge
Difficulty: Level 1

24. Carbon dating is used to determine the absolute age of a rock or fossil.
Answer: True
Key Question: 21
Skill: knowledge
Difficulty: Level 1

25. Heterotrophic organisms can make their own food from inorganic carbon sources.
Answer: False
Key Question: 19
Skill: knowledge
Difficulty: Level 1

Multiple Choice. Choose the **best** answer from the choices provided.

26. The four principle oceans of the Earth are the:
    a. Atlantic, Arctic, Mediterranean, and Pacific Oceans.
    b. Atlantic, Arctic, Indian, and Pacific Oceans.
    c. Atlantic, Antarctic, Mediterranean, and Pacific Oceans.
    d. Antarctic, Caspian, Indian, and Pacific Oceans.
    e. Antarctic, Arctic, Indian, and Pacific Oceans.
Answer: b
Key Question: 1
Skill: knowledge
Difficulty: Level 1

27. One distinction between an "ocean" and a "sea" is that a sea:
    a. contains more shallow water.
    b. is composed of salt water.
    c. is smaller than an ocean.
    d. may be enclosed by either land or ocean currents.
    e. All of the above are correct.

Answer: e
Key Question: 1
Skill: comprehension
Difficulty: Level 2

28. All of the following are **TRUE** concerning the deepest part of the ocean *except*:
    a. The bottom of the trench was visited by Piccard and Walsh in the *Trieste* in 1960.
    b. The deepest part of the ocean is located in a trench off the coast of Japan.
    c. The depth of the trench exceeds the height of Mount Everest.
    d. The depth of the trench is estimated at 12,500 m.
    e. The trench is called the Mariana Trench.
Answer: d
Key Question: 2
Skill: knowledge
Difficulty: Level 1

29. The correct arrangement of astronomical bodies from **oldest** to **youngest** is:
    a. galaxy, solar system, planet.
    b. planet, galaxy, solar system.
    c. planet, solar system, galaxy.
    d. solar system, galaxy, planet.
    e. solar system, planet, galaxy.
Answer: a
Key Question 9
Skill: application
Difficulty: Level 3

30. The **nebular hypothesis** suggest that:
    a. all bodies in the solar system formed from an enormous gas cloud.
    b. Earth's moon is an asteroid captured by the Earth's gravity.
    c. galaxies such as the Milky Way form independent of one another.
    d. the Earth was formed as a cosmic explosion, a "big bang".
    e. the moon is derived from a protoplanet.
Answer: a
Key Question 9
Skill: knowledge
Difficulty: Level 1

31. . The separation of the Earth into layers was the result of the:
    a. decrease in temperature downward toward the core.
    b. differing densities of the rock and mineral materials.
    c. gravitational force created by the rotating Earth.

Introduction to Planet "Earth"

d. initial collection of materials and their position in the Earth.
e. presence of water at Earth's surface.

Answer: b
Key Question 11
Skill: knowledge
Difficulty: Level 1

32. Oceanic crust is primarily:
    a. basalt.
    b. carbonate sedimentary rocks.
    c. clay minerals.
    d. granite.
    e. siltstone.

Answer: a
Key Question 13
Skill: knowledge
Difficulty: Level 1

33. Which of the following statements regarding continental and oceanic crust is **TRUE**?
    a. Continental crust and oceanic crust have equivalent densities.
    b. Continental crust is thicker and denser than oceanic crust.
    c. Continental crust is thinner and denser than oceanic crust.
    d. Continental crust is thicker and less dense than oceanic crust.
    e. Continental crust is thinner and less dense than oceanic crust.

Answer: d
Key Question 13
Skill: comprehension
Difficulty: Level 2

34. Earth's primordial atmosphere most likely included:
    a. ammonia, carbon dioxide, and water vapor.
    b. carbon dioxide, water vapor, sulfur dioxide, and methane.
    c. hydrogen, helium, and oxygen.
    d. nitrogen, ozone, and sulfur dioxide.
    e. all of the above.

Answer: b
Key Question 15
Skill: knowledge
Difficulty: Level 1

35. Free oxygen in our atmosphere is important to the development and maintenance of life on Earth because oxygen:
    a. combines with iron in volcanic rocks.

b. can form ozone and block some UV radiation.
c. is necessary for photosynthesis to occur.
d. reduces atmospheric temperature.
e. was very abundant in our early atmosphere.

Answer: c
Key Question 20
Skill: comprehension
Difficulty: Level 2

36. Organisms that break down organic molecules to release energy are called:
    a. autotrophic organisms.
    b. bacteria.
    c. biotic organisms.
    d. fungi.
    e. heterotrophic organisms.

Answer: e
Key Question 19
Skill: knowledge
Difficulty: Level 1

37. Radioactive isotopes can sometimes be used to determine the:
    a. absolute age of the rock.
    b. chemical composition of the rock.
    c. formation method.
    d. metamorphism.
    e. relative age of the rock.

Answer: a
Key Question 21
Skill: comprehension
Difficulty: Level 2

Word Analysis. Examine the five words and/or phrases and determine the relationship among the majority of words/phrases. Choose the one option that does not fit the pattern.

38. A. Baltic   B. Black   C. Caspian   D. Indian   E. Mediterranean.
Answer: D
Key Question: 1
Skill: analysis
Difficulty: Level 4

39. A. Erastosthenes B. Herodotus   C. Ptolemy   D. Pytheas   E. Strabo

Introduction to Planet "Earth"

Answer: E
Key Question: 3
Skill: analysis
Difficulty: Level 4

39. A. Cook   B. Cosmas   C. Darwin   D. Herodotus E. Mercator
Answer: C
Key Question: 4, 5, & 6
Skill: analysis
Difficulty: Level 4

40. A. autotrophic   B. chemosynthesizers   C. cyanobacteria   D. heterotrophs
                    E. sulfur bacteria
Answer: D
Key Question: 19
Skill: analysis
Difficulty: Level 4

CHAPTER

2

Plate Tectonics and the Ocean Floor

Matching. Match the term or person with the appropriate phrase. You may use each answer once, more than once or not at all.

1. hydrothermal vents
2. island arc
3. mountains
4. oceanic trench
5. rift valley
6. volcanoes

A. convergent plate boundary
B. divergent plate boundary

Answers: 1-B, 2-A, 3-B, 4-B, 5-A, 6-B
Key Question: 4
Skill: comprehension
Difficulty: Level 2

---

7. ancient precursor of the Pacific Ocean
8. supercontinent 200 million years ago
9. depression along ridge axis
10. study of changes in the character of oceans due to geographic changes
11. study of magnetism over geologic time

A. Gondwanaland
B. Laurasia
C. paleogeology
D. paleomagnetism
E. paleoceanography
F. Pangea
G. Panthalassa
H. rift valley
I. subduction zone

Answers: 7-G, 8-F, 9-H, 10-E, 11-D
Key Question: 4 & 6
Skill: comprehension

Difficulty: Level 2

True-False Questions.   Read each question carefully, write "T" if the statement is true, and write "F" if the statement is false.

12. The relatively young age of the seafloor supports the idea that subduction must take place.
Answer: True
Key Question: 3
Skill: comprehension
Difficulty: Level 2

13. The magnetic north pole has remained very close to the geographic North Pole through all of geologic time.
Answer: False
Key Question: 3
Skill: comprehension
Difficulty: Level 2

14. Paleomagnetism confirms that at particular times in the geologic past Earth has had more than one magnetic north pole.
Answer: False
Key Question: 2 & 3
Skill: comprehension
Difficulty: Level 2

15. New crust is formed at trenches and old crust is subducted at ridges.
Answer: False
Key Question: 4
Skill: comprehension
Difficulty: Level 2

16. The oldest rocks are located at mid-ocean ridges.
Answer: False
Key Question: 3 & 4
Skill: application
Difficulty: Level 3

17. Earthquakes are common along fracture zones.
Answer: False
Key Question: 4

Skill: comprehension

Difficulty: Level 2

18. Deep focus earthquakes are often associated with deep-sea trenches.
Answer: True
Key Question: 4
Skill: comprehension
Difficulty: Level 2

19. The magnetic field of the Earth reverses itself each time that magma erupts at a mid-ocean ridge.
Answer: False
Key Question: 2 & 3
Skill: comprehension
Difficulty: Level 2

20. Fast-moving spreading ridges tend to be more gently sloped that slow-moving ridges.
Answer: True
Key Question: 3 & 4
Skill: application
Difficulty: Level 3

21. Deep-sea trenches are found at convergent plate boundaries.
Answer: False
Key Question: 4
Skill: comprehension
Difficulty: Level 2

22. At divergent plate boundaries, only shallow focus earthquakes can be found.
Answer: True
Key Question: 4
Skill: comprehension
Difficulty: Level 2

Multiple Choice.   Choose the one **best** answer from the choices provided.

23. Fossils found in sediments can be used to:
    a. indicate the relative age of the sediments.
    b. provide evidence for plate movement.
    c. suggest ancient climate characteristics.
    d. support the idea that land masses were joined.
    e. all of the above.

Answer: E
Key Question: 1
Skill: application
Difficulty: Level 3

24. All continents fit together with the least number of overlaps and gaps when the continents are matched along:
    a. contours at around 2000 meters in depth.
    b. current shorelines.
    c. edge of the continental shelf.
    d. edges of the deep sea floor.
    e. oceanic trenches in subduction zones.
Answer: A
Key Question: 1 & 2
Skill: comprehension
Difficulty: Level 2

25. Fossils of ancient polar plants are currently found near the equator because the:
    a. entire earth had polar conditions at the time the plants were living.
    b. plants lived near the poles, but have drifted to current locations.
    c. plants probably were tolerant of both tropical and polar conditions.
    d. plants were distributed to current locations by ancient glacial ice sheets.
    e. poles were at the equator at times in the geologic past.
Answer: B
Key Question: 1
Skill: application
Difficulty: Level 3

26. Climate distribution on Earth is primarily controlled by:
    a. Earth's geologic history.
    b. latitude.
    c. longitude.
    d. presence or absence of glacial debris.
    e. plants and animals that live in an area.
Answer: B
Key Question: 1 & 2
Skill: comprehension
Difficulty: Level 2

27. All of the following provide evidence for continental drift **except:**
    a. age of selected continental rocks.
    b. apparent polar wandering.
    c. location of coral reef fossils.

d.   seafloor magnetic pattern.

e.   shape of continental margins.

Answer: D
Key Question: 1
Skill: comprehension
Difficulty: Level 2

28. Continental drift was **confirmed** through the use of the:
   a.   age of rocks on distant continents.
   b.   location of ancient coral reefs.
   c.   location of deep sea trenches.
   d.   location of magnetic poles through geologic time.
   e.   the shape of the continental margins.

Answer: D
Key Question: 2 & 3
Skill: comprehension
Difficulty: Level 2

29. Which of the following statements best describes the relationship between Earth's geographic and magnetic poles?
   a.   The geographic pole and the magnetic pole are always the same.
   b.   The geographic pole wobbles, but stays near the magnetic pole.
   c.   The geographic poles have reversed themselves periodically through geologic time.
   d.   The location of the magnetic pole is unrelated to the location of the geographic pole.
   e.   The magnetic pole wobbles, but stays near the geographic pole.

Answer: E
Key Question: 3
Skill: application
Difficulty: Level 3

30. Vine and Matthews determined that new ocean floor was being produced at ocean ridges by examining:
   a.   apparent polar wandering.
   b.   fossils in marine sediments.
   c.   glacial debris at various locations.
   d.   the location of ancient coral reefs.
   e.   the magnetic pattern on the seafloor.

Answer: E
Key Question: 3
Skill: comprehension
Difficulty: Level 2

31. Confirmation of seafloor spreading was supported by the:

a. age of seafloor.
b. apparent polar wandering.
c. magnetic reversals found in continental rocks.
d. match of rocks from distant continents.
e. sediment analysis from different areas of the seafloor.

Answer: A
Key Question: 2 & 3
Skill: comprehension
Difficulty: Level 2

32. The seafloor magnetic pattern is be best described as:
   a. not related to the location of oceanic ridges.
   b. parallel to and symmetric about ocean ridges.
   c. parallel to, but not symmetric about ocean ridges.
   d. perpendicular to and symmetric about ocean ridges.
   e. perpendicular to, but not symmetric about ocean ridges.

Answer: B
Key Question: 3
Skill: comprehension
Difficulty: Level 2

33. Oceans become deeper moving away from ridges due to:
   a. decreasing thickness of the lithosphere.
   b. increasing density of oceanic basalts.
   c. increases in sediment accumulations.
   d. polar wandering.
   e. thermal contraction of hot asthenosphere.

Answer: E
Key Question: 3
Skill: comprehension
Difficulty: Level 2

34. Differences in height between continental crust and oceanic crust are explained by:
   a. continental drift.
   b. density.
   c. isostasy.
   d. ophiolites.
   e. paleomagnetism.

Answer: C
Key Question: 4 & 5
Skill: comprehension
Difficulty: Level 2

35. Which of the following statements is **true** of the asthenosphere?
   a. The asthenosphere is composed of continental and oceanic plates.
   b. The asthenosphere is composed of outer mantle material.
   c. The asthenosphere is composed of the crust and a portion of the outer mantle.
   d. The asthenosphere is composed of the inner portion of the mantle and the outer core.
   e. The asthenosphere is composed only of crust.

Answer: B
Key Question: 2 & 3
Skill: comprehension
Difficulty: Level 2

36. Which of the following statements is **true** of the lithosphere?
   a. The lithosphere is composed of outer mantle material.
   b. The lithosphere is composed of igneous rock.
   c. The lithosphere is composed of metamorphic rock.
   d. The lithosphere is composed of the crust and the topmost portion of the outer mantle.
   e. The lithosphere is composed of the inner portion of the mantle and the outer core.

Answer: D
Key Question: 2 & 3
Skill: comprehension
Difficulty: Level 2

37. Moving from oceanic ridge to oceanic trench, the thickness of the lithosphere:
   a. decreases in proportion to the distance.
   b. is unrelated to the distance from the ridge.
   c. increases in proportion to the distance.
   d. randomly varies.
   e. remains the same.

Answer: C
Key Question: 3
Skill: comprehension
Difficulty: Level 2

38. Deep ocean trenches are associated with:
   a. rift valleys.
   b. subduction zones.
   c. submarine canyons.
   d. transform faults.
   e. turbidity currents.

Answer: B
Key Question: 4
Skill: application
Difficulty: Level 3

39. The Hawaiian Islands are located where the Pacific plate is:
    a. being subducted beneath the North American plate.
    b. being subducted beneath Japan.
    c. being thrust over the North American plate.
    d. diving under Japan.
    e. moving over a hot spot.
Answer: E
Key Question: 5
Skill: comprehension
Difficulty: Level 2

40. The Mid-Atlantic Ridge is an example of a:
    a. convergent boundary (continent-continent).
    b. convergent boundary (continent-oceanic).
    c. convergent boundary (oceanic-oceanic).
    d. divergent boundary.
    e. transform fault boundary.
Answer: D
Key Question: 4
Skill: knowledge
Difficulty: Level 1

41. Which of the following is associated with convergent plate boundaries on the seafloor?
    a. crest of the mid-ocean ridge
    b. deep sea trenches
    c. deep focus earthquakes
    d. island arcs

    e. offset of the mid-ocean ridge
Answer: A
Key Question: 4
Skill: comprehension
Difficulty: Level 2

42. Which of the following is characteristic of oceanic-oceanic convergent plate boundaries?
        a. andesitic volcanoes
        b. fracture zones
        c. hot spots
    d. mid-ocean ridges
    e. volcanic island arcs
Answer: E

Key Question: 4
Skill: knowledge
Difficulty: Level 1

43. Which of the following is characteristic of oceanic-continental convergent plate boundaries?
    a. andesitic volcanoes
    b. fracture zones
    c. hot spots
    d. mid-ocean ridges
    e. volcanic island arcs
Answer: A
Key Question: 4
Skill: knowledge
Difficulty: Level 1

Word Analysis. Examine the five words and/or phrases and determine the relationship among the majority of words/phrases. Choose the one option that does not fit the pattern.

42. A. hydrothermal vents   B. island arc   C. mountains   D. oceanic trench   E. volcanoes
Answer: A
Key Question: 4 & 5
Skill: application
Difficulty: Level 4

43. A. Aleutian Islands   B. Andes Mountains   C. Hawaiian Islands   D. Japan   E. Mariana Trench
Answer: C
Key Question: 4 & 5
Skill: application
Difficulty: Level 4

44. A. hydrothermal vents   B. rift valley   C. oceanic ridge   D. oceanic trench   E. spreading center
Answer: D
Key Question: 4
Skill: application
Difficulty: Level 4

45. A. Gondwanaland B. Panamerica   C. Pangea D. Panthalassa E. Tethys Sea
Answer: B
Key Question: 6
Skill: application
Difficulty: Level 4

CHAPTER

3

Marine Provinces

Matching. Match the term or person with the appropriate phrase. You may use each answer once, more than once, or not at all.

1. bathymetry
2. GLORIA
3. hypsometric curve
4. PDR
5. seismic survey

A. cumulative plot of area versus depth or elevation
B. device used for side-scan sonar
C. measurement of ocean depth and seafloor topography
D. used echo soundings in 1952 to identify mid-ocean ridge in South Atlantic
E. used to determine shape and position of boundaries
F. used to map ocean floor from space
G. uses high-frequency sound waves to measure ocean depth

Answers: 1-C, 2-B, 3-A, 4-G, 5-E
Key Question: 1
Skill: knowledge
Difficulty: Level 1

Refer to the figure below. Match the term to the numbered ocean floor feature on the figure. You may use each answer once, more than once, or not at all.

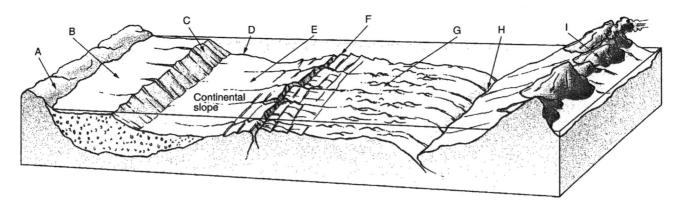

6. abyssal plain
7. continental rise
8. continental slope
9. oceanic ridge
10. trench

Answers: 6-E, 7-D, 8-C, 9-F, 10-H
Key Question: 2, 3, 4, & 5
Skill: comprehension
Difficulty: Level 2

True–False Questions. Read each question carefully, write "True" if the statement is true, and write "False" if the statement is false.

11. Abyssal plains are more extensive on the floor of the Atlantic compared to those on the floor of the Pacific
Answer: True
Key Question: 4
Skill: comprehension
Difficulty: Level 2

12. Sediments of the continental rise can exhibit characteristics similar to those formed by rivers on land.
Answer: True
Key Question: 4
Skill: comprehension
Difficulty: Level 2

13. A sediment-laden current that flows off of the continental shelf is called a turbidity current.
Answer: True
Key Question: 3
Skill: knowledge
Difficulty: Level 1

14. The deepest portions of the ocean are part of the relatively narrow features called submarine canyons.
Answer: False
Key Question: 4
Skill: knowledge
Difficulty: Level 1

15. Subduction zones appear to remain nearly stationary over long periods of time.
Answer: False
Key Question: 4 & 6
Skill: comprehension
Difficulty: Level 2

16. Trenches change their position over time.
Answer: True
Key Question: 4 & 6

Skill: comprehension
Difficulty: Level 2
17. Seamounts form from ancient tablemounts.
Answer: False
Key Question: 5
Skill: knowledge
Difficulty: Level 1

18. Mid-ocean ridges are rises that occupy a small portion of the deep ocean basin, only around 10%.
Answer: False
Key Question: 5
Skill: knowledge
Difficulty: Level 1

19. Hydrothermal vents have a significant impact on ocean chemistry.
Answer: True
Key Question: 5
Skill: application
Difficulty: Level 3

20. Because of the very harsh environment, few organisms are found in association with hydrothermal
   vents.
Answer: False
Key Question: 5
Skill: comprehension
Difficulty: Level 2

Multiple Choice.   Choose the **best** answer from the choices provided.

21. The two relatively flat areas on the hypsometric curve represent:
    a.   continental mountains and abyssal plains.
    b.   continental mountains and mid-ocean ridges.
    c.   continental slopes and deep-sea trenches.
    d.   some interior continental areas/ coastal plains and abyssal plains.
    e.   some interior continental areas/ coastal plains and mid-ocean ridges.
Answer: d
Key Question: 1
Skill: comprehension
Difficulty: Level 2

22. The method that is most frequently used to investigate sediment and rock layers of the sea floor is:
    a.   direct observation.
    b.   drilling.
    c.   light waves.
    d.   satellite observation.
    e.   sound waves.
Answer: e
Key Question: 1

Skill: knowledge
Difficulty: Level 1

23. Satellites are used to map the ocean floor because they:
    a. are unaffected by surface weather.
    b. can cover areas where ships have not produced surveys.
    c. can "see" large areas of the seafloor at a time.
    d. the shape of the ocean surface itself reflects large features on the seafloor below.
    e. All of the above statements are correct.
Answer: e
Key Question: 1
Skill: comprehension
Difficulty: Level 2

24. Passive continental margins are characterized by all of the following **except**:
    a. broad continental shelf.
    b. deep-sea trenches.
    c. shallow coastal waters.
    d. thick sediment accumulation.
    e. very little volcanic and earthquake activity.
Answer: b
Key Question: 2
Skill: knowledge
Difficulty: Level 1

25. Characteristics of active continental margins include all of the following **except**:
    a. broad continental shelf.
    b. chains of islands.
    c. deep-sea trenches.
    d. thin sediment accumulation.
    e. volcanic and earthquake activity.
Answer: a
Key Question: 2
Skill: knowledge
Difficulty: Level 1

26. The correct order of marine provinces from the coast to the mid-ocean ridge is:
    a. abyssal plain, rise, slope, shelf.
    b. abyssal plain, shelf, slope, rise.
    c. rise, abyssal plain, slope, shelf.
    d. shelf, slope, rise, abyssal plain.
    e. slope, rise, shelf, abyssal plain.
Answer: d
Key Question: 2
Skill: comprehension
Difficulty: Level 2

27. Directly seaward of the continental shelf is a more steeply sloping region called the:
    a. abyssal plain.

    b.   continental rise.
    c.   continental slope.
    d.   mid-ocean ridge.
    e.   trench.
Answer: c
Key Question: 2
Skill: knowledge
Difficulty: Level 1

28. All of the following are considered part of the continental margin **except** the:
    a.   continental rise.
    b.   continental shelf.
    c.   continental slope.
    d.   fracture zone.
    e.   submarine canyon.
Answer: d
Key Question: 2
Skill: knowledge
Difficulty: Level 1

29. Continental rises are formed:
    a.   as a result of the slow accumulation of sediments from the water column.
    b.   by many deep sea fans.
    c.   in association with hydrothermal vents
    d.   next to submarine canyons.
    e.   on the flank of a mid-ocean ridge.
Answer: b
Key Question: 2 & 5
Skill: knowledge
Difficulty: Level 1

30. Submarine canyons were most likely formed by
    a.   deposition of terrestrial sediment.
    b.   earthquake activity.
    c.   erosion by major rivers in the past.
    d.   erosion by turbidity currents.
    e.   scouring by glacier during the last ice age.
Answer: d
Key question: 3
Skill: comprehension
Difficulty: Level 2

31. The sea floor feature in the figure is most likely a result of:

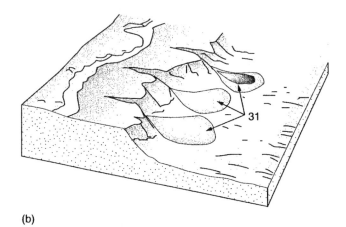

(b)

    a. pillow lava.
    b. submarine fans.
    c. turbidity currents.
    d. underwater boundary currents.
    e. volcanic activity.
Answer: c
Key Question: 3
Skill: comprehension
Difficulty: Level 2

32. The most rapid change in slope in the ocean is found at the:
    a. abyssal plain.
    b. continental slope.
    c. oceanic trench.
    d. submarine canyon.
    e. volcanic seamount.
Answer: c
Key Question: 4
Skill: knowledge
Difficulty: Level 1

33. The most gradual change in slope in the ocean can be found at the:
    a. abyssal plain.
    b. continental rise.
    c. continental shelf.
    d. deep-ocean trench.
    e. mid-ocean ridge.
Answer: a
Key Question: 4
Skill: knowledge
Difficulty: Level 1

Refer to the figure below. Use the labeled features on the figure to answer questions 34-36.

Marine Provinces

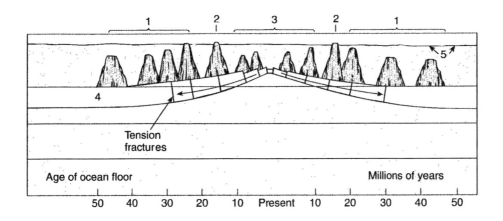

Tension fractures

Age of ocean floor   Millions of years

50   40   30   20   10   Present   10   20   30   40   50

34. Tablemounts are the features labeled:
    a. 1.
    b. 2.
    c. 3.
    d. 4.
    e. 5.
Answer: a
Key Question: 5
Skill: knowledge
Difficulty: Level 1

35. Wave action and plate movement are significant factors in the formation of the feature labeled:
    a. 1.
    b. 2.
    c. 3.
    d. 4.
    e. 5.
Answer: a
Key Question: 5
Skill: comprehension
Difficulty: Level 2

36. Seamounts are the feature labeled:
    a. 1.
    b. 2.
    c. 3.
    d. 4.
    e. 5.
Answer: c
Key Question: 5
Skill: knowledge
Difficulty: Level 1

37. Old lithosphere is destroyed in association with:
    a. deep-sea trenches
    b. fracture zones

c. hydrothermal vents
d. mid-ocean ridges
e. spreading centers.

Answer: a
Key Question: 5
Skill: comprehension
Difficulty: Level 2

38. Abyssal hills are only visible in the Pacific Ocean because:
    a. sediment has covered those found in the other ocean basins.
    b. there are none in the Atlantic and Indian ocean basins.
    c. they are higher in the Pacific than in the other ocean basins
    d. they have been destroyed in active plate margins.
    e. turbidity currents have eroded abyssal hills in the other ocean basins.

Answer: c
Key Question: 4
Skill: application
Difficulty: Level 3

39. New lithosphere is produced in association with:
    a. deep-sea trenches.
    b. fracture zones.
    c. hydrothermal vents.
    d. mid-ocean ridges.
    e. transform faults.

Answer: d
Key Question: 2 & 5
Skill: knowledge
Difficulty: Level 1

40. Warm-water hydrothermal vents form:
    a. abyssal hills.
    b. black smokers.
    c. cold seeps.
    d. turbidity currents.
    e. white smokers.

Answer: e
Key Question: 6
Skill: knowledge
Difficulty: Level 1

41. These organisms are most likely found in:

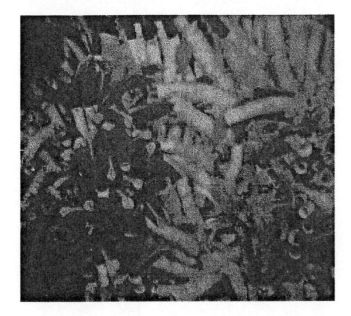

    a. abyssal hills.
    b. cold seeps.
    c. hydrothermal vents.
    d. submarine canyons.
    e. trenches.
Answer: c
Key Question: 6
Skill: application
Difficulty: Level 3

42. The direction of motion along a seafloor transform fault is:
    a. associated with turbidity currents.
    b. in the same direction as the plates are spreading.
    c. in the same direction as the ridge offset.
    d. influenced by underwater boundary currents.
    e. perpendicular to the direction of plate movement.
Answer: b
Key Question: 6
Skill: comprehension
Difficulty: Level 2

43. With respect to mid-ocean ridges, transform faults are:
    a. associated with hydrothermal vents.
    b. located in submarine canyons.
    c. parallel to the direction of plate movement.
    d. parallel to the rift valley.
    e. perpendicular to the ridge axis.
Answer: e
Key Question: 6
Skill: comprehension
Difficulty: Level 2

Word Analysis. Examine the five words and/or phrases and determine the relationship among the majority of words/phrases. Choose the one option that does not fit the pattern.

44. A. global positioning satellite (GPS)   B. GLORIA   C. precision depth recorder (PDR)

        D. SeaBeam   E. SeaMarc

Answer: A
Key Question: 1
Skill: analysis
Difficulty Level: 4

45. A. abyssal plain   B. continental flood basalt   C. continental rise   D. continental shelf
                                        E. continental slope

Answer: B
Key Question: 2
Skill: analysis
Difficulty: Level 4

46. A. black smoker   B. deep focus earthquake   C. hydrothermal vent   D. rift valley   E. white smoker

Answer: D
Key Question: 6
Skill: Analysis
Difficulty: 4

47. A. abyssal hill   B. guyot   C. ridge crest   D. sea knoll   E. tablemount

Answer: C
Key Question: 5
Skill: Analysis
Difficulty: 4

CHAPTER

4

Marine Sediments

Matching. Match the term or person with the appropriate phrase. You may use each answer once, more than once or not at all.

1. coccolithophores
2. diatomaceous ooze
3. foraminiferans
4. halite
5. manganese nodules
6. metal sulfides
7. oolites
8. silaceous ooze
9. stromatolites
10. tektites

A. biogenous sediment
B. cosmogenous sediment
C. hydrogenous sediment

Answers: 1-A, 2-A, 3-A, 4-C, 5-C, 6-C, 7-C, 8-A, 9-A, 10-B
Key Question: 3
Skill: knowledge
Difficulty: Level 1

---

11. CCD
12. ice rafting
13. lysocline
14. turbidite
15. Wentworth Scale

A. associated with deep sea fans
B. associated with glacial deposits
C. depth at which all carbonate is in solution
D. depth at which carbonate begins to dissolve
E. microscopic biogenous sediment
F. particle size classification
G. silicoflagellate ooze

Answers: 11-C, 12-B, 13-D, 14-A, 15-F
Key Question: 3, 4, & 5
Skill: knowledge
Difficulty: Level 1

True-False Questions. Read each question carefully, write "T" if the statement is true, and write "F" if the statement is false.

16. Texture refers to the size and shape of sediment particles.
Answer: True
Key Question: 2
Skill: knowledge
Difficulty: Level 1

17. Sediments derived from weathered rock and volcanic activity are called biogenous sediments.
Key Question: 3
Answer: False
Skill: knowledge
Difficulty: Level 1

18. Beach sand is usually well-sorted.
Answer: True
Key Question: 2
Skill: comprehension
Difficulty: Level 2

19. A glacial deposit is well-sorted.
Answer: False
Key Question: 2
Skill: comprehension
Difficulty: Level 2

20. A well-sorted sand deposit with rounded particles might be called immature.
Answer: False
Key Question: 2
Skill: comprehension
Difficulty: Level 2

21. The Wentworth scale is used to arrange the amount of sorting in a sediment deposit.
Answer: False
Key Question: 1 & 2
Skill: knowledge
Difficulty: Level 1

22. Calcareous shells will not accumulate on the ocean floor when the water depth exceeds about 4500 meters (around 15,000 feet).
Answer: True
Key Question: 3
Skill: comprehension
Difficulty: Level 2

23. The deposition of radiolarian oozes is affected by the carbonate compensation depth.
Answer: False
Key Question: 3
Skill: application
Difficulty: Level 3

Marine Sediments

24. Radiolarian oozes form near the equator.
Answer: True
Key Question: 3
Skill: comprehension
Difficulty: Level 2

25. Phosphate nodules are found on the continental shelf.
Answer: True
Key Question: 3
Skill: knowledge
Difficulty: Level 1

26. Organisms that live on the ocean floor may be responsible for keeping manganese nodules from being buried in the sediment.
Answer: True
Key Question: 4
Skill: application
Difficulty: Level 3

Multiple Choice. Choose the one **best** answer from the choices provided.

27. The major force bringing continental sediments to the open ocean is (are):
    a. glaciers.
    b. neritic currents.
    c. rivers.
    d. turbidity currents.
    e. wind.
Answer: E
Key Question: 2
Skill: knowledge
Difficulty: Level 1

28. Which of the following is **not** an important control on oceanic sediment accumulation?
    a. degree of preservation
    b. dilution
    c. input from other sediment types
    d. rate of deposition
    e. All of the above factors are important.
Answer: E
Key Question: 2
Skill: application
Difficulty: Level 3

29. High energy environments are most likely to contain which one of the following?
    a. clay-sized particles
    b. cosmogenous sediments
    c. large particles such as gravel
    d. manganese nodules
    e. silt-sized particles

Answer: C
Key Question: 2
Skill: comprehension
Difficulty: Level 2

30. Sediments which are poorly sorted and made of a variety of minerals could have been deposited by:
    a. a glacier.
    b. a river delta.
    c. turbidity currents.
    d. a volcanic eruption.
    e. the wind.

Answer: A
Key Question: 2
Skill: comprehension
Difficulty: Level 2

31. Which of the following contains calcium carbonate ($CaCO_3$)?
    a. diatoms
    b. foraminiferans
    c. glauconite
    d. phosphorites
    e. radiolarians

Answer: B
Key Question: 3
Skill: comprehension
Difficulty: Level 2

32. Which of the following contains silica (SiO_2)?
    a. coccolithophores
    b. corals
    c. foraminiferans
    d. phosphorites
    e. radiolarians

Answer: E
Key Question: 3
Skill: comprehension
Difficulty: Level 2

33. Sediments derived form preexisting rocks are called:
    a. cosmogenous.
    b. biogenous.
    c. hydrogenous.
    d. lithogenous.
    e. volcagenous.

Answer: D
Key Question: 3
Skill: knowledge
Difficulty: Level 1

Marine Sediments

34. Sediments produced by plants and animals in the sea called:
    a. cosmogenous.
    b. biogenous.
    c. hydrogenous.
    d. lithogenous.
    e. volcagenous.
Answer: B
Key Question: 3
Skill: knowledge
Difficulty: Level 1

35. Sediments produced as a result of chemical reactions in seawater are called:
    a. cosmogenous.
    b. biogenous.
    c. hydrogenous.
    d. lithogenous.
    e. volcagenous.
Answer: C
Key Question 3
Skill: knowledge
Difficulty: Level 1

36. Sediments with an extraterrestrial origin are called:
    a. cosmogenous.
    b. biogenous.
    c. hydrogenous.
    d. lithogenous.
    e. volcagenous.
Answer: A
Key Question 3
Skill: knowledge
Difficulty: Level 1

37. All of the following are lithogenous sediments **except**:
    a. beach sand.
    b. diatom ooze.
    c. glacial deposits.
    d. illite clays.
    e. volcanogenic particles.
Answer: B
Key Question: 3
Skill: comprehension
Difficulty: Level 2

Items 38-41. Refer to the figure below illustrating the world-wide distribution of marine sediments. Different areas of ocean sediments are indicated by different numbers. Use these numbers to answer the questions below.

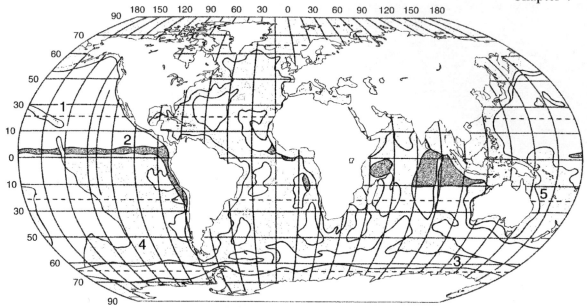

1 = Pacific basin abyssal clay
deposit

2 = Pacific equatorial
radiolarion ooze

3 = diatomaceous (siliceous
ooze) north of Antartica

4 = calcareous ooze in
South Pacific

5 = neritic deposits off
eastern Australian
coast

38. Sediments that are derived primarily from the weathering on continental material are indicated by the
number(s):
   a.   1.
   b.   2.
   c.   2 & 3.
   d.   3 & 4.
   e.   1 & 5.
Answer: E
Key Question: 3 & 4
Skill: application
Difficulty: Level 3

39. Biogenous sediments are indicated by the number(s):
   a.   1.
   b.   2 & 3.

Marine Sediments

    c. 2 & 4.
    d. 2, 3, & 4.
    e. 2, 3, 4, & 5.
Answer: D
Key Question: 3 & 4
Skill: application
Difficulty: Level 3

40. Calcareous oozes are represented by the number(s);
    a. 1.
    b. 2 .
    c. 4.
    d. 2 & 3.
    e. 3 & 4.
Answer: C
Key Question: 3 & 4
Skill: application
Difficulty: Level 3

41. The sediments that are produced in areas of high primary productivity are indicated by the number(s):
    a. 1.
    b. 2.
    c. 3.
    d. 2 & 3.
    e. 3 & 4.
Answer: D
Key Question: 3 & 4
Skill: application
Difficulty: Level 3

42. Manganese nodules are an example of a:
    a. biogenous sediments.
    b. cosmogenous sediments.
    c. hydrogenous sediments.
    d. terrigenous sediments.
    e. volcagenous sediments.
Answer: C
Key Question: 3 & 6
Skill: comprehension
Difficulty: Level 2

43. All of the following are hydrogenous sediments **except**:
    a. evaporites.
    b. halites.
    c. manganese nodule.
    d. phosphates.
    e. stromatolites.
Answer: E
Key Question: 3 & 6
Skill: comprehension
Difficulty: Level 2

44. Calcium carbonate is most likely to dissolve in water with which characteristics?
    a. low carbon dioxide and warm temperatures
    b. lots of carbon dioxide and cold temperatures
    c. lots of carbon dioxide and warm temperatures
    d. low pressure and warm temperatures
    e. low pressure and cold temperatures

Answer: B
Key Question: 5
Skill: application
Difficulty: Level 3

45. The element found in some sediments which suggest that a meteorite or asteroid impact occurred nearby is:
    a. iridium.
    b. manganese.
    c. strontium.
    d. uranium.
    e. yttrium.

Answer: A
Key Question: 3
Skill: knowledge
Difficulty: Level 1

46. The most likely place to find abundant manganese nodules is on the:
    a. abyssal plain far from a continent.
    b. continental rise.
    c. continental shelf.
    d. crest of a mid-ocean ridge.
    e. All of the above locations are contain manganese nodules.

Answer: A
Key Question: 5 & 6
Skill: comprehension
Difficulty: Level 2

47. In contrast to manganese nodules which form on the abyssal plain, phosphate-rich nodules form in:
    a. continental shelf waters..
    b., estuaries.
    c. hydrothermal vent areas.
    d. intermediate to shallow depth water.
    e. mid-ocean ridges.

Answer: D
Key Question: 5 & 6
Skill: comprehension
Difficulty: Level 2

48. Sediments found on continental margins are called:
    a. continental.
    b. estuarine.
    c. neritic.
    d. oceanic.
    e. pelagic.

Answer: C

Marine Sediments

Key Question: 5
Skill: knowledge
Difficulty: Level 1

49. In general, polar neritic sediment has more:
    a. clay than in temperate waters.
    b. coral debris than in tropical waters.
    c. rock and gravel than in tropical waters.
    d. shell fragments than in temperate waters.
    e. silt and sand than in tropical waters.
Answer: C
Key Question: 5
Skill: application
Difficulty: Level 3

50. A pelagic clay contains lots of material that settle to the seafloor through the water column and are:
    a. less than 30% biogenous material.
    b. more than 30% biogenous material.
    c. more than 30% hydrogenous material.
    d. less than 30% neritic material.
    e. more than 30% neritic material.
Answer: A
Key Question: 5
Skill: knowledge
Difficulty: Level 1

51. A very important way to increase the settling rate of fine particles in the open ocean is via:
    a. carbonate dissolution.
    b. deposit feeders.
    c. fecal pellets.
    d. precipitation.
    e. Wind.
Answer: C
Key Question: 5
Skill: comprehension
Difficulty: Level 2

Word Analysis. Examine the five words and/or phrases and determine the relationship among the majority of words/phrases. Choose the one option that does not fit the pattern.

52. A. biogenous B. calcareous C. cosmogenous D. hydrogenous E. lithogenous
Answer: B
Key Question: 2
Skill: Analysis
Difficulty: Level 4

53. A. coccolithophores B. diatoms C. foraminiferans   D. oolites E. radiolarians
Answer: D
Key Question: 3
Skill: Analysis
Difficulty: Level 4

54. A. chalk B. coccolithophores C. diatoms   D. foraminiferans E. stromatolites
Answer: C
Key Question: 3
Skill: Analysis
Difficulty: Level 4

55. A. halides B. manganese nodules C. metal sulfides D. phosphates   E. tektites
Answer: E
Key Question: 6
Skill: Analysis
Difficulty: Level 4

56. A. manganese nodules   B. methane hydrates   C. phosphorite D. quartz sand E. shell fragments
Answer: E
Key Question: 6
Skill: Analysis
Difficulty: Level 4

57. A. abyssal clay B. calcareous ooze C. coarse lithogenic sediment   D. manganese nodule E. silaceous ooze
Answer: C
Key Question: 5
Skill: Analysis
Difficulty: Level 4

CHAPTER
5
Water and Seawater

Matching. Match the term or person with the appropriate phrase. You may use each answer once, more than once or not at all.

1. evaporation
2. high temperature
3. low latitude
4. precipitation
5. river input
6. sea ice formation

A. decrease seawater salinity
B. increase seawater salinity

Answers: 1-B, 2-B, 3-B, 4-A, 5-A, 6-B
Key Question: 6
Skill: application
Difficulty: Level 3

---

7. change in phase from solid to gas
8. change in phase from gas to liquid
9. change in phase from liquid to gas
10. rapid change in density with slight change in depth
11. rapid change in salinity with slight change in depth

A. condensation
B. evaporation
C. isocline
D. halocline
E. pycnocline
F. sublimation
G. thermocline

Answers: 7-F, 8-A, 9-B, 10-E, 11-D
Key Question: 2 & 7
Skill: knowledge
Difficulty: Level 1

True-False Questions. Read each question carefully, write "T" if the statement is true, and write "F" if the statement is false.

12. Water can pile up higher than the edge of a container due to its low surface tension.
Answer: False

Key Question: 1
Skill: knowledge
Difficulty: Level 1

13. Water is a polar molecule.
Answer: True
Key Question: 1
Skill: knowledge
Difficulty: Level 1

14. Water molecules exhibit strong cohesion.
Answer: True
Key Question: 1
Skill: knowledge
Difficulty: 1

15. Latent heat of vaporization is the same as latent heat of sublimation.
Answer: False
Key Question: 2
Skill: knowledge
Difficulty: Level 1

16. The latent heat of vaporization of water is larger than the latent heat of melting.
Answer: True
Key Question: 2
Skill: comprehension
Difficulty: Level 2

17. Evaporation causes cooling in the residual liquid.
Answer: True
Key Question: 2
Skill: comprehension
Difficulty: Level 2

18. Heat capacity of liquid water is 1 calorie per gram per degree C.
Answer: True
Key Question: 2
Skill: knowledge
Difficulty: Level 1

19. Halite, sodium chloride, is the most abundant salt in seawater.
Answer: True
Key Question: 3
Skill: knowledge
Difficulty: Level 1

20. Salinity refers to all of the solid materials in seawater including dissolved and suspended substances.
Answer: False
Key Question: 3

Skill: knowledge
Difficulty: Level 1

21. The density of seawater is affected by salinity and temperature.
Answer: True
Key Question: 3
Skill: comprehension

Difficulty: Level 2

22. The alkalinity of a solution is an estimate of its acid buffering capacity.
Answer: True
Key Question: 5
Skill: comprehension
Difficulty: Level 2

23. Any solution with a pH of greater than 7.0 is acidic.
Answer: False
Key Question: 5
Skill: knowledge
Difficulty: Level 1

24. As a whole, the ph of the ocean is slightly alkaline.
Answer: True
Key Question: 5
Skill: knowledge
Difficulty: Level 1

25. pH will tend to rise in areas of the ocean with high primary productivity.
Answer: True
Key Question: 5
Skill: application
Difficulty: Level 3

Multiple Choice. Choose the one **best** answer from the choices provided.

26. The phase in which water exists water is determined by:
    a. density and pressure.
    b. density and salinity.
    c. pressure and salinity.
    d. temperature and pressure.
    e. temperature and salinity.
Answer: D
Key Question: 1
Skill: comprehension
Difficulty: Level 2

27. Hydrogen bonds form between neighboring water molecules because of:
    a. electron sharing.
    b. electron transfer.
    c. polarity of water molecules.
    d. surface tension.
    e. viscosity of water.
Answer: C
Key Question: 1
Skill: comprehension
Difficulty: Level 2

28. The surface tension of water is
    a. increases as density decreases.
    b. related to salinity.
    c. relatively high.
    d. relatively low.
    e. very similar to similar liquids.
Answer: A
Key Question: 1
Skill: comprehension
Difficulty: Level 1

29. Covalent bonds form between hydrogen and oxygen atoms in a water molecule as a result of the:
    a. polarity of water molecules.
    b. sharing of electrons between atoms.
    c. surface tension of water.
    d. transfer of electrons between atoms.
    e. viscosity of water.
Answer: B
Key Question: 1
Skill: knowledge
Difficulty: Level 1

30. Water can pile up short distance above a container's rim due to:
    a. high capillary action.
    b. high surface tension.
    c. high viscosity.
    d. low surface tension.
    e. low viscosity.
Answer: B
Key Question: 1
Skill: comprehension
Difficulty: Level 2

31. Some insects can glide across the surface of water due to water's:
    a. capillarity.
    b. hydrogen bonds.

© 2005 Pearson Education, Inc., Upper Saddle River, NJ. All rights reserved. This material is protected under all copyright laws as they currently exist. No portion of this material may be reproduced, in any form or by any means, without permission in writing from the publisher.

    c. polarity.
    d. surface tension.
    e. viscosity.
Answer: A
Key Question: 1
Skill: comprehension
Difficulty: Level 2

32. Many of the unique properties of water are attributed to the fact that water:
    a. contains hydrogen bonds.
    b. exists in three phases at the earth's surface.
    c. is a polar molecule.
    d. is a universal solvent.
    e. requires heat to condense.
Answer: C
Key Question: 1

Skill: application
Difficulty: Level 3

33. The amount of energy that is necessary to raise the temperature of one gram of water by one degree C is called the:
    a. boiling point elevation.
    b. calorie.
    c. latent heat of condensation.
    d. latent heat of evaporation.
    e. thermal capacity.
Answer: B
Key Question: 2
Skill: knowledge
Difficulty: Level 1

34. Which property of water causes coastal communities to have only moderate differences in daily highs and lows when compared to inland communities?
    a. high heat capacity
    b. high salinity
    c. high viscosity
    d. low heat capacity
    e. low viscosity
Answer: A
Key Question: 2
Skill: application
Difficulty: Level 3

35. Latent heat is used to:
    a. break chemical bonds.
    b. change molecular structure.
    c. change states of matter.
    d. change the temperature of a substance.

e. form chemical bonds.

Answer: D
Key Question: 2
Skill: comprehension
Difficulty: Level 2

36. A beaker contains a mixture of ice and pure water at 0°C. What happens to the temperature of the mixture as heat is added?
   a. It immediately begins to rise slowly.
   b. It remains constant until the ice melts; then it begins to rise.
   c. It rises rapidly as the ice melts.
   d. It rises slowly until it reaches 32°C; then it remains constant as the ice melts.
   e. The temperature pattern cannot be predicted.

Answer: B
Key Question: 2
Skill: application
Difficulty: Level 3

37. When water evaporates from the ocean surface:
   a. energy is transferred from the atmosphere to the remaining liquid.
   b. sea surface temperature increases.
   c. sea surface salinity decreases.
   d. the remaining water is cooled.
   e. the remaining water is warmed.

Answer: D
Key Question: 2
Skill: comprehension
Difficulty: Level 2

38. In comparison to most other liquids, the heat capacity of water is:
   a. a function of salinity.
   b. about the same as other liquids.
   c. higher than other liquids.
   d. lower than other liquids.
   e. related to solvent concentration.

Answer: C
Key Question: 2
Skill: comprehension
Difficulty: Level 2

39. The average salinity of sea water is:
   a. 0.35%
   b. 2.0%
   c. 3.5%
   d. 10%
   e. 25%

Answer: C
Key Question: 3
Skill: knowledge

Difficulty: Level 1

40. The Principle of Constant Proportions states that:
    a. ocean salinity varies as a function of season.
    b. ocean salinity varies with geographical location.
    c. the percentage of chloride varies with geographical location.
    d. the percentage of sodium varies with ocean depth.
    e. the relative concentration of seawater ions does not change.
Answer: E
Key Question: 3
Skill: knowledge
Difficulty: Level 1

41. Which of the following statements regarding pH is **not true?**
    a. A pH of 3.0 is acidic and a pH of 10.0 is alkaline.
    b. As a whole, the pH of the ocean is slightly acidic.
    c. Buffers prevent large changes in the pH of a solution.
    d. pH will increase in areas of rapid plant or algal growth.
    e. pH relates to relative acid-base ion balance in a solution.
Answer: B
Key Question: 4

Skill: comprehension
Difficulty: Level 2

42. The ion in sea water that is serves as a buffer is:
    a. Ca^{+2}.
    b. Cl^-.
    c. CO_2.
    d. HCO_3^-.
    e. Na^+.
Answer: D
Key Question: 4
Skill: comprehension
Difficulty: Level 2

43. The transfer of water from the atmosphere to the oceans to the continents is known as the:
    a. closed cycle.
    b. geologic cycle.
    c. hydrobiological cycle.
    d. hydrologic cycle.
    e. meteorological cycle.
Answer: D
Key Question: 6
Skill: knowledge
Difficulty: Level 1

44. As the salinity of seawater increases, its:

a. density decreases.
b. heat capacity decreases.
c. residence time increases
d. residence time decreases
e. residence time does not change.
Answer: E
Key Question: 6
Skill: comprehension
Difficulty: Level 2

45. A rapid change in ocean temperature with change in depth is the:
a. barocline.
b. halocline.
c. isocline.
d. pycnocline.
e. thermocline.
Answer: E
Key Question: 7
Skill: knowledge
Difficulty: Level 1

46. A rapid change in ocean density with change in depth is the:
a. barocline.
b. halocline.
c. isocline.
d. pycnocline.
e. thermocline.
Answer: D
Key Question: 7
Skill: knowledge
Difficulty: Level 1

Word Analysis. Examine the five words and/or phrases and determine the relationship among the majority of words/phrases. Choose the one option that does not fit the pattern.

47. A. boiling point B. buffering capacity C. freezing point D. heat capacity E. surface tension
Answer: B
Key Question: 2
Skill: analysis
Difficulty: Level 4

48. A. carbonate ion B. bicarbonate ion C. chloride ion D. hydrogen ion E. hydroxide ion
Answer: D
Key Question: 5
Skill: analysis
Difficulty: Level 4

49. A. latitude B. pH   C. precipitation D. salinity E. temperature

Answer: B
Key Question: 6
Skill: analysis
Difficulty: Level 4

CHAPTER
6
Air-Sea Interface

Matching. Match the term or person with the appropriate phrase. You may use each answer once, more than once or not at all.

1. Intertropical Convergence Zone
2. Trade Winds
3. Tropic of Cancer
4. Tropic of Capricorn
5. Westerlies

A. area where air falls close to the equator
B. located at 23.5° N latitude
C. located at 23.5° S latitude
D. located at 30° S latitude
E. located at 90° N latitude
F. prevailing wind pattern at temperate latitudes
G. prevailing wind pattern at tropical latitudes
H. prevailing wind pattern at polar latitudes

Answers: 1-A, 2-G, 3-B, 4-C, 5-F
Key Question: 4
Skill: knowledge
Difficulty: Level 1

---

6. anthropogenic greenhouse gas
7. atmospheric compound with greatest
   infrared absorption rate
8. contributes to ozone layer depletion
9. produced only in burning hydrocarbons
10. component of the troposphere

A. CFCs
B. CO_2
C. H_2O
D. methane
E. N_2O
F. O_3

Answers: 6-B, 7-A, 8-A, 9-E, 10-F
Key Question: 7
Skill: comprehension
Difficulty: Level 2

Air-Sea Interaction

True-False Questions. Read each question carefully, write "T" if the statement is true, and write "F" if the statement is false.

11. The wavelength of energy radiated from the Earth back into the atmosphere is longer than the incoming solar
radiation.
Answer: True
Key Question: 1
Skill: comprehension
Difficulty: Level 2

12. The angle at which direct sunlight strike the ocean's surface is important in determining the amount of solar energy that is absorbed.
Answer: True
Key Question: 1
Skill: comprehension
Difficulty: Level 2

13. Near the poles, more energy is reflected back into space than is absorbed.
Answer: True
Key Question: 1
Skill: knowledge
Difficulty: Level 1

14. The jet stream is a fast moving easterly flowing air mass.
Answer: True
Key Question: 3
Skill: knowledge
Difficulty: Level 1

15. A cold front is likely to have heavy, brief showers associated with it.
Answer: True
Key Question: 3
Skill: comprehension
Difficulty: Level 2

16. The trade winds can be found between 30° and 60° N and S latitudes.
Answer: False
Key Question: 4
Skill: knowledge
Difficulty: Level 1

17. A maritime polar air mass is likely to be dry and cold.
Answer: False
Key Question: 4
Skill: comprehension
Difficulty: Level 2

18. The doldrums can be found at the Equator.

Answer: True
Key Question: 4
Skill: knowledge
Difficulty: Level 1

19. A hurricane is a very strong high-pressure system.
Answer: False
Key Question: 5
Skill: knowledge
Difficulty: Level 1

20. A hurricane contains more energy than has been generated in the US over the last twenty years.
Answer: True
Key Question: 5
Skill: application
Difficulty: Level 3 ·

21. Sound travels more slowly in the SOFAR channel than in the areas of the ocean immediately above and below it.
Answer: True
Key Question: 6
Skill: comprehension
Difficulty: Level 2

22. An iceberg is a variety of sea ice.
Answer: True
Key Question: 6
Skill: knowledge
Difficulty: Level 1

23. The greenhouse gas that accounts for most of the natural greenhouse effect in Earth's atmosphere is carbon dioxide.
Answer: False
Key Question: 7
Skill: comprehension
Difficulty: Level 2

24. A mole of methane is able to absorb much more heat than one mole of carbon dioxide.
Answer: True
Key Question: 7
Skill: application
Difficulty: Level 3

25. The best climate models indicate that Earth's average surface temperature has risen by 5°C in the last 100 years.
Answer: False
Key Question: 7
Skill: application
Difficulty: Level 3

___

Multiple Choice. Choose the one **best** answer from the choices provided.

26. With respect to incoming solar radiation, radiation emitted back into the atmosphere has:
    a. a longer wave frequency.
    b. a longer wavelength.
    c. a shorter wave period.
    d. a shorter wavelength.
    e. the same wavelength.
Answer: B
Key Question: 1
Skill: knowledge
Difficulty: Level 1

27. The percentage of solar radiation absorbed by the Earth's oceans and landmasses is about:
    a. 25%.
    b. 30%.
    c. 50%.
    d. 70%.
    e. 90%
Answer: C
Key Question: 1
Skill: knowledge
Difficulty: Level 1

28. With respect to the amount of energy absorbed by the atmosphere, the amount of energy radiated back into space between 35°N and 40°S latitude is:
    a. about the same as the amount of energy absorbed by the atmosphere.
    b. dependent upon the weather conditions such as cloud cover in the local area.
    c. greater than the amount of energy absorbed by the atmosphere.
    d. less than the amount of energy absorbed by the atmosphere,
    e. unrelated to latitude.
Answer: C
Key Question: 2
Skill: comprehension
Difficulty: Level 2

29. The percentage of solar radiation directed to Earth absorbed by the clouds and the atmosphere is about:
    a. 10%.
    b. 25%.
    c. 30%.
    d. 50%.
    e. 70%.
Answer: B
Key Question: 1 & 7
Skill: knowledge
Difficulty: Level 1

30. The Tropic of Capricorn is located at:
    a. 0° longitude.
    b. 23.5°N latitude.
    c. 23.5°S latitude.
    d. 30°N latitude.
    e. 60°S latitude.

Answer: C
Key Question: 2
Skill: knowledge
Difficulty: Level 1

31. As a result of the Coriolis effect in the northern hemisphere, winds are deflected:
    a. at a 45° angle form the original direction.
    b. at a 90° angle from the original direction.
    c. to the east of the original direction.
    d. to the left of the original direction.
    e. to the right of the original direction.
Answer: E
Key Question: 2
Skill: comprehension
Difficulty: 2

32. The deflection of air masses to the right or left (depending on latitude) as they move from one latitude to another is called the:
    a. Coriolis effect.
    b. Cyclonic effect.
    c. Ekman spiral.
    d. Hadley cell.
    e. Saffir-Simpson scale.
Answer: A
Key Question: 2 & 3
Skill: knowledge
Difficulty: Level 1

33. A maritime tropical air mass is likely to be:
    a. dry and cold.
    b. dry and warm.
    c. wet and cold.
    d. wet and the same temperature.
    e. wet and warm.
Answer: E
Key Question: 3
Skill: comprehension
Difficulty: Level 2

34. A cold air mass moving into an area occupied by relatively warm air is called a(n)
    a. cold front.
    b. high pressure system.

    c.   low pressure system.
    d.   occluded front.
    e.   warm front.
Answer: A
Key Question: 3
Skill: knowledge
Difficulty: Level 1

35. Idealized pressure belts and wind systems are significantly modified by Earth's tilted axis of rotation and:
    a.   differences in the heat capacity of ocean and land.
    b.   differences in the latitudinal albedo.
    c.   Ekman transport.
    d.   variations in incoming solar radiation over many years
    e.   variations in the Coriolis effect.

Answer: E
Key Question: 3
Skill: comprehension
Difficulty: Level 2

36. Winds blowing from the north in the southern hemisphere will appear to :
    a.   be deflected toward the east.
    b.   be deflected toward the west.
    c.   circulate counterclockwise.
    d.   circulate clockwise.
    e.   travel in a straight line.
Answer: A
Key Question: 3
Skill: application
Difficulty: Level 3

Refer to the figure below and use the numbers that correspond to global wind belts and latitudes to answer questions 37-40.

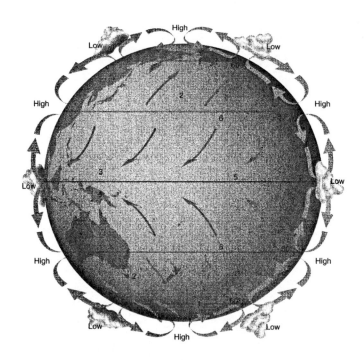

37. The wind belt that corresponds to the doldrums is labeled:
    a. 1.
    b. 2.
    c. 3.
    d. 5.
    e. 6.

Answer: D
Key Question: 4
Skill: knowledge
Difficulty: Level 1

38. The westerlies wind belt is the area corresponding to:
    a. 1.
    b. 2.
    c. 3.
    d. 4.
    e. 5.
Answer: B
Key Question: 4
Skill: knowledge
Difficulty: Level 1

39. The area of the globe (latitude) that is characterized by falling air masses and little precipitation is:
    a. 1.
    b. 2.
    c. 3.
    d. 5.

e. 6.

Answer: E
Key Question: 4
Skill: comprehension
Difficulty: Level 2

40. The strongest winds on Earth are:
    a. 1 & 2.
    b. 1 & 3
    c. 2 & 3.
    d. 2 & 4.
    e. 3 & 4.

Answer: E
Key Question 4
Skill: application
Difficulty: Level 3

41. The doldrums refer to the same region as the:
    a. intertropical convergence zone
    b. jet stream
    c. subtropical jet stream.
    d. subtropics.
    e. trade winds

Answer: A
Key Question: 4
Skill: comprehension
Difficulty: Level 2

42. The temperate regions are characterized by:
    a. cold fronts.
    b. high pressure.
    c. easterly winds.
    d. trade winds.
    e. westerly winds.

Answer: E
Key Question: 4
Skill: knowledge
Difficulty: Level 1

43. Low pressure systems in the northern hemisphere rotate:
    a. at a 45° angle from the prevailing wind direction.
    b. clockwise.
    c. counterclockwise.
    d. to the left.
    e. to the right.

Answer: C
Key Question: 4 & 5
Skill: comprehension
Difficulty: Level 2

44. The strength of a hurricane is ranked from 1 to 5 on the"
    a. Coriolis Scale.
    b. Fugita Scale.
    c. Moh's Scale.
    d. Richter Scale.
    e. Saffir-Simpson Scale.
Answer: E
Key Question: 5
Skill: knowledge
Difficulty: Level 1

45. Hurricanes are an efficient way to:
    a. decrease salinity in affected estuaries.
    b. eradicate rainfall deficits.
    c. raise local sea level due to storm surge.
    d. redistribute heat from one area to another.
    e. remove old-growth coastal forests.
Answer: D
Key Question: 5
Skill: comprehension
Difficulty: Level 2

Refer to the figure below, and use the information on the map corresponding to the ocean's climatic regions to
answer questions 46 and 47.

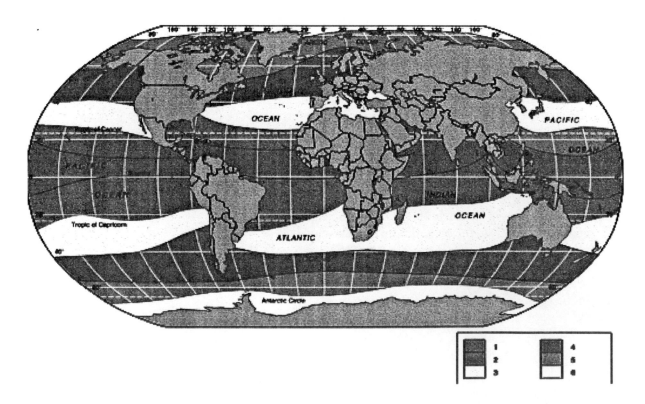

46. The oceanic climate region(s) in the majority of strong cyclonic storms are produced is indicated by the number:
    a. 1.
    b. 1 & 2
    c. 2.
    d. 3.
    e. 3 & 4.
Answer: B
Key Question: 5
Skill: comprehension
Difficulty: Level 2

47. The oceanic climate region that is characterized by sea ice coverage in the winter and open water (but cold) in the summer is indicated by the number:
    a. 2.
    b. 3.
    c. 4.
    d. 5.
    e. 6.
Answer: D
Key Question: 6
Skill: comprehension
Difficulty: Level 2

48. Colder air moving over significantly warmer ocean surface water may produce:
    a. a cold front.
    b. a warm front.
    c. changes in coastal wind direction.

    d. increased coastal precipitation..
    e. sea smoke.
Answer: E
Key Question: 5
Skill: knowledge
Difficulty: Level 1

49. When ice forms from seawater, the remaining seawater will have a:
    a. darker color.
    b. decreased density.
    c. higher salinity.
    d. higher temperature.
    e. lower temperature.
Answer: C
Key Question: 6
Skill: application
Difficulty: Level 3

50. The zone ocean where sound can travel extremely long distances is called the:
    a. pycnocline.

    b. SOFAR channel.
    c. SONAR channel.
    d. surface mix layer.
    e. thermocline.
Answer: C
Key Question: 6
Skill: knowledge
Difficulty: Level 1

51. Worldwide, the SOFAR channel is located at an approximate ocean depth of:
    a. 100 meters.
    b. 250 meters.
    c. 500 meters.
    d. 1000 meters.
    e. 4000 meters.
Answer: D
Key Question: 6
Skill: knowledge
Difficulty: Level 1

52. The atmospheric component that contributes to the majority of greenhouse warming on Earth is:
    a. carbon dioxide.
    b. methane.
    c. nitrous oxide.
    d. ozone.
    e. water vapor
Answer: E
Key Question: 7
Skill: comprehension
Difficulty: Level 2

53. The gas(es) that is (are) increasing atmospheric concentration relative to other gases in the atmosphere annually is (are):
    a. carbon dioxide.
    b. chlorofluorocarbons.
    c. methane.
    d. nitrous oxide.
    e. ozone.
Answer: B
Key Question: 7
Skill: comprehension
Difficulty: Level 2

54. Which of the following atmospheric constituents has the greatest ability to absorb heat (a per mole basis)?
    a. carbon dioxide
    b. chlorofluorocarbons
    c. methane
    d. ozone

e. water vapor

Answer: B
Key Question: 7
Skill: comprehension
Difficulty: Level 2

55. Which of the following is not a consequence of global warming?
    a. droughts in prime agricultural areas
    b. increasing hurricane frequency
    c. melting of glacial ice
    d. sea level rise
    e. All of the above are consequences of global warming.

Answer: E
Key Question: 7
Skill: comprehension
Difficulty: Level 2

56. Burning of fossil fuels is chemically similar to:
    a. autotrophic processes.
    b. chemosynthesis.
    c. metabolism.
    d. photosynthesis.
    e. respiration.

Answer: E
Key Question: 7
Skill: application
Difficulty: Level 3

57. Since 1750, the amount of carbon dioxide in our atmosphere has increased by almost:
    a. 10%.
    b. 20%.
    c. 30%.
    d. 40%.
    e. 50%.

Answer: C
Key Question: 7
Skill: knowledge
Difficulty: Level 1

58. An agreement amongst 60 nations to voluntarily limit greenhouse gas emissions is called the:
    a. Coriolis Protocol.
    b. IPCC.
    c. Keating Conference.
    d. Kyoto Protocol.
    e. United Nations Environmental Programme.

Answer: D
Key Question: 7
Skill: knowledge
Difficulty: Level 1

CHAPTER

7

Ocean Circulation

Matching. Match the term or person with the appropriate phrase. You may use each answer once, more than once or not at all.

1. downwelling
2. Ekman transport
3. geostrophic flow
4. upwelling

A. driven by gravity and modified by the Coriolis force
B. replacement water coming from the bottom to the top of the water column
C. replacement water coming from the top to the bottom of the water column
D. seasonal wind pattern
E. transport of water to the left or right of the wind direction
F. unit of current velocity
G. water mass found in the Sargasso Sea

Answers: 1-C, 2-E, 3-A, 4-B
Key Question: 2, 3, & 4
Skill: knowledge
Difficulty: Level 1

Matching. Match the current with the appropriate descriptive phrase or phrases. You may use each answer once, more than once or not at all. More than one descriptor may apply to each current.

5. Benguela Current
6. California Current
7. Canary Current
8. Gulf Stream
9. Kurishio Current
10. West Wind Drift

A. cold current
B. northern hemisphere
C. polar latitudes
D. southern hemisphere
E. temperate latitudes
F. tropical latitudes
G. warm current

Answers: 5-A, D, E; 6-A, B, E; 7-A, B, E; 8-B, E, G; 9- B, E, G; 10-A, C, D
Key Question: 2
Skill: comprehension
Difficulty: Level 2

True-False Questions.   Read each question carefully, write "T" if the statement is true, and write "F" if the statement is false.

11. Dynamic topography can be used to compute current direction and velocity.
Answer: True
Key Question: 1
Skill: knowledge
Difficulty: Level 1

12. The largest current by volume in the oceans is the Antarctic Circumpolar Current.
Answer: True
Key Question: 2
Skill: comprehension
Difficulty: Level 2

13. The circular pattern of surface water currents is called a gyre.
Answer: True
Key Question: 2
Skill: knowledge
Difficulty: Level 1

14. The Gulf Stream moves water away from the equator; the Benguela Current moves some of this same water back toward the equator.
Answer: False
Key Question: 2
Skill: comprehension
Difficulty: Level 2

15. In the northern hemisphere, Ekman transport pushes surface water to the right of the wind direction.
Answer: True
Key Question: 2
Skill: comprehension
Difficulty: Level 2

16. An eastern boundary current is narrow and swift.
Answer: False
Key Question: 3
Skill: comprehension
Difficulty: Level 2

17. Downwelling may be the result of winds blowing parallel to a coastline.
Answer: True
Key Question: 4
Skill: comprehension
Difficulty: Level 2

18. Thermohaline circulation is wind-driven.
Answer: False

Key Question: 6
Skill: comprehension
Difficulty: Level 2

19. Deep ocean currents often move cold, dense water away from the poles.
Answer: True
Key Question: 6
Skill: comprehension
Difficulty: Level 2

20. The Mediterranean Sea has little influence on the water of the Atlantic Ocean.
Answer: False
Key Question: 6
Skill: application
Difficulty: Level 3

21. The source of some deep ocean water masses can be identified by the amount of dissolved oxygen in the water mass.
Answer: True
Key Question: 6
Skill: application
Difficulty: Level 3

22. Deep ocean water does not travel across the equator.
Answer: False
Key Question: 6
Skill: comprehension
Difficulty: Level 2

23. Deep ocean water masses have characteristic temperatures and salinities.
Answer: True
Key Question: 6
Skill: comprehension
Difficulty: Level 2

24. The most dense ocean water is North Atlantic Deep Water.
Answer: False
Key Question: 6
Skill: comprehension
Difficulty: Level 2

25. All deep water in ocean basins originates in the Atlantic Ocean.
Answer: True
Key Question: 6
Skill: comprehension
Difficulty: Level 2

Ocean Circulation

Multiple Choice. Choose the one **best** answer from the choices provided.

26. The unit of measurement used to describe the rate at which a volume of ocean water moves in a current is a(n):
    a. calorie.
    b. ft/s^2.
    c. km/h.
    d. ml/g.
    e. sverdrup.

Answer: E
Key Question: 1
Skill: knowledge
Difficulty: Level 1

27. Equatorial currents are driven by the:
    a. Coriolis force.
    b. density.
    c. Ekman transport.
    d. trade winds.
    e. westerlies.

Answer: D
Key Question: 2
Skill: comprehension
Difficulty: Level 2

28. Surface ocean circulation is driven primarily by _____ and modified by _____.
    a. density differences; the Coriolis effect and land
    b. density differences; differences in salinity and temperature
    c. latitude; differences in salinity and land
    d. wind; the Coriolis effect and land
    e. wind; gravity and density

Answer: D
Key Question: 2
Skill: comprehension
Difficulty: Level 2

29. Convection cells driven by the relatively weak winds near the center of gyres are called:
    a. Ekman transport.
    b. geostrophic circulation.
    c. Langmuir circulation.
    d. thermohaline circulation.
    e. upwelling.

Answer: C
Key Question: 2
Skill: comprehension
Difficulty: Level 2

30. Which of the following is true of surface water circulation near Antarctica?
    a. A gyre is formed here.

    b. Two circumpolar currents dominate it, one current that moves water to the east and one current that moves water to the west.

    c. It is dominated by water flow directly away from the polar region toward the north.

    d. The surface ocean has no strong currents.

    e. The polar easterlies drive the circulation of water around the Antarctic continent.

Answer: B
Key Question: 2
Skill: comprehension
Difficulty: Level 2

31. The Sargasso Sea is located in the:
    a. Arctic Ocean.
    b. Indian Ocean.
    c. North Atlantic Ocean.
    d. North Pacific Ocean.
    e. South Atlantic Ocean.

Answer: C
Key Question: 2
Skill: knowledge
Difficulty: Level 1

32. When a meander from the Gulf Stream pinches off and isolates a body of water within the center of the North Atlantic gyre, the body of water is called a:
    a. cold core ring.
    b. cyclonic circulation.
    c. geostrophic circulation.
    d. Langmuir cell.
    e. warm core ring.

Answer: A
Key Question: 2
Skill: knowledge
Difficulty: Level 1

33. Identify the mismatched pair.
    a. Agulhas Current – West Australia Current
    b. Brazil Current - Benguela Current
    c. Canary Current - Gulf Stream
    d. Kuroshio Current – California Current
    e. Labrador Current – Humbolt Current

Answer: E
Key Question: 2
Skill: analysis
Difficulty: Level 4

34. During winter months, monsoon winds over the Indian Ocean:
    a. flow from land to sea and are dry.
    b. flow from land to sea and are wet.
    c. flow from sea to land and are dry.
    d. flow from sea to land and are wet.

e. the direction of airflow is unchanged but precipitation increases.

Answer: A
Key Question: 2
Skill: application
Difficulty: Level 3

35. Compared to an eastern boundary current in a gyre, which of the following statements is true for a western boundary current?
    a. deeper current
    b. increased current velocity
    c. intensification in subtropical latitudes
    d. narrower current
    e. All of the above statements are true of western boundary currents.

Answer: E
Key Question: 3
Skill: comprehension
Difficulty: Level 2

36. Which of the following is a western boundary current?
    a. Benguela Current
    b. Brazil Current
    c. Canary Current
    d. California Current
    e. Peru Current

Answer: B
Key Question: 3
Skill: knowledge
Difficulty: Level 1

37. Compared to a western boundary current, which of the following statements is true for an eastern boundary current?
    a. Eastern boundary currents are broad and deep.
    b. Eastern boundary currents are broad and slow.
    c. Eastern boundary currents are deep and swift.
    d. Eastern boundary currents are narrow and deep.
    e. Eastern boundary currents are shallow and swift.

Answer: B
Key Question: 3
Skill: comprehension
Difficulty: Level 2

38. Which of the following is **not** an eastern boundary current?
    a. California Current
    b. Canary Current
    c. Gulf Stream
    d. Peru Current
    e. W. Australian Current

Answer: C
Key Question: 3
Skill: knowledge

Difficulty: Level 1

39. Geostrophic circulation is within a gyre driven by:
    a. density.
    b. gravity.
    c. temperature.
    d. the Coriolis effect.
    e. wind.
Answer: B
Key Question: 3
Skill: knowledge
Difficulty: Level 1

40. Westward intensification causes:
    a. a steeper slope of surface water in the western section of the gyre as compare to the eastern section of the gyre.
    b. equatorial countercurrents.
    c. the center of the gyre to be shift to the west.
    d. very swift western boundary currents.
    e. All of the above statements are the result of westward intensification.
Answer: E
Key Question: 3
Skill: comprehension
Difficulty: Level 2

41. When surface waters are pushed away from land and replaced by nutrient-rich bottom water through:
    a. convergence.
    b. downwelling.
    c. land breezes.
    d. sea breezes.
    e. upwelling.
Answer: E
Key Question: 4
Skill: knowledge
Difficulty: Level 1

42. Strong upwelling occurs in all of the following **except**:
    a. between the North and South Equatorial Currents.
    b. in areas of surface current divergence
    c. in the area surrounding the Galapagos Islands.
    d. where deep ocean water currents are formed.
    e. where water is constantly pushed away from a coastline.
Answer: D
Key Question: 4
Skill: comprehension
Difficulty: Level 2

43. Deep ocean water generally has high amounts of:
    a. dissolved organic matter.
    b. nutrients only.
    c. oxygen only.

    d. nutrients and oxygen.

    e. suspended solids.

Answer: D

Key Question: 4 & 6

Skill: knowledge

Difficulty: Level 1

44. The worldwide effect of El Niño include all of the following **except**:

    a. coral reef deaths in the Pacific Ocean.

    b. crop failure in the Philippines.

    c. drought in the US Gulf coastal states.

    d. increased Pacific cyclone activity.

    e. water shortages in Sri Lanka.

Answer: C

Key Question: 5

Skill: application

Difficulty: Level 3

45. The El Niño Southern Oscillation can best be described as:

    a. relative changes between two different atmospheric pressure systems.

    b. the relationship between sea surface temperature and high altitude pressure.

    c. tidal differences between coastal Peru and Darwin, Australia.

    d. variation in wind speed over the Pacific Ocean.

    e. wind speed and wind direction differences along the equator.

Answer: B

Key Question: 5

Skill: comprehension

Difficulty: Level 2

46. The El Niño weather pattern is associated with:

    a. about a 0.5 meter difference in sea surface height between Tahiti and Darwin, Australia.

    b. cold, nutrient-rich water close to the sea surface near the coast of Peru.

    c. drought and fires in Australia.

    d. high pressure sitting over coastal Peru.

    e. trade winds blowing east to west.

Answer: C

Key Question: 5

Skill: comprehension

Difficulty: Level 2

47. The Ekman spiral is driven by:

    a. density differences in the water column.

    b. gravity.

    c. the Coriolis effect

    d. the pycnocline.

    e. wind.

Answer: E

Key Question: 6

Skill: comprehension

Difficulty: Level 2

48. In the southern hemisphere, the direction of Ekman transport is:
    a. at a 45° angle from the wind direction.
    b. perpendicular to the wind direction.
    c. to the east of the wind direction.
    d. to the left of the wind direction.
    e. to the right of the wind direction.
Answer: D
Key Question: 6
Skill: comprehension
Difficulty: Level 2

49. Which type of flow works in opposition to Ekman transport in a gyre?
    a. counter-current circulation.
    b. density-driven circulation.
    c. geostrophic circulation.
    d. Langmuir circulation.
    e. thermohaline circulation.
Answer: C
Key Question: 6
Skill: comprehension
Difficulty: Level 2

50. Thermohaline circulation is driven by:
    a. density.
    b. gravity.
    c. latitude.
    d. temperature.
    e. wind
Answer: A
Key Question: 6
Skill: comprehension
Difficulty: Level 2

51. Compared to Antarctic Bottom Water, North Atlantic Deep Water is:
    a. colder.
    b. denser.
    c. higher in nutrients.
    d. higher in salinity.
    e. lower in oxygen.
Answer: E
Key Question: 6
Skill: comprehension
Difficulty: Level 2

52. The location where water flow uninterrupted between the Pacific, the Atlantic, and the Indian Oceans is
    a. in the Arctic Ocean.
    b. in the Southern Ocean.
    c. near Alaska.
    d. near the equator.

    e.   This does not occur.

Answer: B
Key Question: 6
Skill: knowledge
Difficulty: Level 1

53. The arrangement of water masses in the southern Atlantic Ocean from the surface to the bottom is:
    a.   Antarctic Bottom Water, Antarctic Intermediate Water, North Atlantic Deep Water.
    b.   Antarctic Intermediate Water, Antarctic Bottom Water, North Atlantic Deep Water.
    c.   Antarctic Intermediate Water, North Atlantic Deep Water, Antarctic Bottom Water.
    d.   North Atlantic Deep Water, Antarctic Bottom Water, Antarctic Intermediate Water.
    e.   North Atlantic Deep Water, Antarctic Intermediate Water, Antarctic Bottom Water.

Answer: C
Key Question: 6
Skill: comprehension
Difficulty: Level 2

54. Scientists have concluded that deep Pacific Ocean water is old is due to its low:
    a.   density.
    b.   nutrient levels.
    c.   oxygen levels.
    d.   salinity.
    e.   temperature.

Answer: C
Key Question: 6
Skill: application
Difficulty: Level 3

55. Deep water circulation in the Pacific Ocean is influenced by
    a.   extreme cooling and the formation of Pacific Bottom Water.
    b.   hydrothermal vents from the East Pacific Rise.
    c.   sea ice formation and resulting increased salinity of surface water in the south Pacific.
    d.   the size of the Pacific basin.
    e.   the Southern Oscillation.

Answer: B
Key Question: 6
Skill: comprehension
Difficulty: Level 2

56. Deep ocean water in the Indian Ocean includes Red Sea water which has
    a.   high salinity and low oxygen.
    b.   high salinity and low temperature.
    c.   low salinity and low oxygen.
    d.   low temperature and high oxygen.
    e.   low temperature and low salinity.

Answer: A
Key Question: 6
Skill: comprehension
Difficulty: Level 2

Word Analysis. Examine the five words and/or phrases and determine the relationship among the majority of words/phrases. Choose the one option that does not fit the pattern.

57. A. Gulf of Alaska   B. Indian Ocean   C. North Atlantic   D. South Atlantic   E. South Pacific
Answer: A
Key Question: 2
Skill: Analysis
Difficulty: Level 4

58.   A. Agulhas Current   B. Benguela Current   C. California Current
                        D. Canary Current   E. West Australian Current
Answer: A
Key Question: 2
Skill: analysis
Difficulty: Level 4

59.   A. Gulf Stream   B. Kuroshio Current   C. North Equatorial Current
                        D. Peru Current   E. Somali Current
Answer: D
Key Question: 2
Skill: Analysis
Difficulty: Level 4

60. A. Australian drought   B. decreased fish stock in coastal Peru   C. flooding rains in southeastern US
                        D. Peruvian upwelling stops   E. strong trade winds
Answer: E
Key Question: 5
Skill: Analysis
Difficulty: Level 4

CHAPTER
8
Waves and Water Dynamics

Matching. Match the wave characteristics with the equation used to calculate the corresponding value. You may use each answer once, more than once or not at all.

1. depth at which waves break
2. depth of the circular motion of water molecules
3. diameter of orbital wave
4. minimum depth for generation of deep water waves
5. wave speed

A. $1.25 \ (depth(m))^{1/2}$
B. $5.67 \ (depth(ft))^{1/2}$
C. 1/period
D. steepness=1:7
E. wave height
F. wavelength/period
G. wavelength/2
H. wavelength/20

Answers: 1-D, 2-G, 3-E, 4-H, 5-F
Key Question: 2 & 3
Skill: comprehension
Difficulty: Level 2

Matching. Match the type of wave with the generating force. You may use each answer once, more than once, or not at all.

6. capillary wave
7. gravity wave
8. internal wave
9. rouge wave
10. swell
11. tide
12. tsunami

A. constructive interference
B. density
C. destructive interference
D. gravitational forces
E. reflection
F. refraction
G. tectonic activity
H. wind

Answers: 6-H, 7-G, 8-B, 9-A, 10-H, 11-D, 12-G
Key Question: 2, 3, & 7
Skill: application
Difficulty: Level 3

True-False Questions. Read each question carefully, write "T" if the statement is true, and write "F" if the statement is false.

13. Internal waves have never been directly observed.
Answer: False
Key Question: 1
Skill: knowledge
Difficulty: 1

14. The vertical distance between the wave trough and the wave crest is the wavelength.
Answer: False
Key Question: 2
Skill: knowledge
Difficulty: Level 1

15. The horizontal distance between two successive troughs is called the wave height.
Answer: False
Key Question: 2
Skill: knowledge
Difficulty: Level 1

16. A shallow water wave must form in water depth less than 100 meters.
Answer: False
Key Question: 3
Skill: comprehension
Difficulty: Level 2

17. A wave will break when wave steepness is equal to 1/20.
Answer: False
Key Question: 3
Skill: comprehension
Difficulty: Level 2

18. The orbital motion of water molecules in a wave goes down to a depth equal to the wavelength divided by two.
Answer: True
Key Question: 3
Skill: comprehension
Difficulty: Level 2

19. The speed of a shallow water wave is a function of wave period.
Answer: False
Key Question: 3
Skill: comprehension
Difficulty: Level 2

20. A wave train is caused by wave energy moving more slowly than individual waves.
Answer: True
Key Question: 4
Skill: comprehension
Difficulty: Level 2

21. Swells are examples of free waves.
Answer: True
Key Question: 5
Skill: knowledge
Difficulty: Level 1

22. A curling wave formed over an air pocket is called a plunging breaker.
Answer: True
Key Question: 5
Skill: knowledge
Difficulty: Level 1

23. A storm surge might form in association with a seafloor avalanche.
Answer: False
Key Question: 5
Skill: knowledge
Difficulty: Level 1

24. Wave energy is focused on headlands due to wave refraction.
Answer: True
Key Question: 6
Skill: knowledge
Difficulty: Level 1

25. A standing wave is caused by wave reflection.
Answer: True
Key Question: 6
Skill: knowledge
Difficulty: 1

Multiple Choice. Choose the one **best** answer from the choices provided.

26. The largest wind-generated waves tend to be associated with the:
    a. doldrums.
    b. horse latitudes.
    c. polar regions.
    d. trade winds.
    e. westerlies.
Answer: E
Key Question: 1

Skill: comprehension
Difficulty: Level 1

Refer to the figure below detailing wave characteristics. Use the information on the figure to answer questions 27-30.

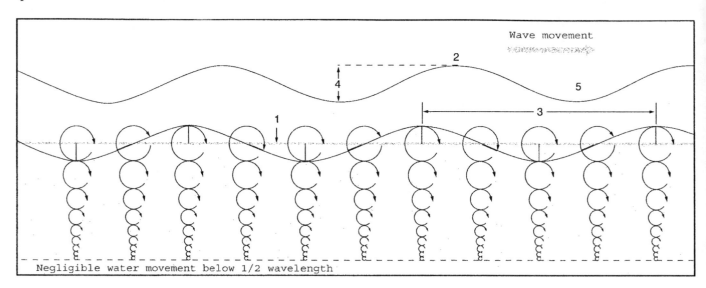

27. The crest is the portion of the wave corresponding to the number:
    a. 1.
    b. 2.
    c. 3.
    d. 4.
    e. 5.
Answer: B
Key Question: 2
Skill: knowledge
Difficulty: Level 1

28. The lowest part of the wave corresponds to the number:
    a. 1.
    b. 2.
    c. 3.
    d. 4.
    e. 5.
Answer: E
Key Question: 2
Skill: knowledge
Difficulty: Level 1

29. The wavelength is labeled with the number:
    a. 1.
    b. 2.

c. 3.
d. 4.
e. 5.
Answer: C
Key Question: 2
Skill: knowledge
Difficulty: Level 1

30. The portion of the wave that is also known as the zero energy level is indicated by the number:
    a. 1.
    b. 2.
    c. 3.
    d. 4.
    e. 5.
Answer: A
Key Question: 2
Skill: comprehension
Difficulty: Level 2

31. The ratio of wave height to wavelength is called the:
    a. frequency.
    b. period.
    c. wave height.
    d. wavelength.
    e. wave steepness.
Answer: E
Key Question: 2
Skill: knowledge
Difficulty: Level 1

32. The time between two successive waves is called the:
    a. crest.
    b. frequency.
    c. height.
    d. period.
    e. trough.
Answer: D
Key Question: 2
Skill: knowledge
Difficulty: Level 1

33. Water waves are:
    a. capillary waves.
    b. longitudinal waves.
    c. refracted waves.
    d. orbital waves.
    e. transverse waves.
Answer: D

Key Question: 2
Skill: knowledge
Difficulty: Level 1

34. Wave speed is equal to
    a. wave height divided by frequency.
    b. wave height divided by period.
    c. wavelength divided by fetch.
    d. wavelength divided by frequency.
    e. wavelength divided by period.
Answer: E
Key Question: 2
Skill: comprehension
Difficulty: Level 2

35. Storm surges are generated by intense:
    a. earthquakes.
    b. high-pressure systems.
    c. landslides.
    d. low-pressure systems.
    e. thunderstorms
Answer: D
Key Question: 2
Skill: knowledge
Difficulty: Level 1

36. The circular motion of water molecules extends to a depth that is equal to:
    a. wave height/wavelength.
    b. wave height/wave period.
    c. wavelength/wave height.
    d. wavelength/2.
    e. wavelength/20.
Answer: D
Key Question: 3
Skill: comprehension
Difficulty: Level 2

37. The diameter of a wave orbital at the surface is equal to:
    a. wave height.
    b. wave height/wavelength.
    c. wavelength.
    d. wavelength/wave period.
    e. wave period.
Answer: A
Key Question: 3
Skill: comprehension
Difficulty: Level 2

38. A deep-water wave occurs when the water depth is equal to:
    a. the fetch.
    b. wave height.
    c. wavelength.
    d. ½ of wavelength.
    e. 1/20 of wavelength.
Answer: E
Key Question: 3
Skill: comprehension
Difficulty: Level 2

39. All of the following are shallow-water waves **except:**
    a. near shore wind-generated waves.
    b. surf.
    c. tides.
    d. tsunamis.
    e. All of the above are examples of shallow-water waves.
Answer: E
Key Question: 3
Skill: comprehension
Difficulty: Level 2

40. The speed of a shallow-water wave is proportional to:
    a. water depth.
    b. wave frequency.
    c. wave height.
    d. wave period.
    e. wavelength.
Answer: A
Key Question: 3
Skill: comprehension
Difficulty: Level 2

41. The speed of a deep-water wave is proportional to:
    a. water depth.
    b. wave frequency.
    c. wave height.
    d. wave period.
    e. wavelength.
Answer: D
Key Question: 3
Skill: comprehension
Difficulty: Level 2

42. Capillary and gravity waves are named for the:
    a. dominant restoring force.
    b. force that creates them.
    c. rate at which they travel.
    d. wave dispersion.

e. wave refraction pattern they create.

Answer: A
Key Question: 3
Skill: knowledge
Difficulty: Level 1

43. The height of a wave depends upon
    a. fetch.
    b. fetch and wind speed.
    c. fetch, wind duration, and wind speed.
    d. wind duration.
    e. wind duration and wind speed.

Answer: C
Key Question: 3
Skill: comprehension
Difficulty: Level 2

44. The fetch refers to:
    a. a method of shoreline erosion control.
    b. a type of wave-cut platform.
    c. the circular pattern made by water particles when a wave passes.
    d. the distance between the trough of a wave and the still water level.
    e. the distance over which wind blows without interruption.

Answer: E
Key Question: 3
Skill: comprehension
Difficulty: Level 2

45. An internal wave might form:
    a. at a density boundary within the ocean.
    b. at the boundary between the atmosphere and the ocean.
    c. at the boundary between the ocean and the seafloor.
    d. close to shore as it moves into shallow water.
    e. only as a result of tidal activity.

Answer: A
Key Question: 3
Skill: comprehension
Difficulty: Level 2

46. As a wave begins to feel bottom near a shoreline, its wave height:
    a. decreases and steepness decreases.
    b. decreases and wavelength increases.
    c. increases and frequency decreases.
    d. increases and wavelength decreases
    e. increases and wavelength remains the same.

Answer: D
Key Question: 3
Skill: application
Difficulty: Level 3

47. Constructive interference results in larger waves while destructive interference produces:
    a. capillary waves.
    b. rouge waves.
    c. smaller waves.
    d. swells.
    e. tsunamis.
Answer: C
Key Question: 4
Skill: comprehension
Difficulty: Level 4

48. A wave will break when:
    a. distance from shore < wavelength.
    b. steepness = 1:7.
    c. water depth = wave height.
    d. water depth = wavelength/20.
    e. wavelength < wave height.
Answer: D
Key Question: 5
Skill: comprehension
Difficulty: Level 2

49. Waves that are moving faster than local wind and are sorted out be wavelength are called:
    a. capillary waves.
    b. constructive waves.
    c. surf.
    d. swell.
    e. wind waves.
Answer: D
Key Question: 5
Skill: knowledge
Difficulty: Level 1

50. Waves that are breaking along the shore and are forming a curling crest over an air pocket are called:
    a. gravity waves.
    b. plunging breakers.
    c. spilling breakers.
    d. surf.
    e. swells.
Answer: B
Key Question: 5
Skill: knowledge
Difficulty: Level 1

51. If a surfer wishes to have a really long ride, what type of wave should he or she look for?
    a. gravity waves
    b. plunging breakers
    c. spilling breakers
    d. surf

e. swells
Answer: C
Key Question: 5
Skill: knowledge
Difficulty: Level 1

52. Waves converge on headlands due to:
    a. constructive interference.
    b. destructive interference.
    c. wave diffraction.
    d. wave reflection.
    e. wave refraction.
Answer: E
Key Question: 5
Skill: comprehension
Difficulty: Level 2

53. Which of the following from earliest to latest represents the typical order of formation of waves?
    a. sea, surf, swell
    b. sea, swell, surf
    c. surf, swell, sea
    d. surf, sea, swell
    e. swell, sea, surf
Answer: B
Key Question: 5
Skill: comprehension
Difficulty: Level 2

54. Rogue waves tend to occur:
    a. in areas where wind belts converge.
    b. In coastal areas where the ocean depth rapidly decreases.
    c. in upwelling zones.
    d. only in the southern ocean below 60ºS latitude.
    e. where storm waves move against strong surface currents.
Answer: E
Key Question: 6
Skill: comprehension
Difficulty: Level 2

55. Standing waves may be caused by:
    a. constructive interference.
    b. destructive interference.
    c. wave diffraction.
    d. wave reflection.
    e. wave refraction
Answer: D
Key Question: 6
Skill: knowledge
Difficulty: Level 1

Water and Water Dynamics

56. A tsunami may result from:
    a. a large deep-water wave.
    b. a storm surge.
    c. an intense storm.
    d. constructive wave interference.
    e. tectonic activity on the seafloor.
Answer: E
Key Question: 7
Skill: comprehension
Difficulty: Level 2

57. A tsunami is considered to be a:
    a. capillary wave.
    b. deep-water wave.
    c. reflected wave.
    d. refracted wave
    e. shallow water wave.
Answer: E
Key Question: 7
Skill: comprehension
Difficulty: Level 2

Word Analysis. Examine the five words and/or phrases and determine the relationship among the majority of words/phrases. Choose the one option that does not fit the pattern.

58. A. longitudinal   B. orbital   C. progressive   D. spilling   E. transverse
Answer: D
Key Question: 2
Skill: analysis
Difficulty: Level 4

59. A. crest   B. height   C. length   D. period   E. trough
Answer: D
Key Question: 3
Skill: analysis
Difficulty: Level 4

60. A. plunging breaker B. spilling breaker C. surf   D. surging breaker E. swell
Answer: E
Key Question: 5
Skill: analysis
Difficulty: Level 4

CHAPTER
9
Tides

Matching. Match the term with the appropriate phrase. You may use each answer once, more than once or not at all.

1. centripetal
2. diurnal
3. ebb
4. gravitational
5. mixed
6. resultant
7. rotary

A. tidal current
B. tidal force
C. tidal pattern

Answers: 1-B, 2-C, 3-A, 4-B, 5-C, 6-B, 7-A
Key Question: 1, 5, & 6
Skill: comprehension
Difficulty: Level 2

Matching. Match the phrase with its best descriptor. You may use each answer once, more than once or not at all.

8. center of an open ocean tidal system
9. highest tidal range in the lunar cycle
10. smallest tidal range in the lunar cycle
11. steep wave front surging up a river as a result of tides
12. water moving out from an inlet due to approaching low tide

A. amphidromic point
B. cotidal point
C. ebb current
D. flood current
E. neap tide
F. spring tide
G. tidal bore
H. tidal current

Answers: 8-A, 9-F, 10-E, 11-G, 12-C

Tides

Key Question: 4, 5, & 6
Skill: comprehension
Difficulty: Level 2

True-False Questions. Read each question carefully, write "T" if the statement is true, and write "F" if the statement is false.

13. The tide-generating force is inversely proportional to the cube of the distance.
Answer: True
Key Question: 1
Skill: comprehension
Difficulty: Level 2

14. The plane through the ellipse that marks the revolution of the Earth around the Sun is called the ecliptic.
Answer: True
Key Question: 1
Skill: knowledge
Difficulty: Level 1

15. A lunar day is shorter than a solar day.
Answer: False
Key Question: 2
Skill: comprehension
Difficulty: Level 2

16. There is no horizontal tide-generating force on Earth at points directly below and opposite the Moon.
Answer: True
Key Question: 3
Skill: comprehension
Difficulty: Level 2

17. The sun and the moon have relatively equal tide-generating forces on earth.
Answer: False
Key Question: 3
Skill: comprehension
Difficulty: Level 2

18. The barycenter follows a smooth orbit around the Sun.
Answer: True
Key Question: 3
Skill: knowledge

Difficulty: Level 1

19. Tides are much greater during apogee than during perigee.
Answer: False
Key Question: 3
Skill: comprehension
Difficulty: Level 2

20. A spring tide occurs once per month.
Answer: False
Key Question: 3
Skill: knowledge
Difficulty: Level 1

21. Due to the shape of the North Sea, it develops two amphidromic points.
Answer: True
Key Question: 4
Skill: comprehension
Difficulty: Level 2

22. A semidiurnal tide is common along the Pacific coast of the United States.
Answer: False
Key Question: 5
Skill: comprehension
Difficulty: Level 2

23. The maximum tidal range in the Bay of Fundy is on the order of 15 meters.
Answer: True
Key Question: 6
Skill: knowledge
Difficulty: Level 1

24. The seaward flow of water due to tidal forces through an inlet is called ebb current.
Answer: True
Key Question: 6
Skill: knowledge
Difficulty: Level 1

25. Grunion depend upon the pattern of erosion and deposition of sand for the survival of their eggs.
Answer: True
Key Question: 6
Skill: analysis
Difficulty: Level 3

Multiple Choice. Choose the one **best** answer from the choices provided.

Tides

26. The force that pulls an orbiting body toward the center of that orbit is called:
    a. amphidromic.
    b. centrifugal.
    c. centripetal.
    d. gravitational.
    e. tidal.
Answer: B
Key Question: 1
Skill: knowledge
Difficulty: Level 1

27. The difference between centripetal forces and gravitational forces is call the:
    a. diurnal force.
    b. dynamic force
    c. lunar force.
    d. residual force.
    e. tidal force.
Answer: C
Key Question: 1
Skill: comprehension
Difficulty: Level 2

28. The center of mass of the Earth-Moon system is called the:
    a. aphelion.
    b. apogee.
    c. barycenter.
    d. perigee.
    e. perihelion.
Answer: C
Key Question: 2
Skill: knowledge
Difficulty: Level 1

29. The barycenter follows:
    a. a path that is perpendicular to the Earth's ecliptic.
    b. a pattern that parallels the Moon's orbit.
    c. a smooth orbit around the Sun.
    d. a wavy path around the Sun.
    e. the Earth's declination.
Answer: C
Key Question: 2
Skill: knowledge
Difficulty: Level 1

30. The tide-generating force varies:

    a.   directly with the cube of the distance between the objects.

    b.   directly with the square of the distance between the objects.
    c.   directly with the square of the distances of the objects divided by the product of the masses.
    d.   inversely with the cube of the distance between the objects.
    e.   inversely with the square of the distance between the objects.

Answer: D
Key Question: 2
Skill: comprehension
Difficulty: Level 2

31. The tide-generating force varies:
    a.   directly with the product of the object masses.
    b.   directly with the product of the cube of the object masses.
    c.   directly with the square of the distance between the objects.
    d.   inversely with the product of object masses.
    e.   inversely with the product of the cube of the object masses.

Answer: A
Key Question: 2
Skill: comprehension
Difficulty: Level 2

32. Compared with a solar day, a lunar day is:
    a.   equal to a solar day.
    b.   half the length of a solar day.
    c.   longer than a solar day.
    d.   shorter than a solar day.
    e.   twice the length of a solar day.

Answer: C
Key Question: 2
Skill: knowledge
Difficulty: Level 1

33. The angular distance of the orbital plane of the Sun or Moon above or below the Earth's equatorial plane is called the:
    a.   apogee.
    b.   declination.
    c.   ecliptic.
    d.   perihelion.
    e.   syzygy.

Answer: B
Key Question: 2
Skill: knowledge
Difficulty: Level 1

34. A spring tide has:

Tides
   a.   moderate high and low tides.

   b.   occurs at a blue moon.
   c.   occurs at the vernal equinox.
   d.   very high high tides and very low low tides
   e.   very little difference between high and low tides.
Answer: D
Key Question: 3
Skill: knowledge
Difficulty: Level 1

35. A neap tide has:
   a.   moderately high tidal range.
   b.   moderately low tidal range.
   c.   no tidal range.
   d.   very high tidal range.
   e.   very low tidal range.
Answer: E
Key Question: 3
Skill: knowledge
Difficulty: Level 1

36. Spring tide occurs about:
   a.   once per month
   b.   once per season.
   c.   once per year.
   d.   twice per month.
   e.   twice per year.
Answer: D
Key Question: 3
Skill: knowledge
Difficulty: Level 1

37. Neap tides occur:
   a.   at summer and winter solstice.
   b.   during a storm surge.
   c.   when the moon is full or new.
   d.   when the moon is at quadrature.
   e.   when the sun is at perihelion or aphelion.
Answer: D
Key Question: 3
Skill: comprehension
Difficulty: Level 2

38. When the earth is at its greatest distance from the sun, it is said to be at:
   a.   apogee.
   b.   aphelion.

c. perigee.

d. perihelion.
e. proxigean.

Answer: B
Key Question: 3
Skill: knowledge
Difficulty: Level 1

39. The side of the Earth that faces the moon experiences a high tide, the side of the Earth that is opposite from the moon will have a(n):

    a. high tide.
    b. low tide.
    c. neap tide.
    d. proxigean tide.
    e. spring tide.

Answer: A
Key Question: 3
Skill: comprehension
Difficulty: Level 2

40. The vertical difference between high and low tides is called the

    a. ebb tide.
    b. flood tide.
    c. tidal bore.
    d. tidal height.
    e. tidal range.

Answer: E
Key Question: 4
Skill: knowledge
Difficulty: Level 1

41. Tidal ranges will be greatest when the Earth and the Moon are at:

    a. apogee.
    b. aphelion
    c. perigee.
    d. perihelion.
    e. proxigean.

Answer: C
Key Question: 4
Skill: comprehension
Difficulty: Level 2

42. The center of an open ocean tidal system is called a(n):

    a. amphidromic center.
    b. cotidal center.

Tides
    c. rotary center.
    d. seiche.
    e. tidal flux.
Answer: A
Key Question: 4
Skill: knowledge
Difficulty: Level 1

43. An area that experiences semidiurnal tides will have:
    a. one high tide and one low tide daily.
    b. one high tide and two low tides daily.
    c. one low tide and two high tides daily.
    d. two high tides and two low tides of nearly equal height daily.
    e. two unequal low and high tides daily.
Answer: D
Key Question: 5
Skill: knowledge
Difficulty: Level 1

44. An area that experiences diurnal tides will have:
    a. one high tide and one low tide daily.
    b. one high tide and two low tides daily.
    c. one low tide and two high tides daily.
    d. two high tides and two low tides of nearly equal height daily.
    e. two unequal low and high tides daily.
Answer: A
Key Question: 5
Skill: knowledge
Difficulty: Level 1

45. The most common tidal pattern around the world are:
    a. diurnal tides.
    b. mixed tides.
    c. proxigean tides.
    d. semidiurnal tides.
    e. spring tides.
Answer: B
Key Question: 5
Skill: knowledge
Difficulty: Level 1

46. To make accurate coastal tidal predicting, one must consider:
    a. diurnal tides.
    b. partial tides.
    c. semidiurnal tides
    d. tidal bores.
    e. tidal currents.

Answer: B

Key Question: 5 & 6
Skill: comprehension
Difficulty: Level 2

47. In the United States one can find semidiurnal tides along the:
    a. Atlantic coast.
    b. Gulf of Alaska.
    c. Gulf of Mexico coast.
    d. Florida Keys.
    e. Pacific coast.
Answer: A
Key Question: 5
Skill: comprehension
Difficulty: Level 2

48. A full tidal cycle is:
    a. 12 hours in duration.
    b. 12 hours 25 minutes in duration.
    c. 24 hours in duration.
    d. 24 hours and 50 minutes in duration.
    e. 48 hours in duration.
Answer: D
Key Question: 5
Skill: knowledge
Difficulty: Level 1

49. In the United States one can find mixed tides along the:
    a. Atlantic coast.
    b. Cape Cod.
    c. Gulf of Mexico coast
    d. Florida Keys.
    e. Pacific coast.
Answer: E
Key Question: 5
Skill: comprehension
Difficulty: Level 2

50. The Bay of Fundy is well known for which tidal characteristic?
    a. large tidal bore.
    b. two amphidromic points.
    c. very large seiche.
    d. very low tidal range.
    e. very high tidal range.
Answer: E
Key Question: 6

Tides
Skill: knowledge
Difficulty: Level 1

51. This wave formed on a river by the flood tide current is called a:

    a. ebb tide.
    b. flood tide.
    c. seiche
    d. tidal bore.
    e. tsunami.
Answer: D
Key Question: 6
Skill: knowledge
Difficulty: Level 1

52. Water flowing out of an enclosed basin due to the tides is called:
    a. ebb current.
    b. flood current.
    c. neap tide
    d. spring tide.
    e. tidal bore.
Answer: A
Key Question: 5 & 6
Skill: knowledge
Difficulty: Level 1

53. The maximum tidal currents are reported:
    a. about half way between high and low tides.
    b. at high tide.
    c. at low tide.
    d. during neap tides.
    e. in the intertidal zone.

Answer: A
Key Question: 6
Skill: application
Difficulty: Level 3

54. Tidal current can produce rotary currents called:
    a. ebb currents.
    b. flood currents.
    c. shoals.
    d. tidal bores.
    e. whirlpools.

Answer: E
Key Question: 6
Skill: knowledge
Difficulty: Level 1

55. Which of the following is a tidal current?
    a. both ebb tides and flood tides.
    b. both neap tides and spring tides.
    c. ebb tide.
    d. flood tide.
    e. spring tide.

Answer: A
Key Question: 6
Skill: knowledge
Difficulty: Level 1

CHAPTER
10
The Coast: Beaches and Shoreline Processes

Matching. Match the pattern of sediment transport along the coastline with the type of coast. You may use each answer once, more than once or not at all.

1. barrier island
2. sea arches
3. spit
4. tombolo
5. wave-cut cliffs

A. depositional-type shore
B. erosional-type shore

Answers: 1-A, 2-B, 3-A, 4-A, 5-B
Key Question: 4
Skill: comprehension
Difficulty: Level 2

Matching. Match the term with the appropriate phrase. You may use each answer once, more than once or not at all.

6. foreshore
7. longshore current
8. low marsh
9. offshore
10. rip current

A. beyond the low-tide breakers
B. colonized by grasses; very productive
C. deposit at mouth of a river
D. exposed at low tide and covered at high tide
E. flows parallel to shore within surf zone
F. found between dunes and high marsh
G. moves water from swash zone out to sea
H. young features formed by non-marine processes

Answers: 6-D, 7-E, 8-B, 9-A, 10-G
Key Question: 1, 2, & 3
Skill: comprehension
Difficulty: Level 2

True-False Questions.   Read each question carefully, write "T" if the statement is true, and write "F" if the statement is false.

11. The backshore is found between the normal high tide mark and the coastline.
Answer: True
Key Question: 1
Skill: knowledge
Difficulty: Level 1

12. The nearshore is equivalent to the intertidal zone.
Answer: False
Key Question: 1
Skill: knowledge
Difficulty: Level 1

13. A summer beach typically has more sediment on it than a winter beach.
Answer: True
Key Question: 2
Skill: comprehension
Difficulty: Level 2

14. The velocity of the longshore current will be higher when wave heights are higher.
Answer: True
Key Question: 3
Skill: comprehension
Difficulty: Level 2

15. Waves will cause much more erosion in an area that has a large tidal range when compared to an area with a small tidal range.
Answer: False
Key Question: 3
Skill: comprehension
Difficulty: Level 2

16. The longshore current is caused by waves striking the beach at an angle.
Answer: True
Key Question: 3
Skill: comprehension
Difficulty: Level 2

17. Elevated wave-cut platforms in southern California are evidence that this coastal area is emergent.
Answer: True
Key Question: 4
Skill: comprehension
Difficulty: Level 2

The Coast: Beaches and Shoreline Processes

18. Eustatic changes in sea level refer to changes in the volume of seawater or changes in the volume of the ocean basin.
Answer: True
Key Question: 5
Skill: knowledge
Difficulty: Level 1

19. An increase in the spreading rate at a mid-ocean ridge will cause a decrease in sea level.
Answer: False
Key Question: 5
Skill: comprehension
Difficulty: Level 2

20. Sea caves and sea stacks are more likely to occur in an area with very hard bedrock.
Answer: True
Key Question: 5
Skill: comprehension
Difficulty: Level 2

21. The Pacific coast of the US is an example of a coast where active erosion occurs.
Answer: False
Key Question: 6
Skill: knowledge
Difficulty: Level 1

22. Seawalls are quite effective at controlling beach erosion.
Answer: False
Key Question: 7
Skill: knowledge
Difficulty: Level 1

23. Groins are constructed for the purpose of maintaining or widening beaches that are losing sand.
Answer: True
Key Question: 7
Skill: knowledge
Difficulty: Level 1

Multiple Choice. Choose the one **best** answer from the choices provided.

24. The section of the coast that is exposed at low tide and submerged at high tide is called the:
    a. backshore.
    b. foreshore.
    c. nearshore.
    d. offshore.
    e. shoreline.

Answer: B
Key Question: 1
Skill: knowledge
Difficulty: Level 1

25. The section of the coast that extend from normal high tide level to the highest elevation on land that is effected by storm waves is called the:
    a. backshore.
    b. foreshore.
    c. nearshore.
    d. offshore.
    e. shoreline.
Answer: A
Key Question: 1
Skill: knowledge
Difficulty: Level 1

26. Eroded material along coastlines is carried from high wave energy areas to:
    a. active offshore bars.
    b. low wave energy areas.
    c. the backshore.
    d. the foreshore.
    e. the nearshore zone.
Answer: B
Key Question: 2
Skill: comprehension
Difficulty: Level 2

27. Winter beaches:
    a. are narrower than summer beaches due to high-energy waves during the winter.
    b. are wider than summer beaches due to low-energy waves during the winter.
    c. contain more sediment than summer beaches due to high-energy waves during the winter.
    d. contain less sediment than summer beaches due to low-energy waves during the winter.
    e. have better smaller offshore bars to sand deposition on the beach during the winter.
Answer: A
Key Question: 2
Skill: application
Difficulty: Level 3

28. Sediment is supplied to the coastal zone by:
    a. coastal erosion.
    b. local biological activity.
    c. rivers.
    d. All of the above are sources of sediment in the costal zone.
    e. Only **a** and **b** are sources of sediment in the coastal zone.
Answer: D
Key Question: 3

The Coast: Beaches and Shoreline Processes

Skill: comprehension
Difficulty: Level 2

29. Which of the following will decrease the velocity of the longshore current?
    a. increased beach slope.
    b. increased wave frequency.
    c. increased wave period.
    d. larger waves.
    e. faster wind speed.
Answer: C
Key Question: 3
Skill: comprehension
Difficulty: Level 2

30. Narrow currents flowing across the surf zone toward the open ocean are called:
    a. longshore currents.
    b. nearshore currents.
    c. rip currents.
    d. surf flow.
    e. swash.
Answer: C
Key Question: 3
Skill: comprehension
Difficulty: Level 2

31. The rate of wave erosion along a coastline is determined by all of the following **except** the:
    a. amount of open ocean exposure.
    b. coastal bedrock composition.
    c. direction of the longshore current.
    d. tidal range.
    e. wave height and wave period.
Answer: C
Key Question: 3
Skill: comprehension
Difficulty: Level 2

32. If one were to walk from the ocean landward across a barrier island complex, in which order would one encounter the following environments?
    a. barrier flat, dune, beach, low marsh, high marsh
    b. beach, dune, barrier flat, high marsh, low marsh
    c. beach, dune, barrier flat, low marsh, high marsh
    d. dune, barrier flat, beach, high marsh, low marsh
    e. low marsh, high marsh, barrier flat, dune, beach
Answer: B
Key Question: 4
Skill: comprehension

Difficulty: 2

33. The area of the barrier island complex that would contain thickets and woodlands would be the:
    a. barrier flat.
    b. dune.
    c. high marsh.
    d. lagoon.
    e. low marsh.
Answer: A
Key Question: 4
Skill: knowledge
Difficulty: Level 1

34. The most biologically productive part of a salt marsh would be the:
    a. barrier flat.
    b. dune.
    c. high marsh.
    d. low marsh.
    e. lagoon.
Answer: D
Key Question: 4
Skill: comprehension
Difficulty: Level 2

35. Large deposits of sediment at the mouths of rivers are called
    a. barrier flats.
    b. barrier islands.
    c. bay-mouth bar.
    d. deltas.
    e. tombolos.
Answer: D
Key Question: 4
Skill: knowledge
Difficulty: Level 1

36. All of the following are examples of features found along primary coasts **except:**
    a. coasts with extensive coral reefs.
    b. drowned river valleys.
    c. drowned glacial valleys.
    d. subaerial deltas.
    e. volcanic coasts.
Answer: A
Key Question: 4
Skill: comprehension
Difficulty: Level 2

The Coast: Beaches and Shoreline Processes

37. Which of the following landforms shows the greatest erosion rate along US coasts?
    a. coralline structures of the Florida Keys
    b. crystalline rocks of New England
    c. mud flats
    d. sandy beaches
    e. sedimentary rocks of Pacific Northwest
Answer: C
Key Question: 4
Skill: comprehension
Difficulty: Level 2

38. Which of the following landforms shows the least amount of erosion along US coasts?
    a. coralline structures of the Florida Keys
    b. crystalline rocks of New England
    c. mud flats
    d. sandy beaches
    e. sedimentary rocks of Pacific Northwest
Answer: B
Key Question: 4
Skill: comprehension
Difficulty: Level 2

39. Which of the following materials you expect to be found on the steepest beach?
    a. coarse sand
    b. fine sand
    c. large gravel
    d. small pebbles
    e. cannot be determined based solely on particle size
Answer: C
Key Question: 4
Skill: comprehension
Difficulty: Level 2

40. Which of the following pairs does not belong together?
    a. Atlantic-type: thick sediment wedge
    b. emergent: drowned beaches
    c. Pacific-type: earthquake activity
    d. secondary coast: mangroves
    e. submergent: submerged dune topography
Answer: B
Key Question: 4 & 6
Skill: analysis
Difficulty: Level 4

41. Emergent coasts might have all of the following characteristics **except:**
    a. cliffs.
    b. drowned beaches.

c. exposed wave-cut bench.
d. marine terraces.
e. shell debris found well above current shoreline.
Answer: B
Key Question: 5
Skill: application
Difficulty: Level 3

42. Submergent coasts might have all of the following characteristics **except:**
    a. drowned beaches.
    b. drowned river delta.
    c. marine terraces.
    d. river mouths found below sea level.
    e. submerged dune topography.
Answer: C
Key Question: 5
Skill: application
Difficulty: Level 3

43. A linear ridge of sediment attached to land at one end might be called a:
    a. barrier island.
    b. bay barrier.
    c. bay-mouth bar.
    d. spit.
    e. tombolo.
Answer: D
Key Question: 5
Skill: knowledge
Difficulty: Level 1

44. Isostatic movement of a coastline might occur due to:
    a. additional seawater.
    b. changes in the rate of seafloor spreading.
    c. the removal of a large glacier that rested in that area.
    d. underwater landslides.
    e. uplift related to earthquake activity.
Answer: C
Key Question: 5
Skill: comprehension
Difficulty: Level 2

45. Eustatic changes in sea level might include:
    a. increase glacial and sea ice melting due to the global warming.
    b. rise in sea level due to a large weight of glacier on a continental mass.
    c. sinking of the crust due to large increases in sediment load.
    d. uplift related to earthquake activity..
    e. volcanic activity resulting in the formation of new continental crust .

Answer: A
Key Question: 5
Skill: comprehension
Difficulty: Level 2

46. When seafloor spreading rates increase:
    a. new continental crust is formed.
    b. sea level falls.
    c. subduction increases.
    d. there is a rise in sea level.
    e. there is no change in sea level.
Answer: D
Key Question: 5
Skill: application
Difficulty: Level 3

47. Which US coast is being most starved for sediments due to the damming of rivers?
    a. Alaskan
    b. Atlantic
    c. Great Lake states
    d. Gulf
    e. Pacific
Answer: E
Key Question: 6
Skill: knowledge
Difficulty: Level 1

48. Nor'easters affect which area of the US coastline during the fall and winter?
    a. Gulf coast
    b. northern Atlantic coast
    c. northern Pacific coast
    d. southern Atlantic coast
    e. southern Pacific coat
Answer: B
Key Question: 6
Skill: knowledge
Difficulty: Level 1

49. Which US coastline has the greatest average loss due to erosion?
    a. Alaskan
    b. Atlantic
    c. Gulf
    d. New England
    e. Pacific
Answer: C
Key Question: 6

Skill: knowledge
Difficulty: Level 1

50. The most common barriers constructed along a coastline are
    a. breakwaters.
    b. groins.
    c. jetties at harbor entrances.
    d. seawalls.
    e. spits.
Answer: C
Key Question: 7
Skill: knowledge
Difficulty: Level 1

51. Which of the following structures is designed to prevent or retard shoreline erosion?
    a. beach nourishment
    b. groin
    c. seawall
    d. All of these structures prevent or retard shoreline erosion.
    e. Both the groin and seawall prevent or retard shoreline erosion.
Answer: D
Key Question: 7
Skill: knowledge
Difficulty: Level 1

52. In terms of erosion protection from wave action, seawalls:
    a. are cost effective.
    b. are ineffective.
    c. are moderately effective.
    d. are very effective.
    e. require very little maintenance.
Answer: B
Key Question: 7
Skill: comprehension
Difficulty: Level 2

Word Analysis. Examine the five words and/or phrases and determine the relationship among the majority of words/phrases. Choose the one option that does not fit the pattern.

53. A. barrier flat B. beach face C. berm D. longshore bar E. trough
Answer: A
Key Question: 2
Skill: Analysis
Difficulty: Level 4

54. A. marine terrace   B. sea arches   C. sea caves   D. tombolo   E. wave-cut cliffs
Answer: D
Key Question: 4
Skill: analysis
Difficulty: Level 4

55. A. bay-mouth bar   B. delta   C. sea stack D. spit E. tombolo
Answer: C
Key Question: 4
Skill: Analysis
Difficulty: Level 4

56. A. formation of large inland lakes   B. increased seafloor spreading rates   C. melting glacial ice
D. melting sea ice   E. uplifted crust
Answer: E
Key Question: 5
Skill: Analysis
Difficulty: Level 4

CHAPTER
11
The Coastal Oceans

Matching. Match the definition with the correct term. Use each choice once, more than once, or not at all.

1. a layer of water in which the salinity changes rapidly with changes in depth

2. a layer of water in which the temperature changes rapidly with changes in depth

3. coastal wetland that occurs at latitudes devoid of killing frosts

4. coastal wetland occurring at temperate latitudes that experience seasonal frosts

5. equal salinity

6. equal temperature

A. coral reef
B. halocline
C. isocline
D. isohaline
E. isothermal
F. mangrove swamp
G. pycnocline
H. salt marsh
I. sea grass bed
J. thermocline

Answers: 1-B, 2-J, 3-F, 4-H, 5-D, 6-E
Key Question: 2, 3, & 4
Skill: knowledge
Difficulty: Level 1

Matching. Match the description of the estuary with its name. Use each choice once, more than once, or not at all.

7. a long, narrow, deep U-shaped inlet that usually represents the seaward end of a submerged glacial valley

8. a shallow lagoon separated from the open ocean by a bar deposit such as a barrier island

A. bar-built estuary
B. coastal plain estuary
C. fjord
D. highly stratified estuary
E. salt wedge estuary
F. vertically-mixed estuary

The Coastal Oceans

9. a very deep river mouth with a large volume of
   freshwater flow beneath which a wedge of salt
   water from the ocean invades

10. shallow estuaries in which freshwater and salt
    water are totally mixed from the top to the
    bottom of the water column

Answers: 7-C, 8-A, 9-E, 10-F
Key Question: 3
Skill: knowledge
Difficulty: Level 1

Matching. Match the pollutant with its general category. Use each answer, once, more than once, or not at all.

11. ammonium nitrate   A. hydrocarbon
12. calcium phosphate   B. nutrient
13. crude oil   C. toxin
14. DDT
15. gasoline
16. heating oil
17. mercury
18. PCBs
19. pesticides
20. sewage

Answers: 11-B, 12-B, 13-A, 14-C, 15-A, 16-A, 17-C, 18-C, 19-C, 20-B
Key Question: 7
Skill: comprehension
Difficulty: Level 2

True-False Questions. Read each question carefully, write "T" if the statement is true, and write "F" if the statement is false.

21. Prevailing offshore winds tend to decrease surface water salinity in a coastal plain estuary.
Answer: False
Key Question: 2
Skill: comprehension
Difficulty: Level 2

22. The Coriolis effect is evident in the surface circulation of Chesapeake Bay.

Answer: True
Key Question: 3
Skill: application
Difficulty: Level 3

23. Laguna Madre is a classic coastal plain estuary.
Answer: False
Key Question: 3
Skill: application
Difficulty: Level 3

24. Salt marshes serve as nurseries for over half of the commercially important fish in the southeastern
United States.
Answer: True
Key Question: 4
Skill: knowledge
Difficulty: Level 1

25. Mangrove swamps are protective buffer areas in temperate latitude coastal ecosystems.
Answer: False
Key Question: 4
Skill: comprehension
Difficulty: Level 2

26. Mediterranean Sea water has little impact on the waters of the Atlantic Ocean.
Answer: False
Key Question: 5
Skill: comprehension
Difficulty: Level 2

27. Pollutants are any substance that has a negative effect on the environment.
Answer: True
Key Question: 6
Skill: knowledge
Difficulty: Level 1

28. The greatest sources of hydrocarbons in the marine environment are urban run-off and shipping.
Answer: True
Key Question: 7
Skill: knowledge
Difficulty: Level 1

29. Bioremediation involves the use of microorganisms to degrade pollutants such as crude oil.
Answer: True
Key Question: 7
Skill: knowledge
Difficulty: Level 1

The Coastal Oceans

30. The largest single oil pollution event was the result of the Persian Gulf War in 1991.
Answer: False
Key Question: 7
Skill: knowledge
Difficulty: Level 1

31. Primary sewage treatment involves the removal of inorganic nutrients from the liquid effluent.
Answer: False
Key Question: 7
Skill: knowledge
Difficulty: Level 1

32. Nitrates and hydrocarbons are examples of persistent organic pollutants in marine ecosystems.
Answer: False
Key Question: 7
Skill: comprehension
Difficulty: Level 2

33. The decreased calcium content in the shells of piscivorous birds was a result bioaccumulation of pesticides in the food chain.
Answer: True
Key Question: 7
Skill: application
Difficulty: Level 3

34. Biomagnification is a result of the inefficiency of trophic transfer in the food web.
Answer: True
Key Question: 7
Skill: application
Difficulty: Level 3

35. Minamata disease was caused by mercury contamination.
Answer: True
Key Question: 7
Skill: knowledge
Difficulty: Level 1

Multiple Choice. Choose the one **best** answer from the choices provided.

35. The **Exclusive Economic Zone (EEZ)** extends:
    a. 3 nautical miles form the coast.
    b. 10.5 nautical miles from the coast.
    c. 20 nautical miles from the coast.
    d. 200 nautical miles from the coast.
    e. into open international waters.
Answer: D

Key Question: 1
Skill: knowledge
Difficulty: Level 1

36. Prevailing offshore winds produce coastal waters that:
    a. are biologically diverse.
    b. are cooler.
    c. are identical to the open ocean.
    d. have higher salinities.
    e. have lower salinities.
Answer: D
Key Question: 2
Skill: comprehension
Difficulty: Level 2

37. An example of a coastal plain estuary is the:
    a. Chesapeake Bay.
    b. Laguna Madre.
    c. Monterey Bay.
    d. Pamlico Sound.
    e. San Francisco Bay
Answer: A
Key Question: 3
Skill: comprehension
Difficulty: Level 2

38. An example of a bar-built estuary is:
    a. Aleutian Islands.
    b. Chesapeake Bay.
    c. Laguna Madre.
    d. Puget Sound.
    e. San Francisco Bay
Answer: C
Key Question: 3
Skill: comprehension
Difficulty: Level 2

39. Lagoons that form behind barrier islands are examples of:
    a. bar-built estuaries.
    b. coastal plain estuaries.
    c. fjords.
    d. salt wedge estuaries.
    e. tectonic estuaries.
Answer: A
Key Question: 3
Skill: comprehension
Difficulty: Level 2

40. The type of circulation pattern found in Laguna Madre is:
    a. opposite of the typical estuarine circulation pattern.
    b. salt wedge pattern.
    c. slightly stratified circulation pattern.
    d. vertically mixed circulation pattern.
    e. wind-driven circulation pattern.
Answer: A
Key Question: 3
Skill: knowledge
Difficulty: Level 1

41. An estuary formed from a flooded glacial valley called a:
    a. bar-built estuary.
    b. coastal plain estuary.
    c. fjord.
    d. tectonic estuary.
    e. vertically mixed estuary.
Answer: C
Key Question: 3
Skill: comprehension
Difficulty: Level 2

42. An estuary produced by faulting or folding of rocks that creates a dropped-down section into which a river flows is called a:
    a. bar-built estuary.
    b. coastal plain estuary.
    c. fjord.
    d. salt wedge estuary.
    e. tectonic estuary.
Answer: E
Key Question: 3
Skill: knowledge
Difficulty: Level 1

43. Estuarine circulation associated with a deep, high river volume system where no horizontal salinity gradient exists at the surface is called a:
    a. bar-built estuary.
    b. highly stratified estuary.
    c. salt wedge estuary.
    d. slightly stratified estuary.
    e. vertically mixed estuary.
Answer: C
Key Question: 3
Skill: knowledge
Difficulty: Level 1

44. Estuarine circulation associated with a shallow, low-volume estuary in which river water mixes evenly at all depths with ocean water would be called a:

a. highly stratified estuary.
b. salt wedge estuary.
c. slightly stratified estuary.
d. tectonic estuary.
e. vertically mixed estuary.
Answer: E
Key Question: 3
Skill: knowledge
Difficulty: Level 1

45. The Columbia River estuary received most of its ecological damage from which of the following sources?
a. dikes erected by farmers to prevent flooding
b. dredging of the river to accommodate boat traffic
c. hydroelectric dams
d. pollution due to soil erosion from logging
e. poor farming practices
Answer: C
Key Question: 3
Skill: comprehension
Difficulty: Level 2

46. One major problem associated with Chesapeake Bay and increased human pressure is:
a. an increase salinity during particular times of the year.
b. an increase in nutrients resulting in more frequent kills of bottom-dwelling animals.
c. decreased tributary river flow due to increased water demand.
d. salinity fluctuations due to reduced inflow from rivers.
e. the removal of sediments behind hydroelectric dams
Answer: B
Key Question: 3
Skill: application
Difficulty: Level 3

47. This wetland coastal area occurs:

    a. between 30°N and 30°S latitude.
    b. in coastal areas with low wave energy.
    c. in coastal areas that do not experience seasonal killing frosts.
    d. All of the above conditions control the distribution of this type of coastal wetland.
    e. Only A and B determine the distribution of this type of wetland.
Answer: D
Key Question: 3
Skill: application
Difficulty: Level 3

48. Coastal wetlands are characterized by:
    a. high levels of inorganic nutrients in the tidal zone and oxygen-rich sediments
    b. high levels of organic nutrients in the tidal zone and anoxic sediments.
    c. high levels of organic nutrients in the tidal zone and oxygen-rich sediments.
    d. low levels of inorganic nutrients in the tidal zone and anoxic sediments.
    e. low levels of organic nutrients in the tidal zone and oxygen-rich sediments.
Answer: D
Key Question: 4
Skill comprehension
Difficulty: Level 2

49. The percentage of the original area of wetlands currently left in the United States is approximately:
    a. 10%.
    b. 25%.
    c. 50%.
    d. 65%.
    e. 75%.

Answer: C
Key Question: 4
Skill: knowledge
Difficulty: 1

50. When ocean water enters a marginal sea above a return flow of saltier water, the circulation pattern is called:
   a. estuarine circulation.
   b. fjord circulation.
   c. lagoon circulation.
   d. loop current circulation.
   e. Mediterranean circulation.
Answer: E
Key Question: 5
Skill: knowledge
Difficulty: Level 1

51. The biological response level that is impacted for the longest time period by pollutants in the marine environment is the:
   a. biochemical-cellular level.
   b. community dynamics and structure level.
   c. organismal level.
   d. population dynamics level.
   e. trophic level.
Answer: B
Key Question: 6
Skill: comprehension
Difficulty: Level 2

52. All of the following are examples of pollutants in the marine environment **except**:
   a. heavy metals such as mercury and silver.
   b. hydrocarbons.
   c. nitrate and phosphates.
   d. phytoplankton.
   e. sewage effluent.
Answer: D
Key Question: 6
Skill: comprehension
Difficulty: Level 2

53. The toxicity of marine pollutants is estimated:
   a. by the EPA.
   b. calculating the concentration at which 50% of the test organisms die.
   c. determining the length of time that the pollutant remains in the environment.
   d. determining the total biomass of affected organisms in the environment.
   e. estimating the number of trophic transfers in the food web affected by the pollutant.
Answer: B

The Coastal Oceans

Key Question: 7
Skill: knowledge
Difficulty: Level 1

54. The two most significant sources of oil pollution in the marine environment are:
    a. blowout accidents and urban run-off.
    b. natural seeps and urban run-off.
    c. normal oil tanker/shipping operations and urban run-off.
    d. oil tanker and blowout accidents in marine coastal waters.
    e. tar balls and oil tanker accidents.
Answer: C
Key Question: 7
Skill: comprehension
Difficulty: Level 2

55. The most biologically devastating oil spills in the marine environment are a result of:
    a. blowout accidents on drilling platforms.
    b. collision and/or sinking of oil tankers.
    c. discharge from refueling tankers and ships.
    d. natural deep-sea seeps.
    e. urban run-off.
Answer: B
Key Question: 7
Skill: knowledge
Difficulty: Level 1

56. The largest petroleum spill in the marine waters to date is attributed to the:
    a. *Argo Merchant.*
    b. *Exxon Valdez.*
    c. M/V *New Carissa.*
    d. Persian Gulf War of 1991.
    e. Petroleus Mexicanos drilling operations.
Answer: D
Key Question: 7
Skill: knowledge
Difficulty: Level 1

57. Natural processes which help to remove oil spills from the ocean include all of the following **except**:
    a. evaporation from the ocean surface.
    b. digestion of significant amount by fish populations.
    c. dispersal due to wave and wind action.
    d. sinking due to aggregation into tarry lumps.
    e. sinking of coated particles.
Answer: B
Key Question: 7
Skill: comprehension
Difficulty: Level 2

58. Bioremediation has been particularly effective in marine ecosystems in the clean-up of:
    a. heavy metals.
    b. hydrocarbons.
    c. nitrates.
    d. pesticides
    e. thermal effluents.
Answer: B
Key Question: 7
Skill: comprehension
Difficulty: Level 2

59. Plastics cause significant biological damage in oceans when:
    a. degradation is rapid releasing toxins into the environment.
    b. netting strangles seals and birds.
    c. pellets appear in the sediments.
    d. plastics degrade in DDT.
    e. they result in increased bacteria levels.
Answer: B
Key Question: 7
Skill: knowledge
Difficulty: Level 1

60. Secondary sewage treatment is distinguished form primary sewage treatment by the:
    a. addition of bacteria to process organic contaminants.
    b. aeration of liquid effluent following chlorination.
    c. chlorination of the liquid effluent.
    d. removal of inorganic nutrients from the liquid effluent.
    e. separation of the suspended solids from the liquid effluent.
Answer: C
Key Question:
Skill: knowledge
Difficulty: Level 1

61. The deep water dumping site for sewage sludge off the US East Coast initially seemed to be a good choice because:
    a. a well-developed pycnocline should isolate the sewage
    b. internal waves would decrease water mixing
    c. it had been a well-studies method of sewage disposal
    d. thermal mixing occurred between the surface and deep water.
    e. tsunamis are uncommon in this area
Answer: A
Key Question: 7
Skill: comprehension
Difficulty: Level 2

62. Which of the following organisms are expected to show the highest concentrations of DDT and other chlorinated hydrocarbons in its tissues?

    a. carnivorous fishes
    b. filter-feeding fishes
    c. phytoplankton
    d. sea otters
    e. zooplankton

Answer: D
Key Question: 7
Skill: application
Difficulty: Level 3

63. Dead zones resulting from hypoxia and anoxia:
    a. are prevalent in coastal waters west of the Mississippi River delta during the summer months.
    b. increase the standing stock of demersal fishes.
    c. occur exclusively in estuarine environments.
    d. result from significant inputs of organic hydrocarbons in marine environments.
    e. stimulate high primary productivity in coastal areas.

Answer: A
Key Question: 7
Skill: knowledge
Difficulty: Level 1

64. Minamata disease is associated with:
    a. dinoflagellates in tropical reef ecosystems.
    b. eutrophication.
    c. harmful algal blooms.
    d. illegal fishing in tropical areas.
    e. ingestion of methyl mercury-contaminated fish and shellfish

Answer: E
Key Question: 7
Skill: knowledge
Difficulty: Level 1

65. Point sources of municipal and industrial wastes in the United States are governed by:
    a. Federal Clean Water Act.
    b. Marine Protection, Research and Sanctuaries Act.
    c. Oceans Act of 2000.
    d. Ocean Dumping Ban Act.
    e. Rivers and Harbors Act.

Answer: A
Key Question: 4
Skill: knowledge
Difficulty: Level 1

12

Marine Life and the Marine Environment

Matching. Match the marine zone with its correct location. Use each choice once, more than once, or not at all.

1. abyssal
2. abyssopelagic
3. bathyl
4. epipelagic
5. hadal
6. littoral
7. mesopelagic
8. subtidal

A. benthic
B. neritic
C. pelagic

Answers: 1-A, 2-C, 3-A, 4-C, 5-A, 6-B, 7-C, 8-A & B
Key Question: 6
Skill: knowledge
Difficulty: Level 1

Matching. Match the description of the marine organism's lifestyle with the correct term. Use each choice once, more than once, or not at all.

9. cannot swim against a current
10. floats for a portion of its life
11. lives above benthic sediments
12. lives in benthic sediments
13. swims for its entire life

A. epifauna
B. holoplankton
C. infauna
D. meroplankton
E. nanoplankton
F. nekton
G. picoplankton

Answers: 9-B, 10-D, 11-A, 12-C, 13-F
Key Question: 2
Skill: knowledge
Difficulty: Level 1

Marine Life and the Marine Environment

True-False Questions. Read each question carefully, write "T" if the statement is true, and write "F" if the statement is false.

14. Cold, high viscosity water benefits floating organisms.
Answer: True
Key Question: 5
Skill: comprehension
Difficulty: Level 1

15. Streamlining in fish means that the minimum amount of energy is expended to swim.
Answer: True
Key Question: 5
Skill: comprehension
Difficulty: Level 2

16. Osmosis occurs when salt ions diffuse through a membrane with a lower ion concentration.
Answer: False
Key Question: 4
Skill: knowledge
Difficulty: Level 1

17. A euryhaline organism would be poorly adapted to living in coastal environments.
Answer: False
Key Question: 4
Skill: knowledge
Difficulty: Level 1

18. Stenothermal organisms are likely to be found in deep open ocean water.
Answer: True
Key Question: 4
Skill: knowledge
Difficulty: Level 1

19. Phytoplankton are small in size as a result of predation pressure.
Answer: False
Key Question: 5
Skill: comprehension
Difficulty: Level 2

20. One reason that polar climates support a high biomass is that cold water can hold more dissolved oxygen.
Answer: True
Key Question: 5
Skill: comprehension
Difficulty: Level 2

21. The majority of marine species are pelagic.

Answer: False
Key Question: 6
Skill: knowledge
Difficulty: Level 1

22. The neritic province is associated with the continental shelf.
Answer: True
Key Question: 6
Skill: knowledge
Difficulty: Level 1

23. The depth of the oxygen minimum is found in the bathypelagic zone.
Answer: False
Key Question: 6
Skill: knowledge
Difficulty: Level 1

24. The depth of the nutrient maximum is found at the base of the mesopelagic zone.
Answer: True
Key Question: 6
Skill: knowledge
Difficulty: Level 1

25. The deep scattering layer is produced by masses of migrating phytoplankton.
Answer: True
Key Question: 6
Skill: knowledge
Difficulty: Level 1

26. The euphotic zone is contained entirely in the epipelagic zone.
Answer: True
Key Question: 6
Skill: knowledge
Difficulty: Level 1

27. Epifauna live deep within benthic sediments.
Answer: False
Key Question: 6
Skill: knowledge
Difficulty: Level 1

28. The hadal zone is associated with deep-ocean trenches.
Answer: True
Key Question: 6
Skill: knowledge
Difficulty: Level 1

Multiple Choice. Choose the one **best** answer from the choices provided.

29. Which of the following statements concerning bacteria is **not true**?
    a. Bacteria can be found living in extreme environments (heat, salinity, cold, etc.).
    b. Bacteria have a cell membrane and a cell wall.
    c. Bacteria lack membrane-bound organelles and a distinct nucleus surrounded by a nuclear membrane.
    d. Bacteria reproduce asexually only.
    e. Bacteria were the first type of cells to evolve on earth.
Answer: D
Key Question: 1
Skill: comprehension
Difficulty: Level 2

30. Which of the following statements shows the correct hierarchical ordering of taxonomic levels in terms of increasing specificity?
    a. class, family, genus, kingdom, order, phylum, species
    b. genus, species order, family, kingdom, phylum, class
    c. kingdom, phylum, class, order, family, genus, species
    d. order, family, genus, species, kingdom, phylum, class
    e. phylum, class, order, kingdom, family, genus, species
Answer: C
Key Question: 1
Skill: comprehension
Difficulty: Level 2

31. Multicellular organisms that are comprised of eukarytotic, heterotrophic cells with cell walls would most likely belong to the kingdom:
    a. Animalia.
    b. Fungi.
    c. Monera.
    d. Plantae.
    e. Protista.
Answer: B
Key Question: 1
Skill: application
Difficulty: Level 3

32. Which of the following associations is **incorrect**?
    a. Kingdom Animalia – dolphins
    b. Kingdom Fungi – mushrooms
    c. Kingdom Monera – bacteria in hydrothermal vents
    d. Kingdom Plantae – macroalgae
    e. Kingdom Protista – phytoplankton
Answer: D
Key Question: 1
Skill: analysis

Difficulty: Level 4

33. A small size is advantageous for marine organisms because it:
    a. increases the ability to absorb nutrients.
    b. increases the ability of wastes to diffuse out of the organism.
    c. increases the surface area to volume ratio that in turn decreases density.
    d. All of the above statements are advantageous to marine organisms.
    e. None of the above statements are advantageous to marine organisms.
Answer: D
Key Question: 2
Skill: comprehension
Difficulty: Level 2

Refer to the Figure below to answer Questions 34 and 35.

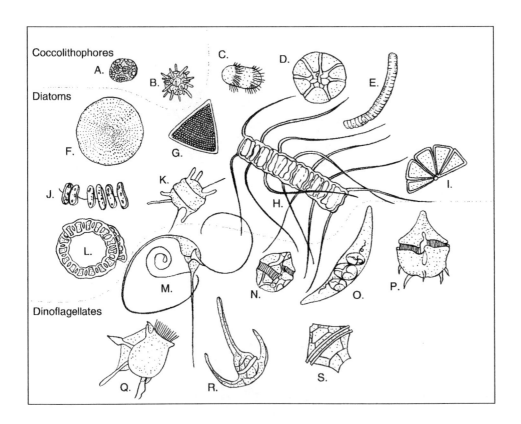

34. These planktonic organisms often have needle-like structures that:
    a. are used as a defense mechanism.
    b. are used as paddles to catch ocean currents.
    c. increase density.
    d. prevent sinking.
    e. serve as a "skeleton" to support the diatom.
Answer: D

Key Question: 2
Skill: comprehension
Difficulty: Level 2

35. The portion of the ocean in which these organisms are most likely to be found is the:
    a. benthic zone.
    b. estuary.
    c. intertidal zone.
    d. pelagic zone.
    e. sediment layer.
Answer: D
Key Question: 2
Skill: Application
Difficulty: Level 3

36. Which of the following word pairs correctly link a descriptor with the way in which the organism lives in the ocean?
    a. benthos – drift
    b. benthos – swim
    c. nekton – bottom-dwelling
    d. nekton – swim
    e. plankton – bottom-dwelling
Answer: D
Key Question: 2
Skill: analysis
Difficulty: Level 4

37. An example of an organism that might be part of the epifauna is a(n):
    a. bull kelp.
    b. feather duster worm.
    c. sea star.
    d. shark.
    e. tuna.
Answer: C
Key Question: 2
Skill: comprehension
Difficulty: Level 2

38. Planktonic organisms that spend part of their life in planktonic form, and the rest of their life as either benthos or nekton are called:
    a. bacterioplankton.
    b. holoplankton.
    c. macroplankton.
    d. meroplankton.
    e. zooplankton.
Answer: D
Key Question: 2
Skill: knowledge

Difficulty: Level 1

39. With respect to their marine environment, these organisms can be referred to as:

    a. benthos.
    b. heterotrophs.
    c. nekton.
    d. plankton.
    e. predators.
Answer: A
Key Question: 2
Skill: comprehension
Difficulty: Level 2

40. Nekton are restricted to particular ocean areas by:
    a. Availability of food.
    b. differences in water pressure with depth.
    c. changes in salinity.
    d. temperature variations with latitude and depth.
    e. All of the above conditions may restrict the distribution of nekton.
Answer: E
Key Question: 2
Skill: comprehension
Difficulty: Level 2

41. When compared to their warmer water counterparts, cold water plankton often:
    a. are larger in size.
    b. are smaller in size.
    c. exhibit countershading.
    d. have more spines and ornamentation on the cell wall.
    e. reproduce asexually only.
Answer: A
Key Question: 3
Skill: comprehension
Difficulty: Level 1

42. High latitude ocean water tends to support large planktonic communities because:
    a. fewer predators that feed on plankton.
    b. longer summer day length.
    c. of higher dissolved gas concentrations.
    d. there is abundant light.
    e. there are abundant nutrients.
Answer: C
Key Question: 3
Skill: comprehension
Difficulty: Level 2

43. All of the following are adaptive solutions employed by marine organisms to prevent sinking **except**:
    a. building a flotation mechanism such as a gas bladder.
    b. decreasing density.
    c. decreasing cellular fat content.
    d. increasing drag in the water.
    e. increasing the surface area to volume ratio.
Answer: C
Key Question: 3
Skill: comprehension
Difficulty: Level 2

44. Plankton which are 2.0 to 0.2 μm in size are called:
    a. nanoplankton.
    b. net plankton.

c. picoplankton.
d. phytoplankton.
e. zooplankton.
Answer: C
Key Question: 3
Skill: knowledge
Difficulty: Level 1

45. Euryhaline organisms:
    a. are less common than stenohaline organisms.
    b. can survive wide salinity fluctuations.
    c. only tolerate small temperature changes.
    d. require less oxygen for survival.
    e. tolerate a narrow range of salinities.
Answer: B
Key Question: 3
Skill: knowledge
Difficulty: Level 1

46. Organisms that cannot withstand large changes in temperature are referred to as:
    a. eurythermal.
    b. euryhaline.
    c. estuarine.
    d. isothermal.
    e. stenothermal.
Answer: E
Key Question: 3
Skill: knowledge
Difficulty: Level 1

47. When an organism has the same salt and water concentration as its environment, it is said to be:
    a. euryhaline.
    b. hypertonic.
    c. hypotonic.
    d. isotonic.
    e. stenohaline.
Answer: C
Key Question: 4
Skill: knowledge
Difficulty: Level 1

48. Osmotic pressure increases as the:
    a. difference in salinity decreases.
    b. difference in salinity increases.
    c. difference in temperature increases.
    d. salinity increases.
    e. temperature increases.

Answer: B
Key Question: 4
Skill: comprehension
Difficulty: Level 2

49. The majority of marine invertebrates are:
    a. adapted to life in the pelagic zone.
    b. estuarine.
    c. found only in benthic environments.
    d. hypertonic with respect to their environment.
    e. isotonic with respect to their environment.
Answer: E
Key Question: 4
Skill: comprehension
Difficulty: Level 2

50. Compared to freshwater fishes, marine fishes:
    a. drink seawater and produce a large volume of urine.
    b. do not drink seawater in an effort to conserve as much water as possible.
    c. produce a large volume of dilute urine in an effort to rid their bodies of excess water.
    d. tend to gain water by osmosis since their internal salt concentration is higher than that of seawater.
    e. tend to lose water by osmosis since their internal salt concentration is lower than that of seawater.
Answer: E
Key Question: 4
Skill: application
Difficulty: Level 3

51. An organism that tolerates a wide range of salinities is referred to as:
    a. euryhaline.
    b. hypertonic.
    c. hypotonic.
    d. isotonic.
    e. stenohaline.
Answer: A
Key Question: 4
Skill: knowledge
Difficulty: Level 1

52. The movement of a substance in solution from an area of higher concentration to an area of lower concentration across a selectively permeable membrane is:
    a. active transport.
    b. Brownian movement.
    c. diffusion.
    d. osmosis.
    e. passive transport.
Answer: D
Key Question: 4

Skill: knowledge
Difficulty: Level 1

53. The color pattern in which marine organisms are light on the bottom and dark on the top of their bodies camouflaging them against the water-air interface is:
    a.   countershading.
    b.   cryptic coloration.
    c.   defensive coloration.
    d.   disruptive coloration.
    e.   warning coloration.
Answer: A
Key Question: 5
Skill: knowledge
Difficulty: Level 1

54. A common body shape that streamlines an organism in the marine environment is a flattened body that:
    a.   has a wide, blunt end.
    b.   tapers at the anterior end.
    c.   tapers at the dorsal surface.
    d.   tapers at the posterior end.
    e.   tapers at the ventral surface.
 Answer: D
Key Question: 5
Skill: comprehension
Difficulty: Level 2

55. The seasonal temperature range in the deep ocean is usually:
    a.   between -2°and 32°C.
    b.   between 0° and 15°C.
    c.   between 2° and 8°C.
    d.   between 8° and °25C.
    e.   negligible.
Answer: E
Key Question: 5
Skill: comprehension
Difficulty: Level 2

56. Coastal waters that are highly productive tend to be:
    a.   brown in color.
    b.   colorless.
    c.   deep blue in color.
    d.   green in color.
    e.   light blue in color.
Answer: D
Key Question: 5

Skill: knowledge
Difficulty: Level 1

57. Most marine species are found in a(n):
      a. bathypelagic environment.
      b. benthic environment.
      c. mesopelagic environment.
      d. oceanic environment.
      e. pelagic environment.
Answer: B
Key Question: 5
Skill: comprehension
Difficulty: Level 2

58. Neritic marine environments would be found:
      a. associated with continental shelves.
      b. at mid-ocean ridges.
      c. deep in the ocean basin.
      d. in subduction zones.
      e. within a deep-sea trench.
Answer: A
Key Question: 6
Skill: knowledge
Difficulty: Level 1

59. Which marine environment exhibits the greatest species diversity?
      a. bathypelagic zone
      b. epipelagic zone
      c. hadal zone
      d. littoral zone
      e. neritic province
Answer: E
Key Question: 6
Skill: comprehension
Difficulty: Level 2

60. The photic zone is confined to the:
      a. abyssopelagic zone.
      b. bathypelagic zone.
      c. epipelagic zone.
      d. mesopelagic zone.
      e. neritic province.
Answer: C
Key Question: 6
Skill: comprehension
Difficulty: Level 2

61. Neritic environments are influenced by:
    a. seasonal salinity variations.
    b. seasonal temperature fluctuations.
    c. tidal movements.
    d. wave energy.
    e. All of the above factors influence neritic environments.
Answer: E
Key Question: 6
Skill: comprehension
Difficulty: Level 2

62. The sublittoral (subtidal) zone is the area:
    a. above the highest tide.
    b. below the intertidal zone on the continental shelf.
    c. between the highest high tide and the lowest low tide.
    d. beyond the continental shelf.
    e. Where demersal and pelagic organisms are found.
Answer: B
Key Question: 6
Skill: knowledge
Difficulty: Level 1

63. Zonation of benthic organisms includes all of the following **except** the:
    a. abyssal zone.
    b. bathyl zone.
    c. hadal zone.
    d. neritic zone.
    e. subtidal zone.
Answer: D
Key Question: 6
Skill: comprehension
Difficulty: Level 2

64. Organisms of the mesopelagic zone are characterized by:
    a. bioluminescence.
    b. large, sensitive eyes.
    c. no eyes.
    d. **a** and **b** are correct.
    e. **a** and **c** are correct.
Answer: D
Key Question: 6
Skill: comprehension
Difficulty: Level 2

65. Organisms with small, expandable bodies, extremely large mouths, and efficient teeth are likely to be found in the:

    a. bathypelagic zone.
    b. epipelagic zone.
    c. mesopelagic zone.
    d. neritic province.
    e. photic zone.
Answer: A
Key Question: 6
Skill: comprehension
Difficulty: Level 2

13
Biological Productivity and Energy Transfer

Matching. Match the organism with its correct descriptor of energy use. Use each choice once, more than once, or not at all.

1. cyanobacteria
2. bacteria
3. flounder
4. kelp
5. *Sargassum*
6. starfish

A. consumer
B. decomposer
C. producer

Answers: 1-C, 2-B, 3-A, 4-C, 5-C, 6-A
Key Question: 5
Skill: knowledge
Difficulty: Level 1

Matching. Match the organism with the correct description of its food preference. Use each choice once, more than once, or not at all.

7. bacteria
8. baleen whale
9. brittle star
10. *Ceratium*
11. diatom
12. dolphin
13. fan worm
14. krill
15. grouper

A. autotroph
B. carnivore
C. decomposer
D. detritivore
E. herbivore
F. omnivore

Answers: 7-C, 8-E, 9-B, 10-A, 11-A, 12-B, 13-F, 14-E. 15-B
Key Question: 5 & 6

Skill: knowledge
Difficulty: Level 1

Matching. Match the organism with the correct description of its food preference. Use each choice once, more than once, or not at all.

16. by-catch
17. mariculture
18. Marine Mammals Act of 1992
19. maximum sustainable yield
20. standing stock

A. available biomass of target species
B. catch limit
C. catch size that reduces the population of target species
D. dolphin protection
E. farming of commercial shellfish and finfish
F. incidental catch
G. maximum catch without reducing the population of target species
H. target species juveniles
I. TEDs

Answers: 16-F, 17-E, 18-D, 19-G, 20-A
Key Question: 7
Skill: knowledge
Difficulty: Level 1

True-False Questions. Read each question carefully, write "T" if the statement is true, and write "F" if the statement is false.

21. The by-products of photosynthesis are carbon dioxide (CO_2) and water (H_2O).
Answer: False
Key Question: 1
Skill: knowledge
Difficulty: Level 1

22. Bacteria that manufacture carbohydrates in the absence of solar energy from inorganic carbon are autotrophs.
Answer: True
Key Question: 1
Skill: knowledge
Difficulty: Level 1

23. Net primary production can be estimated as the amount of photosynthesis plus the amount of respiration.
Answer: False
Key Question: 2

Skill: comprehension
Difficulty: Level 2

24. The group of marine algae with the highest abundance and greatest geographic distribution belong to the Division Rhodophyta.
Answer: True
Key Question: 3
Skill: comprehension
Difficulty: Level 2

25. Most marine algae are limited to depths above 100 meters; red algae have been observed growing at depths of over 250 meters.
Answer: True
Key Question: 3
Skill: knowledge
Difficulty: Level 1

26. Diatoms are classified as members of the Division Chlorophyta.
Answer: False
Key Question: 3
Skill: knowledge
Difficulty: Level 1

27. Marine algae that grow close to the limits of light penetration have accessory photosynthetic pigments that absorb high energy, short-wavelength light in the blue region of the electromagnetic spectrum.
Answer: True
Key Question: 3
Skill: application
Difficulty: Level 3

28. An overabundance of organic matter results in eutrophication.
Answer: False
Key Question: 3
Skill: knowledge
Difficulty: Level 1

29. Tropical marine waters have the highest rate of primary productivity in the world's oceans.
Answer: False
Key Question: 4
Skill: comprehension
Difficulty: Level 2

30. Primary productivity in temperate marine systems is limited by the amount of available solar radiation.
Answer: False
Key Question: 4
Skill: comprehension

Difficulty: Level 2

31. Energy flow is unidirectional in contrast to nutrients, which cycle in ecosystems.
Answer: True
Key Question: 5
Skill: comprehension
Difficulty: Level 2

32. If the total caloric content of the autotrophic organisms in a marine ecosystem were 250,000 KCAL, then the expected caloric value for the second-level consumers would be 25,000 KCAL.
Answer: False
Key Question: 6
Skill: Application
Difficulty: Level 3

33. Consumers, producers, and decomposers are all examples of trophic levels within a food chain or food web.
Answer: True
Key Question: 6
Skill: knowledge
Difficulty: Level 1

Multiple Choice. Choose the one **best** answer from the choices provided.

34. In primary production:
    a. carbon dioxide is released into the water.
    b. oxygen is utilized by plants.
    c. oxygen utilized by animals is less than the oxygen consumed by autotrophs.
    d. proteins are made by animals.
    e. there is a net gain in organic carbon.
Answer: E
Key Question: 1
Skill: comprehension
Difficulty: Level 2

35. Bacteria that make their own carbohydrates by obtaining energy from chemical compounds and not directly from the sun are:
    a. chemoautotrophs.
    b. cyanobacteria.
    c. heterotrophs.
    d. phytoplankton.
    e. protists.
Answer: A
Key Question: 1

Skill: knowledge
Difficulty: Level 1

36. Net primary productivity is:
    a. net gain in organic carbon.
    b. photosynthesis minus cellular respiration.
    c. total amount of photosynthesis.
    d. **A** and **B** are correct.
    e. **A** and **C** are correct.
Answer: D
Key Question: 1
Skill: comprehension
Difficulty: Level 2

37. The nutrients that tend to limit photosynthesis in marine environments include:
    a. carbon dioxide.
    b. nitrogen.
    c. phosphorus.
    d. **A** and **B** are correct.
    e. **B** and **C** are correct.
Answer: E
Key Question: 2
Skill: knowledge

Difficulty: Level 2

38. The depth at which the cellular respiration rate equals the photosynthetic rate is referred to as the:
    a. calcium compensation depth.
    b. epipelagic depth.
    c. euphotic zone.
    d. oxygen compensation depth.
    e. productive zone.
Answer: D
Key Question: 2
Skill: comprehension
Difficulty: Level 2

39. The most abundant marine algae are members of the Division:
    a. Bacillariophyta.
    b. Chlorophyta.
    c. Chrysophyta.
    d. Phaeophyta.
    e. Rhodophyta.
Answer: E
Key Question: 3
Skill: comprehension
Difficulty: Level 2

40. Diatoms, important producers in the epipelagic open ocean, are members of the Division:
    a. Angiospermae.
    b. Bacillariophyta.
    c. Chlorophyta.
    d. Haptophyta.
    e. Pyrrophyta.

Answer: B
Key Question: 3
Skill: knowledge
Difficulty: Level 1

41. The organism that is responsible for *red tides* and *paralytic shellfish poisoning* belongs to the Division:
    a. Bacillariophyta.
    b. Chlorophyta.
    c. Phaeophyta.
    d. Pyrrophyta.
    e. Rhodophyta.

Answer: D
Key Question: 3
Skill: application
Difficulty: Level 3

42. An important marine autotroph that has SiO_2 incorporated in the cell walls are:
    a. coccolithophorids.
    b. cyanobacteria.
    c. diatoms.
    d. dinoflagellates.
    e. radiolarians.

Answer: C
Key Question: 3
Skill: application
Difficulty: Level 3

43. Marine flowering plants include all of the following **except:**
    a. eel grass.
    b. mangroves.
    c. *Spartina alterniflora.*
    d. turtle grass.
    e. *Ulva.*

Answer: E
Key Question: 3
Skill: knowledge
Difficulty: Level 1

44. Overproduction of organic matter resulting in anoxic conditions is attributed to:

a. autotrophication.
b. eutrophication.
c. net primary productivity.
d. photoperiodicity.
e. phototropism.

Answer: B
Key Question: 4
Skill: comprehension
Difficulty: Level 2

45. Harmful algal blooms (HABs):
    a. are attributed to *Vibriobacter cholerae*.
    b. are caused by diatoms and coccolithophorids.
    c. do not affect coastal fisheries.
    d. have decreased in frequency since 1992.
    e. may produce toxins that affect human neurological functioning.

Answer: E
Key Question: 4
Skill: knowledge
Difficulty: Level 1

46. Eutrophication is a type of pollution caused by increased:
    a. concentration of hydrocarbons.
    b. inorganic nutrient input.
    c. primary productivity.
    d. salinity.
    e. water temperature.

Answer: B
Key Question: 4
Skill: knowledge
Difficulty: Level 1

47. The relative productivity in the world's oceans from most productive to least productive is:
    a. polar waters, temperate waters, tropical waters.
    b. polar waters, tropical waters, temperate waters.
    c. temperate waters, polar waters, tropical waters.
    d. temperate waters, tropical waters, polar waters.
    e. tropical waters, temperate waters, polar waters.

Answer: A
Key Question: 4
Skill: knowledge
Difficulty: Level 1

48. In temperate oceans during the winter months:
    a. nutrient concentrations are high, solar input is low, and water temperatures decrease.
    b. nutrient concentrations are high, solar input is high, and water temperatures decrease.
    c. nutrient concentrations are high, solar input is high, and water temperatures increase.

d. nutrient concentrations are low, solar input is high, and water temperatures decrease.

e. nutrient concentrations are low, solar input is low, and water temperatures decrease.

Answer: A
Key Question: 4
Skill: application
Difficulty: Level 3

49. In temperate oceans during the summer months:
   a. nutrient concentrations are high, solar input is low, and oxygen solubility decreases.
   b. nutrient concentrations are high, solar input is high, and oxygen solubility decreases.
   c. nutrient concentrations are high, solar input is high, and oxygen solubility increases.
   d. nutrient concentrations are low, solar input is high, and oxygen solubility decreases.
   e. nutrient concentrations are low, solar input is high, and oxygen solubility increases.

Answer: D
Key Question: 4
Skill: application
Difficulty: Level 3

50. Although primary productivity in tropical areas is generally low, which of the following tropical locations have unusually high primary productivity rates?
   a. coastal upwelling zones
   b. coral reefs
   c. equatorial upwelling zones
   d. mangrove swamps
   e. All of the above tropical areas have relatively high primary productivity.

Answer: E
Key Question: 4
Skill: comprehension
Difficulty: Level 2

51. An area of the open ocean where the rate of primary productivity is very low is referred to as a(n):
   a. atrophic zone.
   b. eutrophic area.
   c. oligotrophic area.
   d. photic zone.
   e. polytrophic area.

Answer: C
Key Question: 4
Skill: knowledge
Difficulty: Level 1

52. Productivity in polar oceans is:
   a. light-limited.
   b. nutrient-limited.
   c. oxygen-limited.
   d. light and nutrient-limited.
   e. nutrient and oxygen-limited.

Answer: A
Key Question: 4
Skill: comprehension
Difficulty: Level 2

53. Productivity in tropical oceans is:
    a. light-limited.
    b. nutrient-limited.
    c. oxygen-limited.
    d. light and nutrient-limited.
    e. nutrient and oxygen-limited.
Answer: B
Key Question: 4
Skill: comprehension
Difficulty: Level 2

54. If 10,000 KCAL of energy were contained in the primary producers, on average how many KCAL of energy would you expect to be transferred to third-order consumers?
    a. 10,000 KCAL
    b. 1000 KCAL
    c. 100 KCAL
    d. 10 KCAL
    e. 1 KCAL
Answer: D
Key Question: 5
Skill: application
Difficulty: Level 3

55. Nutrient flow in an ecosystem is:
    a. bi-directional.
    b. cyclic.
    c. semi-conservative.
    d. top down.
    e. unidirectional.
Answer: B
Key Question: 5
Skill: comprehension
Difficulty: Level 1

56. Energy flow in an ecosystem is:
    a. bi-directional.
    b. cyclic.
    c. semi-conservative.
    d. top down..
    e. unidirectional.
Answer: E
Key Question: 5

Biological Productivity and Energy Transfer

Skill: comprehension
Difficulty: Level 1

57. The efficiency of trophic transfers in ecosystems is on average around:
    a. 75%.
    b. 50%.
    c. 30%.
    d. 10%.
    e. 5%.
Answer: D
Key Question: 5
Skill: knowledge
Difficulty: Level 1

58. Identify the mismatched pair.
    a. barnacles-whales
    b. remora-shark
    c. resurrection ferns-live oak trees
    d. Spanish moss-live oak trees
    e. zooxanthallae-coral
Answer: E
Key Question: 6
Skill: analysis
Difficulty: Level 4

59. Which of the following pairs is an incorrect match between organisms and the type of symbiotic relationship they manifest?
    a. coral-dinoflagellates: mutualism
    b. fish-isopods: parasitism
    c. grouper-cleaner wrasse: commensalism
    d. shark-remora: commensalism
    e. whale-barnacle: mutualism
Answer: E
Key Question: 6
Skill: analysis
Difficulty: Level 4

60. The percentage of biomass regularly recycled in the euphotic zone is about:
    a. 1 %.
    b. 10%
    c. 30%
    d. 50%
    e. 90%.
Answer: E
Key Question: 6
Skill: knowledge
Difficulty: Level 1

61. The percentage of euphotic zone biomass that reaches the deep ocean floor is approximately:
    a. 1 %.
    b. 10%
    c. 30%
    d. 50%
    e. 90%.
Answer: A
Key Question: 6
Skill: knowledge
Difficulty: Level 1

62. A symbiotic relationship in which one organism benefits and the other is unaffected is:
    a. commensalism.
    b. ectoparasitism.
    c. endoparasitism.
    d. mutualism.
    e. predation.
Answer: A
Key Question: 6
Skill: knowledge
Difficulty: Level 1

63. The relationship between cyanobacteria and fungi that results in a lichen is an example of:
    a. commensalism.
    b. ectoparasitism.
    c. endoparasitism.
    d. mutualism.
    e. predation.
Answer: D
Key Question: 6
Skill: comprehension
Difficulty: Level 2

64. The maximum sustainable yield (MSY) is best defined as:
    a. annual harvest that will balance natural mortality and predation.
    b. largest catch that can be taken without overfishing.
    c. largest catch that will cover the minimum cost of fishing.
    d. maximum fishing effort allowed after overfishing occurs.
    e. Minimum catch that will still allow the population to increase.
Answer: B
Key Question: 7
Skill: knowledge
Difficulty: Level 1

65. The area of the ocean that produces the largest standing stock of commercial fish is in the:
    a. coastal areas.
    b. epipelagic zone.

    c. mesopelagic zone.

    d. tropical areas.

    e. upwelling areas.

Answer: A

Key Question: 7

Skill: knowledge

Difficulty: Level 1

66. The term-by catch refers to:

    a. krill and other shellfish.

    b. non-target species that are caught along with commercial species.

    c. species caught as part of traditional fisheries.

    d. species harvested for industrial purposes.

    e. species raised in aquaculture settings.

Answer: B

Key Question: 7

Skill: knowledge

Difficulty: Level 1

67. All of the following are effective means of regulating fisheries **except**:

    a. Limiting the length of the fishing season.

    b. Limiting the size of the boat.

    c. Restricting the location of a legal catch.

    d. Setting catch limits.

    e. Setting gear limits.

Answer: B

Key Question: 7

Skill: comprehension

Difficulty: Level 2

68. Catches above the maximum sustainable yield:

    a. can be increased to prevent overfishing.

    b. produce decreased fishing effort.

    c. result in increased populations of the target species.

    d. result in overfishing.

    e. result in underutilization of the target species.

Answer: D

Key Question: 7

Skill: knowledge

Difficulty: Level 1

69. Purse seines are nets that:

    a. are allowed to drift at the surface.

    b. are dragged along the bottom or through the water column.

    c. float at the surface.

    d. placed along the bottom to trap passing fishes.

    e. surround and trap fishes.

Answer: E
Key Question: 7
Skill: comprehension
Difficulty: Level 2

70. The mass present at a given time of a population of fish is called its:
    a. diversity.
    b. fish stock.
    c. maximum sustainable yield.
    d. recruitment mass.
    e. standing stock.
Answer: E
Key Question: 7
Skill: knowledge
Difficulty: Level 1

CHAPTER
14
Animals of the Pelagic Environment

Matching. Match the organism with the correct taxonomic classification. Use each choice once, more than once, or not at all.

1. blue whale
2. bottlenose dolphin
3. dugong
4. fur seal
5. gray whale
6. killer whale
7. manatee
8. sea lion
9. sperm whale
10. walrus

A. Order Carnivora
B. Order Cetacea, Suborder Mysticeti
C. Order Cetacea, Suborder Odontoceti
D. Order Pinnipedia
E. Order Sirenia

Answers: 1-B, 2-C, 3-E, 4-D, 5-B, 6-C, 7-E, 8-D, 9-C, 10-D
Key Question: 5
Skill: knowledge
Difficulty: Level 1

Matching. Match the organism with the correct caudal fin shape. Use each choice once, more than once, or not at all.

11. blue marlin
12. bluefin tuna
13. flounder
14. gray angelfish
15. herring
16. queen angel
17. salmon
18. silvertip shark
19. tiger shark
20. yellowtail snapper

A. forked caudal fin
B. heterocercal caudal fin
C. lunate caudal fin
D. rounded caudal fin
E. truncate caudal fin

Answers: 11-C, 12-C, 13-D, 14-E, 15-A, 16-D, 17-E, 18-B, 19-B, 20-A

Key Question: 2
Skill: knowledge
Difficulty: Level 1

True-False Questions. Read each question carefully, write "T" if the statement is true, and write "F" if the statement is false.

21. Strategies for staying afloat in pelagic environments include air bladder, increased body fat, and increased density.
Answer: False
Key Question: 1
Skill: comprehension
Difficulty: Level 2

22. Sharks have lunate caudal fins.
Answer: False
Key Question: 2
Skill: knowledge
Difficulty: Level 1

23. Some fish maintain body temperatures significantly higher than the surrounding water using a modified circulatory countercurrent heat exchange system between muscle and blood vessels.
Answer: True
Key Question: 3
Skill: knowledge
Difficulty: Level 1

24. Muscles segments used in locomotion and found along the sides of fish are called myomeres.
Answer: True
Key Question: 4
Skill: knowledge
Difficulty: Level 1

25. Red muscles fiber is abundant in cruisers, while white muscle fiber is abundant in lungers.
Answer: True
Key Question:34
Skill: comprehension
Difficulty: Level 2

26. We currently believe that all marine mammals evolved from land-dwelling mammals.
Answer: True
Key Question: 5
Skill: knowledge
Difficulty: Level 1

27. One adaptation for deep diving is an increase in heart rate during the dive.
Answer: False
Key Question: 5
Skill: comprehension
Difficulty: Level 2

28. Many cetaceans can extract 90% of the oxygen from each breath.
Answer: True
Key Question: 5
Skill: knowledge
Difficulty: Level 1

29. The mysticeti whales include the humpback, the gray, and the sperm whales.
Answer: False
Key Question: 5
Skill: comprehension
Difficulty: Level 2

30. The California gray whale is unusual because it stirs up bottom sediment in order to feed.
Answer: True
Key Question: 6
Skill: knowledge
Difficulty: Level 1

31. The migration routes of marine fishes and mammals are well known by man.
Answer: False
Key Question: 6
Skill: knowledge
Difficulty: Level 1

Multiple Choice. Choose the one **best** answer from the choices provided.

32. All of the following are adaptations to life in the epipelagic zone **except**:
    a. gas-filled bladders.
    b. increased density.
    c. increased surface area.
    d. long appendages.
    e. spines.
Answer: B
Key Question: 1
Skill: comprehension
Difficulty: 2

33. Which of the following is a member of the Phylum Cnidaria?
    a. Copepod

b. jellyfish
c. nautilus
d. salp
e. sea gooseberry

Answer: B
Key Question: 1
Skill: knowledge
Difficulty: Level 1

34. Identify the mismatched pair.
    a. arrow worm – Chaetognatha
    b. krill – Arthropoda
    c. *Physalia* – Cnidaria
    d. Sea gooseberry – Ctenophora
    e. Squid – Annelida

Answer: E
Key Question: 1
Skill: Analysis
Difficulty: Level 4

35. Barrel-shaped animals with openings at each end for current flow are called:
    a. cephalopods.
    b. cnidarians.
    c. crustaceans.
    d. ctenophores.
    e. salps.

Answer: E
Key Question: 2
Skill: knowledge
Difficulty: Level 1

36. Which set of fins is used for turning and breaking?
    a. anal and caudal
    b. anal and dorsal
    c. caudal and dorsal
    d. caudal and pelvic
    e. pectoral and pelvic

Answer: E
Key Question: 2
Skill: comprehension
Difficulty: Level 2

37. Which set of fins is used as stabilizers?
    a. anal and caudal
    b. anal and dorsal
    c. caudal and dorsal

Animals of the Pelagic Environment

    d.   caudal and pelvic
    e.   pectoral and pelvic
Answer: B
Key Question: 2
Skill: comprehension
Difficulty: Level 2

38. Which set of fins is used for moving fast?
    a.   anal and dorsal
    b.   caudal
    c.   caudal and pectoral
    d.   pectoral
    e.   pectoral and pelvic
Answer: C
Key Question: 2
Skill: comprehension
Difficulty: Level 2

39. The shape of the caudal fin of a shark is referred to as:
    a.   forked.
    b.   heterocercal.
    c.   lunate.
    d.   rounded.
    e.   truncate.
Answer: B
Key Question: 2
Skill: comprehension
Difficulty: Level 2

40. The caudal fin of fast-cruising fish such as tuna is:
    a.   forked.
    b.   heterocercal.
    c.   lunate.
    d.   rounded.
    e.   truncate.
Answer: C
Key Question: 2
Skill: comprehension
Difficulty: Level 2

41. The fin(s) that have been modified in rays and skates for efficient movement is (are) the:
    a.   anal fin.
    b.   caudal fin.
    c.   dorsal fin.
    d.   pectoral fins.
    e.   pelvic fin.
Answer: D

Key Question: 2
Skill: comprehension
Difficulty: Level 2

42. The body shape among fishes varies greatly in accordance with habitat and life-style. A torpedo-shaped body is found among:
    a.   bottom-dwelling fishes.
    b.   demersal fishes.
    c.   fast swimming fishes.
    d.   fishes that live among rocks and vegetation.
    e.   slow swimming fishes.
Answer: C
Key Question: 3
Skill: application
Difficulty: Level 3

43. Which of the following is not an adaptation for deep diving in Cetaceans?
    a.   blood flow is shifted from the brain to the extremities.
    b.   collapsing the lungs to compensate for increasing water pressure during deep dives.
    c.   having a lot of myoglobin in the muscles to store oxygen.
    d.   having increased hemoglobin concentrations to store more oxygen.
    e.   slowed cardiac rate.
Answer: A
Key Question: 5
Skill: comprehension
Difficulty: Level 2

44. A modified circulatory system in tuna helps it:
    a.   cruise for long periods of time.
    b.   maintain a relatively high body temperature.
    c.   minimize heat loss.
    d.   swim very fast for short periods of time.
    e.   All of the above statements are a result of modified circulation in tuna.
Answer: E
Key Question: 5
Skill: comprehension
Difficulty: Level 2

45. All of the following are adaptations of mesopelagic fishes **except**:
    a.   Extensible jaws.
    b.   Large mouths
    c.   Large body.
    d.   Nonspecific diet.
    e.   Sharp, needle-like teeth
Answer: B
Key Question: 3

Skill: knowledge
Difficulty: Level 1

46. Bioluminescence is employed by mesopelagic animals for all of the following **except**:
    a. attracting food.
    b. communication.
    c. counter illumination.
    d. predator avoidance.
    e. warning coloration.
Answer: D
Key Question: 3
Skill: comprehension
Difficulty: Level 2

47. Which of the following affect the ability of species to capture food?
    a. body length
    b. body temperature
    c. circulatory system
    d. speed
    e. All of the above affect the ability of pelagic organisms to capture food.
Answer: E
Key Question: 3
Skill: comprehension
Difficulty: Level 2

48. An example of a "cruiser" is a:
    a. flounder.
    b. grouper.
    c. mackerel.
    d. shark.
    e. tuna.
Answer: E
Key Question: 3
Skill: knowledge
Difficulty: Level 1

49. The muscle tissue of a "lunger" is predominantly:
    a. blue.
    b. gray.
    c. pink.
    d. red.
    e. white.
Answer: E
Key Question: 3
Skill: knowledge
Difficulty: Level 1

50. The speed of a fish is closely related to its:
    a. aspect ratio.
    b. length.
    c. number of fins.
    d. size of tail.
    e. width.
Answer: B
Key Question: 3
Skill: knowledge
Difficulty: Level 1

51. Cruisers often have relatively high body temperature because:
    a. it assists them in predator avoidance.
    b. it helps them blend more easily with their environment
    c. it increases the power output of muscle tissue
    d. they are cold blooded
    e. they only need to move periodically
Answer: C
Key Question: 3
Skill: comprehension
Difficulty: Level 2

52. All of the following are benefits the adaptive behavior in the figure because it:

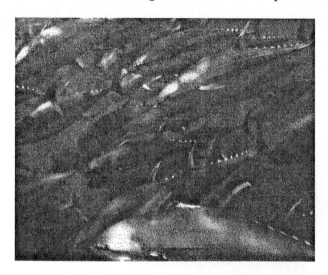

    a. confuses predators by constantly changing positions of the fish within the school.
    b. makes the group of fish appear as one large unit.
    c. reduces the mortality rate for individuals within the school
    d. reduces the probability that a predator will locate the prey species.
    e. All of the above behaviors are beneficial to schooling fish.
Answer: E

Key Question: 4
Skill: application
Difficulty: Level 3

53. All of the following are baleen whales **except**:
    a. blue whales.
    b. fin whales.
    c. gray whales.
    d. right whales.
    e. sperm whales.
Answer: E
Key Question: 5
Skill: knowledge
Difficulty: Level 1

54. Identify the mismatched pair.
    a. dolphin –Cetacea
    b. dugong – Sirenia
    c. manatee – Cetacea
    d. sea otter – Carnivora
    e. walrus – Pinnipedia
Answer: C
Key Question: 5
Skill: Analysis
Difficulty: Level 4

55. This marine mammal:

    a. are small mammals with dense fur and lack an insulating blubber layer.

b. are tropical herbivores found in shallow coastal waters.

c. have anterior flippers covered with hair that cannot be rotated backwards.

d. have posterior flippers than can be moved forward.

e. have thick fur with hollow fur shafts for insulation.

Answer: A

Key Question: 5

Skill: application

Difficulty: Level 2

56. Sea lions are easily distinguished from seals because they:
    a. cannot rotate their anterior flippers backward.
    b. cannot rotate their anterior flippers forward.
    c. have external ears.
    d. have a short neck.
    e. use their posterior flippers for swimming.

Answer: C

Key Question: 5

Skill: knowledge

Difficulty: Level 1

57. The humpback and other baleen whales migrate every year to:
    a. feed in the Arctic and Antarctic regions during the winter.
    b. feed in the tropics during the summer.
    c. feed in the tropics during the winter.
    d. mate and give birth in the Arctic and Antarctic regions during the summer.
    e. mate and give birth in the tropics during the winter.

Answer: D

Key Question: 6

Skill: comprehension

Difficulty: Level 2

Word Analysis. Examine the five words and/or phrases and determine the relationship among the majority of words/phrases. Choose the one option that does not fit the pattern.

58. A. arrow worm   B. copepod   C. ctenophore D. jellyfish   E. salp

Answer: B

Key Question: 1

Skill: Analysis

Difficulty: Level 4

59. A. anal   B. caudal   C. dorsal   D. pelvic   E. ventral

Answer: E

Key Question: 2

Skill: Analysis

Difficulty: Level 4

60. A. blubber B. collapsible ribs   C. gas bladder   D. spines E. swim bladder
Answer: B
Key Question: 3
Skill: Analysis
Difficulty: Level 4

61. A. blue   B. gray   C. killer   D. minke   E. sei
Answer: C
Key Question: 5
Skill: Analysis
Difficulty: Level 4

CHAPTER
15
Animals of the Benthic Environment

Matching. Match the organism with the correct habitat in the rocky intertidal zone. Use each answer once, more than once, or not at all. Some organisms may live in more than one habitat.

1. acorn barnacle
2. *Asterias*
3. buckshot barnacle
4. *Fucus*
5. gooseneck barnacle
6. hermit crab
7. limpet
8. *Lithothamnion*
9. *Littorina*
10. mussel
11. sea anemone
12. sea roach
13. sea urchin
14. shore crab
15. surf grass

A. high water intertidal zone
B. low water intertidal zone
C. middle water intertidal zone
D. supralittoral zone
E. tide pool

Answers: 1-B, 2-B, 3-A, 4-A, 5-B, 6-E, 7-D, 8-C, 9-A&D, 10-B, 11-E, 12-D, 13-E, 14-C, 15-C
Key Question: 1
Skill: comprehension
Difficulty: Level 2

Matching. Match the benthic organism with its habitat and latitude. Use each answer once, more than once, or not at all.

16. coral
17. crown-of-thorns starfish
18. eelgrass
19. kelp
20. *Macrocystis*
21. oyster

A. muddy bottom
B. rocky bottom
C. sandy bottom
D. temperate
E. tropical

Animals of the Benthic Environment

22. sand dollar
23. sea otter
24. sea urchin
25. turtle grass

Answers: 16-B&E, 17-B&E, 18-A&D, 19-B&D, 20-B&D, 21-A&D, 22-C,D,&E, 23-B&D, 24-B&D, 25-A&E
Key Question: 1 & 2
Skill: application
Difficulty: Level 3

True-False Questions. Read each question carefully, write "T" if the statement is true, and write "F" if the statement is false.

26. The supralittoral zone of the rocky shore is the area between the highest high tide and the lowest low tide.
Answer: False
Key Question: 1
Skill: knowledge
Difficulty: Level 1

27. Limpets are commonly found in the middle portion of the intertidal zone on a rocky shore.
Answer: False
Key Question: 1
Skill: knowledge
Difficulty: Level 1

28. Fiddler crabs are commonly found inhabitants of tide pools.
Answer: True
Key Question: 1& 2
Skill: knowledge
Difficulty: Level 1

29. Faunal zonation across a sediment-covered shore is best seen when the shore is gently sloping.
Answer: False
Key Question: 2
Skill: comprehension
Difficulty: Level 2

30. Species diversity is highest in coral reef communities.
Answer: True
Key Question: 3
Skill: comprehension
Difficulty: Level 2

31. Coral reefs contain twenty-five percent of all marine species.
Answer: True
Key Question: 3
Skill: knowledge
Difficulty: Level 1

32. The eastern side of an ocean basin tends to have greater diversity of reef-building corals than the western side.
Answer: False
Key Question: 3
Skill: comprehension
Difficulty: Level 2

33. Coral reefs contain more algal biomass than animal biomass.
Answer: True
Key Question: 3
Skill: knowledge
Difficulty: Level 1

34. The increase in the number of crown-of-thorn sea stars has been strong linked to human activities.
Answer: False
Key Question: 3
Skill: knowledge
Difficulty: Level 1

35. Temperature of ocean water has a significant affect on species diversity of benthic communities.
Answer: True
Key Question: 5
Skill: comprehension
Difficulty: Level 2

36. Benthic diversity decreases below upwelling zones.
Answer: True
Key Question: 5
Skill: comprehension
Difficulty: Level 2

37. Zooxanthellae are important members of hydrothermal vent communities.
Answer: False
Key Question: 6
Skill: knowledge
Difficulty: Level 1

38. One characteristic of hydrothermal vent communities is unusually large organisms such as tubeworms and clams.
Answer: True
Key Question: 6

Animals of the Benthic Environment

Skill: knowledge
Difficulty: Level 1

39. Hypersaline seep communities rely on photosynthesis.
Answer: False
Key Question: 6
Skill: knowledge
Difficulty: Level 1

Multiple Choice. Choose the one **best** answer from the choices provided.

Refer to the Figure below to answer questions 40, 41, and 42.

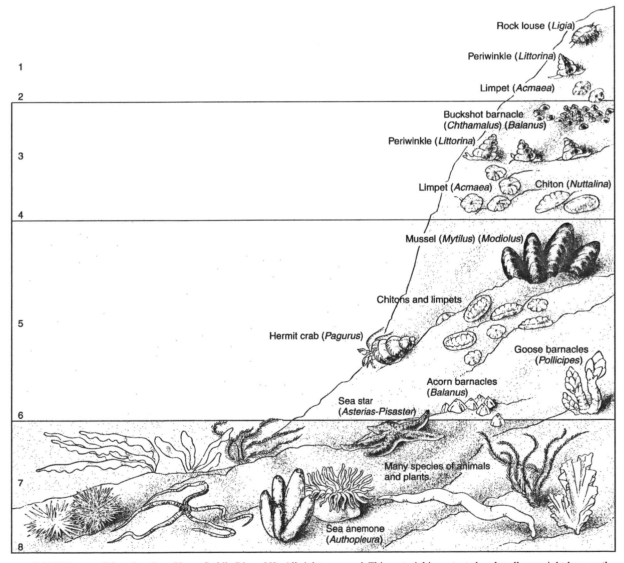

40. Along a rocky shore, the spray zone is indicated by the number:
    a. 1.
    b. 2.
    c. 3.
    d. 5.
    e. 7.
Answer: A
Key Question: 1
Skill: knowledge
Difficulty: Level 1

41. Within the intertidal zone, the area that receives equal amounts of air exposure and water coverage is indicated by the number:
    a. 1.
    b. 3.
    c. 5.
    d. 6.
    e. 7.
Answer: C
Key Question: 1
Skill: comprehension
Difficulty: Level 2

42. The area on a rocky shore that is inhabited by organisms adapted to high wave energy for the majority of the tidal cycle is indicated by the number:
    a. 1.
    b. 2.
    c. 3.
    d. 5.
    e. 7.
Answer: E
Key Question: 1
Skill: comprehension
Difficulty: Level 2

43. All of the following are examples of strategies employed by organisms to reduce wave shock in the rocky intertidal zone **except**:
    a. byssal threads.
    b. flexible stems and blades.
    c. holdfasts.
    d. motile larvae.
    e. the use of suction to attach to rocks.
Answer: D
Key Question: 1
Skill: application
Difficulty: Level 3

44. The most important limiting factor in intertidal communities is:
    a. food.
    b. light.
    c. nutrients.
    d. predation.
    e. space.
Answer: E
Key Question: 1 & 2
Skill: comprehension
Difficulty: Level 2

45. A common inhabitant of the supralittoral zone on the rocky shores of the Pacific Northwest is the:
    a. buckshot barnacle.
    b. limpet.
    c. kelp.
    d. periwinkle snail.
    e. sea urchin.
Answer: D
Key Question: 1
Skill: knowledge
Difficulty: Level 1

46. Two dominant organisms of the rocky shore found high on the rocks of the intertidal zone are:
    a. buckshot barnacle and rockweed.
    b. goose barnacle and mussel.
    c. keyhole limpet and Irish moss.
    d. periwinkle snail and kelp.
    e. sea anemone and hermit crab.
Answer: A
Key Question: 1
Skill: knowledge
Difficulty: Level 1

47. Two frequent inhabitants of a rocky coast tide pools are:
    a. buckshot barnacle and rockweed.
    b. goose barnacle and mussel.
    c. periwinkle snail and kelp.
    d. sea anemone and hermit crab
    e. sea stars and *Ulva*.
Answer: D
Key Question: 1
Skill: knowledge
Difficulty: Level 1

48. Two dominant organisms commonly found at mid-water levels of the rocky intertidal zone are:
    a. buckshot barnacle and rockweed.

    b.   fiddler crab and *Littorina*.
    c.   goose barnacle and mussel.
    d.   periwinkle snail and kelp.
    e.   sea anemone and hermit crab.

Answer: C
Key Question: 1
Skill: knowledge
Difficulty: Level 1

49. Some organisms living in the high water portion of the intertidal zone cannot survive in the
supralittoral zone because they:
    a.   are filter feeders.
    b.   are sessile.
    c.   cannot tolerate desiccation.
    d.   cannot tolerate fluctuating salinity.
    e.   cannot tolerate temperature fluctuations.

Answer: C
Key Question: 1
Skill: comprehension
Difficulty: Level 2

50. The low-water portion of the rocky intertidal zone is dominated by:
    a.   hermit crabs.
    b.   fiddler crabs.
    c.   limpets.
    d.   Mussels.
    e.   seaweeds and surf grasses.

Answer: E
Key Question: 1
Skill: knowledge
Difficulty: Level 2

51. Male fiddler crabs use their enlarged claw to:
    a.   attract a mate.
    b.   defend themselves against predators.
    c.   dig the burrow.
    d.   feed on algae growing on the mud flat surface.
    e,   plug the hole in the burrow when the tide comes in.

Answer: A
Key Question: 2
Skill: comprehension
Difficulty: Level 2

52. Which of the following marine habitats has the lowest species diversity?
    a.   coral reef
    b.   mangrove swamp
    c.   mud flat

d. rocky shore
e. sandy beach

Answer: C
Key Question: 1, 2, & 3
Skill: comprehension
Difficulty: Level 2

53. The most successful adaptation for living on a sediment-covered shore is:
   a. attachment to the substrate.
   b. burrowing into the sediment.
   c. flattened body shape.
   d. sessile lifestyle.
   e. swimming.

Answer: B
Key Question: 2
Skill: comprehension
Difficulty: Level 2

54. The depth to which a bivalve can bury itself depends on the:
   a. composition of the sediment
   b. length of the respiratory structure
   c. oxygen content of the sediment
   d. turbidity of the surface water
   e. wave frequency and water velocity.

Answer: B
Key Question: 2
Skill: comprehension
Difficulty: Level 2

55. The common annelid found in a sandy beach environment is the:
   a. clam.
   b. fan worm.
   c. feather duster worm.
   d. ghost crab.
   e. lugworm.

Answer: E
Key Question: 2
Skill: knowledge
Difficulty: Level 1

56. Organisms that live the spaces between sediment particles are called:
   a. epifauna
   b. microfauna
   c. meiofauna
   d. mesofauna
   e. subfauna.

Answer: C
Key Question: 2
Skill: knowledge
Difficulty: Level 1

57. The sublittoral rocky bottom zone is dominated by:
    a. coralline algae.
    b. green algae.
    c. kelp
    d. *Thalassia.*
    e. *Zostera.*
Answer: C
Key Question: 2
Skill: knowledge
Difficulty: Level 1

58. Oysters prefer:
    a. clear moving water.
    b. clear stagnant water.
    c. muddy bottom substrate.
    d. rocky bottom substrate.
    e. sandy bottom substrate.
Answer: A
Key Question: 2
Skill: knowledge
Difficulty: Level 1

59. All of the following are true of hard corals **except**:
    a. corals are members of the Kingdom Animalia, Phylum Cnidaria, Class Anthozoa.
    b. coral distribution worldwide is limited to areas where the water temperature exceeds 25°C.
    c. corals grow in shallow water with high light and relatively low organic nutrient input.
    d. corals have a motile planula larval form.
    e. corals have obligate endosymbionts.
Answer: B
Key Question: 3
Skill: application
Difficulty: Level 3

60. Which of the following factors does **not** limit coral growth?
    a. high concentrations of calcium carbonate in the water
    b. high sediment load in the water
    c. low light
    d. low nitrogen and phosphorus levels in the water
    e. water temperatures below 18°C
Answer: A
Key Question: 3

Skill: comprehension
Difficulty: Level 2

61. Eutrophication is detrimental to coral growth because it increases the:
    a. amount of inorganic nutrients in the water that stimulates excessive algal growth.
    b. amount of toxic synthetic chemicals that stimulates excessive bacterial growth.
    c. salinity of the water that results in coral bleaching.
    d. water temperature that kills zooxanthellae.
    e. water temperature that results in coral bleaching.

Answer: A
Key Question: 3
Skill: application
Difficulty: Level 3

62. Zooxanthellae are autotrophic marine protists that are found in the living tissues of some simple marine invertebrates such as corals, sea anemones, and jellyfish. Zooxanthellae are members of the:
    a. Division Bacillariophyta.
    b. Division Chrysophyta.
    c. Division Dinoflagellata.
    d. Phylum Ciliophora.
    e. Phylum Foraminfera.

Answer: C
Key Question: 3
Skill: knowledge
Difficulty: Level 1

63. The relationship between the protistan zooxanthellae and the polyps of reef-building corals is best described as a(n):
    a. facultative ectoparasitism.
    b. facultative commensalism.
    c. obligate endoparasitism.
    d. obligate mutualistic endosymbiosis.
    e. obligate commensalism.

Answer: D
Key Question: 3
Skill: application
Difficulty: Level 3

64. Corals with delicate growth patterns are usually found:
    a. below 150 m depth.
    b. in the buttress zone.
    c. in the spur-and-groove zone.
    d. on the reef flat.
    e. on the reef slope.

Answer: E
Key Question: 3

Skill: knowledge
Difficulty: Level1

.

65. The buttress zone of a coral reef is likely to have which variety of coral?
    a. boulder corals.
    b. delicate plate corals
    c. gorgonian corals.
    d. massive branching corals
    e. rounded and smooth corals
Answer: D
Key Question: 3
Skill: knowledge
Difficulty: Level 1

66. Which of the following is a threat to coral reef survival?
    a. boat collisions.
    b. fishing.
    c. scuba and snorkeling.
    d. suspended sediment.
    e. All of the above might contribute to the decline of a coral community.
Answer: E
Key Question: 4
Skill: comprehension
Difficulty: Level 2

67. The loss of color (coral bleaching) in coral reef organisms is caused by:
    a. crown-of-thorn sea stars.
    b. fungal parasite.
    c. increased sediment load.
    d. increased water temperature.
    e. loss of zooxanthellae.
Answer: E
Key Question: 4
Skill: knowledge
Difficulty: Level 1

68. The variables that affect species diversity of benthic animals include:
    a. currents.
    b. organic nutrients.
    c. temperature.
    d. wave energy.
    e. All of the above factors contribute to benthic animal diversity.
Answer: E
Key Question: 5
Skill: comprehension
Difficulty: Level 2

69. The distribution of benthic biomass is related to:
    a. current patterns.
    b. primary productivity.
    c. sediment variety.
    d. thermocline depth.
    e. wave energy.
Answer: B
Key Question: 5
Skill: comprehension
Difficulty: Level 2

70. Primary producers in hydrothermal vent communities are:
    a. algae.
    b. eyeless shrimp.
    c. giant clams.
    d. *Riftia* tubeworms.
    e. sulfur-oxidizing bacteria
Answer: E
Key Question: 6
Skill: knowledge
Difficulty: Level 1

71. These organisms are inhabitants of a(n):

(b)

(c)

    a. active subduction zone.
    b. cold seep.
    c. hypersaline seep.
    d. hydrocarbon seep.
    e. hydrothermal vent.

Answer: D
Key Question: 6
Skill: knowledge
Difficulty: Level 1

72. The three varieties of seeps on the seafloor include hypersaline, hydrocarbon and:
    a. abyssal plain seeps.
    b. deep-sea trench seeps.
    c. mid-ocean ridge seeps
    d. seamount seeps.
    e. subduction zone seeps
Answer: E
Key Question: 6
Skill: knowledge
Difficulty: Level 1

73. Subduction zone seeps support communities from:
    a. hydrocarbon-rich waters.
    b. hydrothermal waters.
    c. inorganic nutrient rich waters.
    d. oxygen-rich waters.
    e. sulfur and methane-rich sedimentary waters.
Answer: B
Key Question: 6
Skill: knowledge
Difficulty: Level 1

74. Most of the hydrothermal vents and cool-water seeps on the seafloor were discovered during which decade?
    a. 1960s
    b. 1970s
    c. 1980s
    d. 1990s
    e. since 2000
Answer: C
Key Question: 6
Skill: knowledge
Difficulty: Level 1

75. Hydrocarbon seeps have been discovered :
    a. along the Galapagos Ridge.
    b. along the Mid-Atlantic Ridge.
    c. in the Gulf of California.
    d. in the Gulf of Mexico.
    e. in the Indian Ocean.
Answer: D
Key Question: 6

Animals of the Benthic Environment

Skill: knowledge
Difficulty: Level 1

76. All of the following are associated with a hypersaline seep **except**:
    a. chemosynthesis.
    b. hydrogen sulfide.
    c. microbial mats.
    d. very high salinity.
    e. very high temperature.
Answer: E
Key Question: 6
Skill: comprehension
Difficulty: Level 2

Test Bank Photo Credits